Y0-BRV-479

SPECIAL REPORT 93

IMPROVED STREET UTILIZATION THROUGH TRAFFIC ENGINEERING

Proceedings of a Conference
Held May 22-24, 1967
National Academy of Sciences
Washington, D.C.

Subject Area

53 Traffic Control and Operations

HIGHWAY RESEARCH BOARD

DIVISION OF ENGINEERING   NATIONAL RESEARCH COUNCIL
NATIONAL ACADEMY OF SCIENCES—NATIONAL ACADEMY OF ENGINEERING

Washington, D.C., 1967   Publication 1550

The Highway Research Board wishes to acknowledge gratefully the support of the Institute of Traffic Engineers in placing a substantial prepublication order for this Special Report.

Price: $7.00, Paper Cover
$8.00, Hard Cover

Available from

Highway Research Board
National Academy of Sciences
2101 Constitution Avenue
Washington, D.C. 20418

388.31
C74i

HIGHWAY RESEARCH BOARD

Officers and Members of the Executive Committee
1967

OFFICERS

EDWARD G. WETZEL
Chairman

DAVID H. STEVENS
First Vice Chairman

OSCAR T. MARZKE
Second Vice Chairman

W. N. CAREY, JR.
Executive Director

Executive Committee

LOWELL K. BRIDWELL, *Federal Highway Administrator, U. S. Department of Transportation* (ex officio)

A. E. JOHNSON, *Executive Director, American Association of State Highway Officials* (ex officio)

JOHN C. KOHL, *Executive Secretary, Division of Engineering, National Research Council* (ex officio)

DONALD S. BERRY, *Chairman, Department of Civil Engineering, Northwestern University* (ex officio, Past Chairman 1965)

J. B. MCMORRAN, *Commissioner, New York State Department of Transportation* (ex officio, Past Chairman 1966)

MASON A. BUTCHER, *County Manager, Montgomery County, Md.*

J. DOUGLAS CARROLL, JR., *Executive Director, Tri-State Transportation Commission, New York City*

HARMER E. DAVIS, *Director, Institute of Transportation and Traffic Engineering, University of California*

GEORGE E. HOLBROOK, *Vice President, E. I. du Pont de Nemours and Company*

JOHN T. HOWARD, *Head, Department of City and Regional Planning, Massachusetts Institute of Technology*

EUGENE M. JOHNSON, *Chief Engineer, Mississippi State Highway Department*

PYKE JOHNSON, *Retired*

THOMAS F. JONES, JR., *President, University of South Carolina*

LOUIS C. LUNDSTROM, *Director, Automotive Safety Engineering, General Motors Technical Center*

OSCAR T. MARZKE, *Vice President, Fundamental Research, U. S. Steel Corporation*

D. GRANT MICKLE, *Vice President, Automotive Safety Foundation*

LEE LAVERNE MORGAN, *Executive Vice President, Caterpillar Tractor Company*

T. E. SHELBURNE, *State Highway Research Engineer, Virginia Highway Research Council*

CHARLES E. SHUMATE, *Chief Engineer, Colorado Department of Highways*

WILBUR S. SMITH, *Wilbur Smith and Associates, Inc., New Haven, Connecticut*

DAVID H. STEVENS, *Chairman, Maine State Highway Commission*

JOHN H. SWANBERG, *Chief Engineer, Minnesota Department of Highways*

EDWARD G. WETZEL, *The Port of New York Authority, New York City*

J. C. WOMACK, *State Highway Engineer, California Division of Highways*

K. B. WOODS, *Goss Professor of Engineering, School of Civil Engineering, Purdue University*

Editorial Staff

EARLE W. JACKSON
Senior Editor

STEPHEN MONTGOMERY
Assistant Editor

BEATRICE G. CROFOOT
Production Manager

2101 Constitution Avenue

Washington, D. C. 20418

The opinions and conclusions expressed in this publication are those of the authors
and not necessarily those of the Highway Research Board

Highway Research Board
Advisory Committee
On Improved Street Utilization
January 1967

Fred W. Hurd, Chairman
Director, Bureau of Highway Traffic
Yale University
New Haven, Connecticut

William L. Carson, Staff Engineer, Institute of Traffic Engineers, Washington, D.C.

Robert E. Conner, Chief, Traffic Engineering Branch, Office of Highway Safety, Bureau of Public Roads, Federal Highway Administration, U.S. Department of Transportation, Washington, D.C.

John F. Exnicios, City Traffic Engineer, City of New Orleans, New Orleans, Louisiana

Edward M. Hall, Street Improvement Administrator, City of Phoenix, Phoenix, Arizona

Daniel J. Hanson, Deputy Director for Traffic Engineering and Operations, D.C. Department of Highways and Traffic, Washington, D.C.

Donald W. Loutzenheiser, Chief, Highway Standards and Design Division, Bureau of Public Roads, Federal Highway Administration, U.S. Department of Transportation, Washington, D.C.

Matthew C. Sielski, Director, Driving Environment, National Highway Safety Bureau, Federal Highway Administration, Washington, D.C.

Asriel Taragin, Assistant Deputy Director, Office of Research and Development, Federal Highway Administration, U.S. Department of Transportation, Washington, D.C.

Ben West, West and West Law Offices, Nashville, Tennessee

Ex-Officio: Harold L. Michael, Associate Director, Joint Highway Research Project, Purdue University, Lafayette, Indiana

HRB Liaison: Edward A. Mueller, Engineer of Traffic and Operations
Paul E. Irick, Assistant Director for Special Projects

Conference on Improved Street Utilization Through Traffic Engineering

CONFERENCE MODERATORS AND SPEAKERS
(Alphabetical Order)

David M. Baldwin, Chief, Operations Division, Office of Traffic and Operations, Bureau of Public Roads, Federal Highway Administration, U.S. Department of Transportation, Washington, D.C.

C. Edwin Brewer, Deputy Director, Department of Traffic and Parking, City of New Haven, New Haven, Connecticut

John A. Bruce, Director of Traffic Engineering, Denver, Colorado

Samuel Cass, Commissioner, Metropolitan Toronto Traffic Engineering Department, Toronto, Ontario, Canada

John P. Cavallero, Jr., Deputy Commissioner, Department of Transit and Traffic, City of Baltimore, Baltimore, Maryland

John F. Exnicios, City Traffic Engineer, City of New Orleans, New Orleans, Louisiana

James L. Foley, Jr., Commissioner of Transit and Traffic, City of Baltimore, Baltimore, Maryland

Edward M. Hall, Street Improvement Administrator and Assistant City Manager for Public Works Development, City of Phoenix, Phoenix, Arizona

Daniel J. Hanson, Deputy Director for Traffic Engineering, District of Columbia Department of Highways and Traffic, Washington, D.C.

Ellis C. Henry, Jr., Traffic Commissioner, City of St. Louis, St. Louis, Missouri

Delbert F. Karmeier, Traffic Commissioner, St. Louis County, St. Louis, Missouri

Peter G. Koltnow, Victor Gruen Associates, Los Angeles, California

John N. LaPlante, Traffic Engineer III, Design and Planning Division, Bureau of Street Traffic, City of Chicago, Chicago, Illinois

Donald W. Loutzenheiser, Chief, Highway Standards and Design Division, Bureau of Public Roads, Federal Highway Administration, U.S. Department of Transportation, Washington, D.C.

William R. McGrath, Transportation Coordinator, Boston Redevelopment Authority, Boston, Massachusetts

Alger F. Malo, Director, Department of Streets and Traffic, City of Detroit, Detroit, Michigan

William R. Marston, Deputy Commissioner, Department of Development and Planning, City of Chicago, Chicago, Illinois

Harold L. Michael, Associate Director, Joint Highway Research Project, Purdue University, Lafayette, Indiana

Paul W. Rice, City Manager, Bethany, Oklahoma

Edmund R. Ricker, Director, Traffic Engineering Bureau, Pennsylvania Department of Highways, Harrisburg, Pennsylvania

Ross T. Shoaf, Assistant City Engineer, City of San Francisco, San Francisco, California

Matthew C. Sielski, Director, Driving Environment, National Highway Safety Bureau, Federal Highway Administration, Washington, D.C.

Harry B. Skinner, Executive Director, New Haven Parking Authority, City of New Haven, New Haven, Connecticut

Wilbur S. Smith, Wilbur Smith and Associates, New Haven, Connecticut

Asriel Taragin, Assistant Deputy Director, Office of Research and Development, Bureau of Public Roads, Federal Highway Administration, U.S. Department of Transportation, Washington, D.C.

Ben West, West and West Law Offices, Nashville, Tennessee

James E. Wilson, Traffic Engineer, California Division of Highways, Sacramento, California

Thomas E. Young, City Traffic Engineer, Cincinnati, Ohio

OTHER CONFERENCE PARTICIPANTS

Paul Box
Conference Secretariat

Lowell K. Bridwell
U.S. Department of Transportation

William N. Carey, Jr.
Highway Research Board

John Cummings
Automobile Manufacturers' Association

Joseph Ewing
U.S. Chamber of Commerce

Nicholas Gal
American Petroleum Institute

Harold Horn
International City Managers' Association

James Keene
The Traffic Institute

Brian Martin
Greater London Council

James Mason
Greater London Council

Carlton C. Robinson
Automotive Safety Foundation

Gordon Sessions
Principal Author

Steiner Silence
U.S. Bureau of Public Roads

Robert Toohey
National League of Cities

W. Powell Walker
U.S. Bureau of Public Roads

Max Wehrly
Urban Land Institute

FOREWORD

These Proceedings are the product of the first phase of a Highway Research Board special project on Improved Street Utilization Through Traffic Engineering. It consists of technical papers presented at a conference bearing on this subject held in Washington, D. C., May 22-24, 1967.

The purpose of the Conference was to provide suitable documentation for a forthcoming informational publication directed to public officials, service organizations, civic leaders, legislators and others to make them aware of the value of traffic engineering applications and to advise them on the basic ingredients of a successful traffic improvement program. The need for such a publication was stressed by an Advisory Committee appointed for this project by the National Academy of Sciences. The committee agreed that many cities are not applying traffic engineering principles and techniques as much as they should; and major obstacles to this application are official and public apathy, opposition to change, or lack of awareness of how better operations can improve street capacity and safety.

Technical papers for the Conference were invited from those traffic professionals known to have access to generally unpublished, factually oriented material on the effects of traffic engineering improvements on street operations. No attempt was made to invite papers covering all aspects of traffic engineering, particularly in those areas already documented by published material. The subject areas for the Conference were chosen to represent relatively low cost improvements afforded by regulations, controls and minor reconstruction. Because of these factors, the Proceedings should be regarded as case examples gathered for a special purpose.

The program for the three-day Conference consisted of six sessions, each containing four presentations. The presentations were followed by separate discussion periods. The discussion portion of the Conference is not included with these Proceedings but, in those instances where the discussion alluded to factual information in extension of the Conference papers, a follow-up to obtain these data was made. This material appears as Addenda to various Proceedings papers.

Members of the Advisory Committee for the Special Project and the Conference are Fred Hurd (Chairman), William Carson, Robert Connor, John Exnicios, Edward Hall, Daniel Hanson, Donald Loutzenheiser, Harold Michael, Matthew Sielski, Asriel Taragin, and Ben West. Development and organization of the Conference was under the direct supervision of Paul Irick and Edward Mueller of the Highway Research Board. Paul Box was secretariat and consultant to the Conference.

Supporting funds for the project were provided by the Automotive Safety Foundation, the Automobile Manufacturers Association, the American Petroleum Institute, and the Highway Research Board.

The verbatim transcript of conference discussion and a corresponding discussion summary prepared by the secretariat are available as privileged documents on a restricted loan basis from the Highway Research Board.

—Fred Hurd

Contents

Keynote Address

LOWELL K. BRIDWELL
Federal Highway Administrator
U.S. Department of Transportation

It was with unusual pleasure that I accepted your kind invitation suggesting that I speak with you here today.

Your Conference is assembled to discuss a subject with a tongue-twisting appellation—the "improved utilization of existing streets and highways through traffic engineering." To you who will participate, the title is informative. It tells each of you—highway engineer, traffic engineer, designer, urban planner, or administrator—that you will be talking in detail about such hard-nosed issues as improved traffic flow, better traffic control devices, parking limitations and provisions, street lighting, and a host of other elements of the total road system.

I compliment you on the range and depth of your planned discussions. And yet, without intending to slight the authors of your program, I am going to offer an amended title to your Conference. I am going to suggest that it could very appropriately and very effectively be called, "The Conference on Improving the American Highway Resource."

That, in effect, is the laudable goal you have set for your discussions over the next three days. It is a goal which, I am afraid, some people in our land believe to be non-existent. And over and above your many other tasks and responsibilities you implicitly share the worthwhile burden of making it clear, as often and in as many ways possible, that a major purpose of "highway engineering" today is the raising of our existing national road resource to new levels of safety, efficiency, productivity and—to wrap it all up into a single term—public service. Your Conference and you, as individuals, are dedicated to the proposition that roads can, should, and will provide ever higher levels of service to all of the public.

You will be dealing in your Conference discussions with facts and practicalities, so I do not intend to start your meeting off in an unwarranted aura of platitudes. You will be talking about things being done or planned on behalf of the traveling public. I want to slightly reverse the order of that relationship, to talk with you briefly about that same traveling public today, and about the effect of your work and your actions upon it.

One need only glance through the list of your agenda items to become aware that the public with the most to gain from your work is the urban public, including those who live in and around urban areas and those who regularly travel into and out of urban areas. As you are aware on a day-to-day working basis, this accounts for an immense portion of our national population.

This urban public is very much in the national eye today. It is intimately a part of our growing concern with the problems of cities and suburbs—overlapping problems of air pollution, lack of space, inadequate services, rising costs, crime, the slum, imbalances in employment, educational facilities, and a myriad other concerns. This public is rather sharply stratified as between core city dweller, city worker living in the suburbs, and suburban dweller working in the suburbs—and it is also stratified, of course, by economic considerations.

Depending on which stratum an individual inhabits, his goals for the future of his urban area may vary greatly. But one goal long shared by most members of this urban public has been adequate transportation—transportation, that is, which meets the often varying requirements of the urban community's citizens to move with relative ease, speed, flexibility, economy, and safety to and from all points within and beyond the urban area. Relative, in this sense, means able to meet those criteria better than any existing service or system.

1

The urban highway and road network was, quite simply, a response to that demand. It was the best available response early in this century, when the advent of the motor vehicle challenged Americans either to drastically improve their roads, or else abandon them as a national resource. And despite the problems it has encountered—and some it has engendered—it is the best available response today. Conferences such as yours, of course, indicate that we intend to keep it that way.

But what about tomorrow? Will our national network of urban streets and highways be the best available response to tomorrow's—next month's, next year's—demands by the urban public for transportation which meets its many standards? And even if so, will our "best available response" be good enough?

I wish that I could give you the final answers to those questions. I do not, of course, have the final answers. You do, and every decision, plan, and project which you advance will determine how these questions are to be resolved. But if you feel, as I do, that our cities' roads and highways can be as good as rising public expectations require, we at least can discuss the atmosphere which surrounds our steps toward improving this basic transportation resource.

As a first principle, perhaps we should agree with the statement carved at the door to the National Archives Building here in Washington. "What Is Past Is Prologue," it declares. We and the public can learn from and build upon our past in highway planning, design, construction and traffic control—but let us not fling the past at each other, either as a weapon of recrimination or a source of smug self-defense.

I do not take too seriously the idea that a great wave of public disenchantment will prompt the tearing down of important segments of our roads, or the withdrawal of our mandate to improve the national road system. By the same token, I cannot endorse the idea that highway engineers are justified in taking a "my way or no way" attitude toward road building. Certainly, the Federal Highway Administration does not take such an attitude.

If the past is instructive prologue, it teaches us that the planning, design, construction, and operation and use of highways is no more static than the continuing expansion of the universe. On the contrary, the evolution of our urban highway and road system is an unparalleled example of motion and growth, and this suggests to me a second principle which we might do well to adopt: The present is our eternal opportunity to influence the future. Perhaps that smacks of platitude, but I believe it has a very practical implication to the future of urban roads. For if we pass up our opportunities today, other forces and considerations of the present certainly will dictate the shape of our road system for the future, whether urban or otherwise.

This opportunity has its greatest possibilities in our urban areas and will come about in the beginning through a more flexible approach to our present roadway development pattern.

It is an interesting paradox that many of our opportunities in road development today are presented in the guise of frustrations. To the planner, builder, engineer, administrator, or anyone else whose life is committed to creating and improving a national highway resource, it is frustrating indeed to be told, by sincere city dwellers, newspapers or officials that "roads are destructive to society," or that "rail transit is better than highways in urban areas," or that such-and-such a stretch of road will "blight the neighborhood." To reply in defense of highways is to court the charge that one is "narrow" and "pro-highway," or "anti-rail." In few areas of national discussion it is difficult to hold the middle view, and so-called "highway people" are forever finding themselves in one extreme corner of an argument they never asked for.

Yet we would be dangerously unwise to withdraw farther into that corner. Tougher though it may be to stay in dead center, that is the only place where we have an opportunity to answer the sound questions, and work toward a restatement of the unsound ones. Moreover, that is the only place in which we can distill our opportunities from the seeming frustrations of the discussion.

We know, for instance, that there is no such thing as "bad" road. There may be poorly built roads, roads needing improvement, or roads which are not operated safely and efficiently—but not "bad" roads in the moral sense. When we leap to the defense of "good" roads, however, our stamp of endorsement implicitly goes on the "good-bad" argument. When our actions—such as this Conference—signify efforts to improve existing roads and the use of existing roads, we are successfully holding the middle ground and making the most of our opportunities.

Likewise, the middle ground is the most productive—and the most difficult to secure—in the "roads are destructive to cities" discussion which flares up with increasing frequency. We know that roads can be destructive to cities, and we know of past instances where, because of poor planning and coordination, false economies, and other reasons, construction of roadway had produced unnecessary injury to segments of the same urban community which benefited as a whole from the involved stretch of road.

But far more important, we also know that roads should not and need not be a destructive element in the city development process. You know, and your Conference signifies, that our existing urban streets and roads are the skeleton upon which America's cities have been built—and that to remove the skeleton would be to eliminate the city, totally. We also are painfully and actively aware—again, witness this Conference—that the skeletal bones need constant attention and strengthening, else the city will become a very sick patient, plagued with the traffic congestion, hazard, and enervation which already has attacked some major urban areas.

In this regard, most of you are familiar with our TOPICS program, initiated early this year by the Bureau of Public Roads. TOPICS is an effort to extend traffic engineering improvements to principal urban streets not previously eligible for Federal-aid highway funds.

TOPICS is a technique—a present, applied technique—to insure that our city road systems remain the best available response to urban America's demand for safe, efficient, economical, flexible transportation. It is not, of course, the only way. One of the opportunities held out by the present is the challenge, put to us by public need and public sentiment, to develop additional improvements both in our urban road system and our use of that system.

Solely in the cause of making our existing urban street system a far more productive resource, we must explore many other avenues of opportunity. The shrinking availability and mounting inconvenience of parking in and around many urban areas offers not only a present opportunity, but a hard challenge, to all of us. Legislation now is being developed which will make a start toward fulfilling the Federal share of this responsibility.

In my personal opinion, we need to do much more in this area to obtain the maximum return from our very large investment in roads. After all, the road itself is only a means to an end—and no place to park makes the trip frustrating, if not downright useless.

I have made clear a number of times already my conviction that our concern must not be limited just to the adequacy and technical acceptability of our existing urban road systems, but also to their productivity. And this, of course, means concern over improving our use of these systems. I for one am sometimes appalled at the uses—more to the point, non-uses—to which we have subjected major portions of our urban street and highway network. History, let us hope, will not relate that the society capable of building the world's most magnificent highway system proved incapable of using that system properly.

A dismaying example of this is our near total failure to recognize and exploit our urban highway system as an effective means of mass transportation—a ludicrous situation in a nation so deeply and justifiably concerned with the problems of moving huge numbers of people into and out of cities during two peak periods of every working day! If ever an opportunity was ripe for fulfillment by highways and so-called "highway people," this is it. It demands the harmonizing of a combination of factors, two of which are first a willingness by the private and public bus industry to commit itself to a true mass transit service and second, cooperation by city and suburban officials, highway designers and administrators, and the public (which, after all, stands to gain the most) in defining and applying the lane control, loading facilities, proper signalization, and other techniques needed to bring about the desired public-service result. Frankly, I am convinced that this is an opportunity demanding fast and aggressive action, and within the scope of my responsibility I intend to promote it as vigorously as possible. TOPICS, by the way, recognizes this aspect and is a start toward doing something about it.

Your Conference by its title and agenda is explicitly concerned with existing streets and highways as contrasted with planned or required future roadway. With this in mind, I have endeavored to keep my comments so far within the framework of your interest at this meeting in discussing and developing means to improve road resources, and the public's use of those resources, which already are in operation.

But as you are acutely aware, the challenge of refining existing roads to better meet public demand is only half the story in highway needs today. The other half is, of course, our growing national need—both in and beyond urban areas—for additional components to the American highway network. And, you certainly recognize that these additional components must be planned, developed, integrated, and physically built with close attention to a wide swatch of other economic and social considerations, particularly in our urban areas.

The basis for an adequate, comprehensive development of new Federal-aid highways in the context of other community needs and desires is provided in the continuing comprehensive transportation planning process required by the 1962 Federal-Aid Highway Act; this planning process is now active in some 230 urban areas. Through it communities can establish their developmental goals and see that highway improvements are compatible both with these goals and with other forms of transportation development.

But as was recognized then, and is even more apparent today, additional techniques and—to use a fashionable Washington word—"inputs" are required if future highway development in urban areas is to be adequately responsive to public demand.

One such technique, which the Federal Highway Administration is working hard to advance, is the so-called "joint-use" approach to urban highway planning. Oversimplified, this is the same kind of multiple-use concept which, applied to highway development, can produce results even more impressive than it has generated in the planning and construction of municipal centers, schools, and other public buildings.

This concept provides for the complementary development of an urban freeway corridor. It has advantages in making the best use of scarce urban space, and in making public dollars do double duty through the economics of land acquisition. It can help provide replacement housing, parks and recreational areas, parking or commercial development, and other community facilities along with needed freeways.

We believe joint development presents a logical, practical approach to a range of difficult urban problems. We are encouraged by the interest it is receiving, as for example here in Washington where feasibility studies point to the construction of apartments over a portion of the Inner Loop. And we look for the profitable application of this approach to urban freeway planning in the years just ahead.

I have talked with you this morning about only a few of the many opportunities which the present holds out to all of us concerned with highway development and improvement. I mean neither to cast criticism where those opportunities are being left untaken, nor to suggest that no frustrations will be encountered as they are pursued. I mean only to make clear my belief, without reservation, that we can and will meet the national demand for an even higher quality, more productive, and more harmonious highway system, that we are capable of distilling, from public comment and public need, a legitimate mandate for change and improvement in response to changing social and economic circumstances—and, finally, that our actions in the coming months and years will continue to demonstrate that highways are for, and not despite, any and every element of the American public.

If I am correct, we have nowhere to go but forward. Thank you.

Selection, Classification, and Designation
Of Major Street Systems

WILLIAM MARSTON
Deputy Commissioner
Department of Development and Planning
City of Chicago

Some years ago in Chicago, in an effort to clear up the confusion in street classification, the term "preferential" was chosen to describe those streets that were important traffic carriers. This was intended to replace a confusion of street classes such as through streets, arterial streets, state-aid streets, state primary, state secondary, and Federal aid. "Preferential" was further broken down into classes, not necessarily describing precise function but merely designating importance. In addition to the limited-access type the classes consisted of the following: Class I, denoting a carrier for principally through movement and which might be likened to the supplemental trunk highway; Class II, those streets carrying large volumes of through movement and also serving as collectors to a great extent; and Class III, streets serving basically as collectors but also as access streets. The balance of the streets were, of course, considered as the "access" system. We are the first to agree that this attempt at classification was less than perfect.

The classification of streets and highways into some logical set of systems is a necessary beginning to proper and efficient administration, financing, and operation of the road network. With respect to rural highways it is relatively easy to develop systems that have reasonably clear-cut characteristic uses. Further, it is fairly easy to assign political responsibility for each system. As streets and highways enter the limits of dense urban areas, the function becomes less clearly defined, as does the responsibility of planning, maintenance, and operation. Types of vehicle trips become quite mixed due to the higher density of land use. Even a limited-access expressway takes on a somewhat different character in a large city like Chicago.

It is generally agreed that streets and highways can best be classified in accord with their use. The main factor that will control the class of a street or highway will be the travel desires of the users and/or potential users. A class of street should not only reflect the desired use for today but that for the future. All roads and streets can be classified into four basic systems: expressways, arterials, collectors, and local streets.

In strictly rural areas, these basic systems require little refinement but the greater trip density of the city adds many problems.

Throughout the states there are a myriad of classification systems and combinations of systems. Imagine the problem of discussing a street that may be administered by a city but constructed by a county government. Or one that is maintained by a city, yet construction costs are split fifty-fifty between the state and the city. Further complicating the problem are through streets constructed and maintained by the city which connect to state routes at city limits.

Historically the urban street has been considered the responsibility of the city. However, the user source of funds has not been distributed on a fair basis for such arteries. This is notwithstanding the fact that one-third of all fatalities occur on city streets and while the urban system is only 14 percent of the total highway mileage, it carries 50 percent of the vehicle-miles of travel. Responsibility for this imbalance can be laid partly to the lack of a systematic classification plan. Inasmuch as the trend is toward designating more funds to city streets, a good street classification plan will soon become a necessity for all municipalities.

5

As stated previously, the complexity of urban travel makes it extremely difficult to arrive at a clear-cut classification of city streets. In Chicago, as well as other large cities, a street is normally placed within a certain system more from the standpoint of city planning considerations than actual use. Because of the high density of trip ends all streets will perform very similar service unless controlled by design.

The expressway with its many ramps in a city serves a trunk highway function. Although its service is not adulterated in giving access to property, it does perform as a collector to some extent because of its many ramps. The ordinary arterial street generally has only width, continuity, and signalization to give it distinction. It serves as a through carrier only because of these characteristics. A neighborhood street may be pressed into such service if an adjacent arterial becomes overloaded, particularly if it is also continuous.

Recognizing that arterial streets serve more than intercommunity traffic in that they must also act as collectors, steps should be taken to curtail materially their function as access streets. This means that there must be control of frontage, curb cuts and entrances of intersecting local streets.

The process of designating streets by class may be controlled by considerations other than just desire lines of current travel. The considerations that must necessarily control the selection of an arterial class street are therefore (a) character of the environment through which the street passes, (b) potential for widening to permit improved traffic service and improved environmental effect, (c) reduction in number of access points, (d) reduction in marginal interferences through frontage lane-use control, (e) reduction in pedestrian-vehicle conflict, and (f) reduction in intersection interferences.

A collector street can be selected as need of land-use needs dictate. In this case, great changes in design are not justified and only good traffic engineering need be considered. Through movement can be reduced by building discontinuity into these streets.

The beginning of a city's arterial network is generally the present grid system of major streets. To determine those streets that have the best possibility of being developed into properly functioning arterials will require extensive and careful study.

There are problems in developing the service standards and reconstruction schedules that are far more difficult to solve than those of estimating traffic demand. In determining the possibility of widening, it is necessary to consider the condition of frontage buildings and relocation problems, as well as the availability of money.

It must be pointed out that the improvement of a short street section will provide additional traffic capacity and efficiency for persons using this improved street section. However, it will provide limited benefit for those making longer trips.

In the early days of the preferential street planning process in Chicago, the grave difficulties encountered in improving surface streets over significant distances led to the conclusion that work should proceed on rebuilding streets to obtainable standards as the opportunity occurred. It was possible to improve intersections and short sections of street and to justify the improvement on the basis that traffic service was being materially improved for, at least, local trips.

It must be emphasized that widened roadways and/or traffic bypass routes must be developed for lengths of several miles if additional through traffic capacity and better traffic service are to be realized. Whether the state, Federal, or local government constructs these widened streets is not important at the moment. The relocation of businesses and homes to the degree necessary for major widening creates the most difficult problem.

Built-up cities are generally faced with the slow process of obtaining widened rights-of-way in conjunction with urban renewal unless major clearance of business street frontage becomes much easier, or unless means can be developed to route traffic onto nearby streets to bypass congested locations. There is a practical limit to the width of a surface street, to the availability of frontage property for widening, and to the availability of side streets of a kind that can handle heavy traffic. The development of high-capacity surface traffic carriers requires careful planning, good street design and considerable change in land use.

TABLE 1

EXAMPLES OF CITY STREET MILEAGE BREAKDOWN

Population of City	Percent of Total Mileage				
	Freeway	Arterial	CBD	Collector	Local
65,000	2	23	1	4	70
150,000	6	27	6	NA	61
950,000	1	32	4	NA	63

Source: Unpublished case studies.

TABLE 2

EXAMPLES OF CITY STREET MILEAGE
BY CLASS OF STREET

Population	Freeway (%)	Arterial (%)	Other (%)
72,000	3	25	72
72,500	0	16	84
131,000	2	16	82
142,000	7	15	78
172,000	5	23	72
500,000	1	20	79
670,000	1	19	80
713,000	4	10	86
940,000	1	32	67

Source: Unpublished case studies.

A study of major city streets will show that more tools for rebuilding than we now have are necessary. A revolving fund could be established for the purchase of frontage or right-of-way as buildings are torn down and rebuilt. Much can also be accomplished by limiting curb access to frontage property. A means of accomplishing this control might be through zoning laws which would give building size or housing density bonuses if access to the structures is from side streets and/or alleys. This matter needs full and intelligent study soon.

There are many problems in developing an improved major street system from an existing street network. Answers are required to a number of questions. How can present streets be widened for any great distance within limits of available money? How can the relocation of businesses and homes be accomplished to the degree necessary to make any great progress toward widening? What is the maximum width of street that can be safely crossed by pedestrians and properly signalized for efficient traffic movement?

To accomplish a planned major street network, judgment must be exercised as to what the design of a surface street should be and how it should relate to the neighborhood through which it passes. Then, there should be an investigation of all major streets and a preliminary and realistic plan developed for each street section keeping in mind that traffic capacity over its length should be relatively uniform except, of course, near street ends. It is extremely important that all traffic estimates be related to a point in time so that traffic volume expansion for that same point in time can be used in testing the network.

MAJOR STREET DATA

Tables 1 and 2 illustrate percentages of street mileages by typical types of streets. The mileage used by streets for significant traffic movement excluding Central Business District (CBD) streets, ranges from 14 percent to 33 percent in these cities. When CBD mileage is included these values would range somewhat higher. These examples may be compared with the suggested mileage divisions shown in Table 3.

The importance of major traffic streets from the safety standpoint is illustrated in Table 4. Regardless of city size, the principal accident problem is on these routes, and the emphasis, priorities and expenditure of funds should be directed at alleviation of these hazards. It is almost redundant to point out that practically all congestion and delay occurs on these routes.

The relative percentages of different accident types on major surface arterials, by general location, are shown in Table 5. In this case

TABLE 3

SUGGESTED DIVISION OF STREET MILEAGES

Population of Metropolitan Areas	Percent of Total Mileage		
	Freeways	Arterial, CBD and Collector	Local
Under 25,000	—a	25 to 35	65 to 75
25,000 to 150,000	—a	20 to 30	70 to 80
150,000 to 500,000	2 to 4	20 to 25	75 to 80
Over 500,000	4 to 6	15 to 20	75 to 80

aDepends on through traffic needs.
Source: Table 8, page 47, Better Transportation for Your City, Public Service Adm., 1958.

TABLE 4

EXAMPLES OF ACCIDENTS RELATED
TO STREET TYPE

Population of City	Percent of All Accidents		
	Freeways	Arterial	Local
65,000[a]	NA	80	20
3,000,000[b]	2	61	37

[a]Unpublished 5-yr study, Skokie, Illinois.
[b]One-yr study, Chicago, Illinois, CATS.

study, more than 40 percent of the major street accidents were found to occur at intersections of two major streets. Improvement priority for these major intersections is self-evident, since these locations also tend to be points of maximum major street congestion.

More than one-third of major street accidents were found to occur in midblock locations, with nearly equal distributions of parked car, driveway or other type accidents such as head-on and sideswipe.

The value of parking prohibition, access control, adequate lane width and median separation in reduction of such accidents is discussed in subsequent papers.

TRUCK ROUTES

Among the more difficult tasks that a traffic engineer faces is the designation of truck routes. In a negative sense, trucks are sometimes restricted to certain routes or streets by posting prohibition signs on streets where trucks are not wanted. In a positive sense, it is possible to post the actual truck route and to prohibit them elsewhere. Merchandise delivery or pick-up is possible if the trucker uses the shortest route to (or from) the unrestricted truck route to (or from) the destination.

Posting truck routes could create legal problems. Landowners could claim damages for deterioration of property values. On the other hand, the system of prohibiting trucks in certain areas is costly. Chicago uses signs at the intersection of a residential street with a major street which read "Residential Street—Load Limit 5 Tons" or "Residential Street—Commercial Vehicles Prohibited." Two signs per half mile are generally sufficient in this case.

Generally speaking, the nature of a large urban center makes it difficult to prohibit trucks on very much of the arterial street system. However, there are parkways, boulevards and residential streets where it may be desirable to do so. It is important to relate city planning and street planning in such a way that street environment will reduce the deteriorating effect of truck traffic.

CONCLUSIONS

To provide a sound basis for determining traffic requirements streets and highways should be assigned to classes that reflect character of use. When logical systems based on function have been determined, administrative and financial responsibilities can be assigned in accord with the most effective level of government. In urban areas, function is considerably controlled by design of the street and character of the neighboring environment.

TABLE 5

PERCENT OF ARTERIAL STREET ACCIDENTS BY CONDITION

Condition	Type of Accident					
	Ped.	Parked Car	Driveway	Fixed Object	Other Veh. Acc.	Total
At intersections						
With major st.	0.7	0.3	0.6	1.6	40.0	43.2
With minor st.	1.0	0.7	0.2	0.7	19.0	21.6
Midblock	0.8	10.7	10.9	2.4	10.4	35.2
Total	2.5	11.7	11.7	4.7	69.4	100.0

Source: Unpublished 5-yr case study, Skokie, Illinois.

Chicago is now engaged in the process of developing and refining its street classification system. The study is predicated on the existing one-mile grid system of
streets. Traffic carrying capacity is to be developed to the optimum level with due
regard to environment and proper use of land. Major streets may be relocated or
their design changed to permit better development of land. Connection of streets to
major highways at the city limits will be recognized as an important consideration in
the arterial designation.

Full use will be made of opportunities to rearrange land use which could come about
by urban renewal procedures, both publicly and privately supported, and of demolition
of structures by any legal means where their removal would improve adjacent properties to a sufficiently high degree.

It is imperative, therefore, that the selection, classification, and development of
major streets be governed not only by traffic service needs but also with full recognition of the environment, effect on environment and possibilities of improving
environment.

REFERENCES

1. McGrath, William R. The Urban Thoroughfare System. Traffic Quarterly, Eno
   Foundation for Highway Traffic Control, Oct. 1966.
2. Osborne, Henry. The Buffalo Truck Route System. Traffic Quarterly, Eno
   Foundation for Highway Traffic Control, July 1953.
3. Wilbur Smith and Assoc. Highway Classification in Illinois. Oct. 1965.
4. Public Administration Service. Procedure Manual—Standards for Street Facilities
   and Services.
5. Barton-Aschman Associates, Inc. Needs and Opportunities for Coordinating
   Renewal and Transportation Improvement.
6. Department of Development and Planning. Comprehensive Plan of Chicago—1966.
   City of Chicago, Ill.
7. Loutzenheiser, D. W. Coordination of Highway and General Urban Planning.
   Proc. 31st Annual Meeting, Institute of Traffic Engineers, 1961.
8. Hammer, Phillip. Proc. 31st Annual Meeting, Institute of Traffic Engineers, 1961.
9. Engelen, R. B. The Opportunity Is Here. Traffic Engineering, April 1962.
10. Fagin, Henry. Transportation Systems Planning as an Influence on Urban Land
    Uses. Traffic Engineering, June 1963.
11. Hammond, H. F., moderator. Excerpts from a Panel Discussion. Traffic
    Engineering, June 1963.
12. Recommended Practices for Subdivision Streets, Project Committee 6E (62).
    [Note: extensive bibliography contained in committee report.] Traffic Engi-
    neering, Jan. 1967.
13. Hurd, F. W. Land Use Planning and Highway Engineering. Public Works, June
    1964.
14. Carroll, J. D., Jr. New Ways To See Land Use and Transportation. Civil
    Engineering, Aug. 1964.
15. Pollard, W. S., Jr. Operations Research Approach to the Reciprocal Impact of
    Transportation and Land Use. Jour. of the Urban Planning and Development
    Division, ASCE, May 1966.
16. Eberhard, J. R. Technology for the City. International Science and Technology,
    Sept. 1966.
17. Arterial Planning Standards. Chicago Area Transportation Study, March 1967.
18. Urbanized Area Transportation Study—Manual of Street and Highway Improvement
    Standards and Typical Cross-Sections. Illinois Division of Highways, Bureau
    of Planning.
19. Box, P. C. and Assoc. Selected Parking and Traffic Generation Data. Feb. 1967.
20. Better Transportation for Your City. Public Service Administration, 1958.

Improvement Priorities—The Factual Approach

EDWARD M. HALL
Street Improvement Administrator and
Assistant City Manager for Public Works Development
City of Phoenix

"Streets for the urban traveler" might well be the battle cry for the 1960's. Across the land one of the great unfulfilled needs of our urban areas is adequate street and freeway systems. Two important and timely contributions of this conference can be to emphasize the importance of efficient street utilization and the great need for additional funds to accomplish vital major street improvements.

The City of Phoenix has a strong and balanced street program. Since 1960 Phoenix has completed or has under construction over 35 miles of major street at a cost of

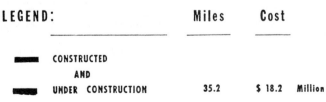

LEGEND:	Miles	Cost
CONSTRUCTED AND UNDER CONSTRUCTION	35.2	$ 18.2 Million

Figure 1. Major street progress, 1960–1967.

10

$18.2 million (Fig. 1). Although progress is good, it must be viewed in the perspective of the Street and Freeway Needs Studies of 1961 and 1965. Both of these studies clearly demonstrate that Phoenix is presently expending at about half the annual rate required to provide all the needed improvements of the major street system within a 20-yr period. The 1965 Deficiency and Needs Study factually showed that an annual investment of $8.2 million would be needed for 20 years to build major streets to serve present and future traffic. The current rate of investment is approximately $4 million per year.

This great urban street and freeway money problem was recently very clearly demonstrated by an excellent report published by the Arizona Highway Department. This report, "Arizona's Highway Needs—1965-1985," summarized the needs and revenues over a 20-yr period for State, county, and city levels of government. It concluded that there was a 20-yr deficit of nearly $900 million. Of this, over two-thirds (or more than $600 million) was allocated to city street systems.

The City of Phoenix has the major street plan, street classification system, workable street policies based on classification, the organization, and abundant facts. Our problem is money—or the lack of it. The funds that have been budgeted from 1960 to 1967 for major street construction, bottleneck elimination, and signalization are given in Table 1.

The funding problem leads to a three-pronged attack on street improvement:

1. Major street construction program—a city responsibility
2. Bottleneck elimination—a city responsibility
3. Local street improvement—property owners' responsibility

The balance of this paper will discuss two fronts—major street construction and bottleneck elimination. The projects that are included in these two programs must be selected to produce the maximum return in improved traffic flow and accident reduction from the funds that are available for street improvement. The factual approach to project selection and establishing priorities is essential.

MAJOR STREET CONSTRUCTION PROGRAM

The City of Phoenix' major street construction program is based on the adopted Major Street and Highway Plan shown in Figure 2. Street policies have been adopted in published form, which are geared to the adopted functional street classification map. A right-of-way standards map has also been adopted, which is based on the plan and functional street classification and tied to the street cross-section standards.

Each year the City publishes a new Six-Year Major Street Capital Improvement Program. The capital program is put together by a committee composed of the Public

TABLE 1

CITY FUNDS FOR MAJOR STREET IMPROVEMENTS
1960-1967—PHOENIX, ARIZONA

Year	Major Street Construction[a]	Bottleneck Elimination	Signals[b]	Total
1960-61	$ 1,582,000	$ 50,000	$ 85,000	$ 1,717,000
1961-62	1,892,000	78,000	59,000	2,029,000
1962-63	806,000	61,000	53,000	920,000
1963-64	969,000	80,000	22,000	1,071,000
1964-65	3,317,000	223,000	37,000	3,577,000
1965-66	5,454,000	133,000	67,000	5,654,000
1966-67	3,960,000	50,000	55,000	4,065,000
1967-68[c]	2,090,000	68,000	57,000	2,215,000
Totals	$20,070,000	$743,000	$435,000	$21,248,000

[a]Includes gasoline tax revenue bonds and city share of state gasoline tax; excludes Federal-aid secondary urban.
[b]New signals and modernization of old; excludes signals on major streets in the construction program.
[c]Tentative.

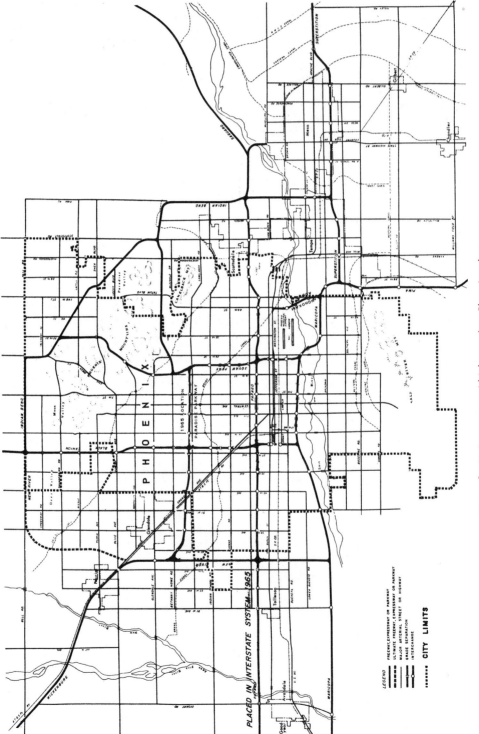

Figure 2. Major street and highway plan, Phoenix urban area.

Works Director, City Engineer, City Traffic Engineer, Planning Director, Real Estate Officer, Finance Director, Research and Budget Officer, and Street Improvement Administrator as chairman. The staff reviews and adjusts the program for any changing conditions or varying revenue forecasts.

The first three years of the 6-yr program are reasonably firm, as they are the design, right-of-way acquisition, and construction years. The second 3-yr portion of the program has flexibility for adjustment to meet changing growth patterns and new developments.

Traffic volume and travel time (delay) data and system development are major criteria for the development of the 6-yr program. The effort to develop long, continuous stretches of major street is shown in Figure 1.

Substantial work has been done toward the development of a major street priority formula. Most of this work is included in two earlier papers (7, 8). This research led to the development in October 1963 of a Priority Formula D, which follows:

MAJOR STREET IMPROVEMENT PRIORITY—FORMULA D

Element		Relative Weight (points)
Delay rate per mile during peak hour		50
Collision index: 2 yr accidents/mile plus accident rate/mile		15
Structural condition		15
Surface and base	5	
Drainage	10	
Traffic: $\dfrac{\text{Present ADT}}{1,500} + \dfrac{\text{5-yr future forecast ADT}}{2\ (\text{present ADT})}$		20
	Maximum possible points	100

Note: Projects to be listed in order of highest point value; program to be developed from list of projects and evaluation of budgetary and administrative considerations.

The delay rate and collision index point-rating scales are shown in Figure 3. Table 2 summarizes the test of Priority Formula D as applied to the projects in the adopted 1963 Six-Year Capital Improvement Program and an additional 25 test segments which had been selected to give a broad spectrum of street and traffic conditions.

The conclusion was that a factual priority formula makes possible a listing of various projects in a relative priority list. It must be emphasized that at this point administrative, coordination, budgetary considerations, and judgment are most properly applied to develop the final capital program that will be the maximum benefit to the public. Further experience has indicated that facts may be applied to the development of a program without necessarily using the priority formula.

In addition to the more complex formula that has been previously described, a simple means of comparing several projects is to divide the measured average daily traffic by the number of traffic lanes. Although this is a rather crude yardstick, it has been found to be useful.

BOTTLENECK ELIMINATION PROGRAM

The bottleneck elimination program is an effective approach to easing high-accident or congested-location problems. It is a spot improvement program which allows Phoenix to take immediate action to solve specific problems. Generally, the best bottleneck project is a specific location that needs immediate action, but one where funds are not available for the construction of a long-term major improvement. It is important that the total street program properly balance the allocation of funds to these two efforts.

The bottleneck program is coordinated with the major street program. Quite often it is possible to use funds from the major street program to make a permanent

14

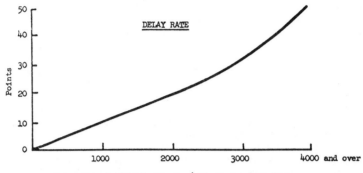

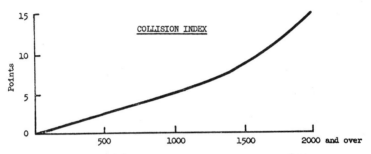

Figure 3. Major street improvement priority Formula C rating scales.

improvement which, at the same time, makes possible the elimination of a bottleneck. In every case, an effort is made to design a bottleneck project to fit into the future major improvements. Normally, a bottleneck project is not programmed unless the major street project is at least two years away.

Traffic Engineering makes full use of accident records, travel time studies, and traffic volume information in developing a priority list of these projects for consideration each budget year. The factual data are combined with a physical condition study to develop the plans for the actual project.

Traffic signals play an important part in the bottleneck elimination program. The signal priority list is developed annually, based on the traffic volume, pedestrian counts, accident records, the number of lanes, signal coordination, relation of school crossings, and special considerations. This factual priority list is reviewed and updated annually. A milestone was reached in the spring of 1967, when the signal priority list was submitted for budget review. This became a current program, with Phoenix having no intersections warranting signals that are not budgeted. New intersections will, of course, become warranted each year, as traffic continues to grow.

The important point is that the bottleneck program and the signal priority lists are carefully coordinated. In many instances widening or the elimination of a specific obstruction is necessary before a signal can be installed. In other words, the signal installation must be safe, and furthermore, the physical room to achieve the potential capacity of the signal must be provided.

TABLE 2

FORMULA D APPLIED TO ADOPTED 6-YEAR PROGRAM AND
25 TEST SEGMENTS

Major Arterial Street	Total Points (100 max.)	Year Scheduled (6-yr program)
Thomas Rd. Black Canyon to 19th Ave.	89.3	3
7th Ave. RR Structure/Jefferson to Grant-Lincoln	80.9	1
* McDowell Rd. 19th Ave. to 7th St. (as it was)	76.0	* *
Indian School Rd. 35th Ave. to Black Canyon	53.1	4-6
7th St. Maricopa Freeway to Grant-Lincoln	52.3	2
* Grand Ave. Thomas to Camelback (as it was)	47.0	* *
* 24th St. Buckeye to McDowell (as it was)	43.8	* *
19th Ave. Buckeye to Van Buren	43.8	2
16th St. Buckeye to Van Buren	43.8	3
* Van Buren 7th St. to 24th St.	43.2	
* Indian School Rd. 7th Ave. to 16th St.	41.7	
7th Ave. Osborn to Bethany Home	41.5	4-6
* 7th St. McDowell to Indian School (as it was)	37.7	* *
* 7th Ave. Van Buren to Thomas	35.0	* *
44th St. Thomas to Camelback	34.2	4-6
Van Buren 39th Ave. to Black Canyon	32.7	2
* 27th Ave. McDowell to Indian School	31.1	
24th St. Maricopa Freeway to Buckeye	31.0	4-6
Washington and Adams Tie-in	30.9	1
* 32nd St. Van Buren to Thomas	30.9	
7th St. Camelback to Glendale	30.8	2
* Camelback 16th St. to 32nd St.	29.3	
Dunlap 7th Ave. to Central	29.2	1
* 44th St. McDowell to Indian School	28.5	
* Van Buren 43rd Ave. to 27th Ave.	28.2	
24th St. Missouri to Lincoln Drive	28.0	4-6
Indian School 51st Ave. to 35th Ave.	26.5	4-6
* Central Ave. Camelback to Glendale	26.0	
16th St. Grand Canal to Camelback	26.0	
* 16th St. Camelback to Glendale	25.0	
16th St. Broadway to Buckeye	24.9	4-6
* Bethany Home 7th Ave. to 16th St.	24.2	3
7th St. Glendale to Dunlap	23.6	3
Thomas Rd. 43rd Ave. to 27th Ave.	23.4	4-6
* Broadway 7th Ave. to 16th St.	23.4	
* 19th Ave. Indian School to Bethany Home	23.4	
* Cave Creek 7th St. to 20th St.	23.1	* *
Papago Park Rd. Van Buren to McDowell	22.8	* *
44th St. Washington to McDowell	21.1	4-6
* 43rd Ave. Bethany Home to Northern	20.8	
* Thomas Rd. 51st Ave. to 35th Ave.	19.5	
* "Q" Ave. 43rd Ave. to Black Canyon	19.3	
* 59th Ave. Van Buren to Thomas	17.8	
* Van Buren 48th St. to 60th St.	15.6	
* Glendale Ave. 16th St. to 32nd St.	14.2	
* Baseline Rd. 16th St. to 32nd St.	8.9	

  * Test segments.
 ** Construction completed.
Note: 75.3 miles of major arterial street rated.

During the past five years, 96 bottleneck projects have been completed. This is an average of nearly 20 a year. These projects ranged in cost from $500 to $45,000—the average was approximately $5,000. These costs include signals where necessary, the relocation of drainage structures, and widening and other improvements.

CONCLUSIONS

Factual data on traffic volume, travel time, and accidents provide the foundation for establishing priorities for major street construction programs and treating high-accident locations and eliminating congestion bottlenecks. These factual data should be applied to develop a balanced street program that will lead toward the construction of a total street system. One important aspect of the major street construction program is that it contributes significantly to the building of a city. This is particularly true in a new city such as Phoenix.

The end product of the continuing comprehensive cooperative urban transportation planning process must be provision of useful and attractive facilities to serve the public. The application of factual data to establish priorities is the key to securing the maximum benefit from the limited funds available for urban street improvement.

REFERENCES

1. Wilbur Smith and Associates. A Major Street and Highway Plan—Phoenix Urban Area—Maricopa County, Arizona, 1960.
2. Street Deficiency Study—1961. City of Phoenix, Arizona.
3. Street and Freeway Needs Study—1965. City of Phoenix, Arizona.
4. Annual Budgets, 1960-61 to 1966-67. City of Phoenix, Arizona.
5. Six-Year Major Street Program—1966. City of Phoenix, Arizona.
6. Arizona Highway Needs, 1965-1985. Arizona Highway Department, Phoenix, Arizona.
7. Haley, Charles E., Hall, Edward M., and Johnson, Arnold A. Travel Time—A Measure of Service and a Criterion for Improvement Priorities. Highway Research Record 35, pp. 1-17, 1963.
8. Hall, Edward M., and Hixon, C. Dwight. The Use of a Priority Formula in Urban Street Programming. Highway Research Record 87, pp. 57-77, 1965.
9. Haley, Charles E. Eliminating Urban Bottlenecks. City of Phoenix, Arizona, June 1966.

Directional Flow Improvements on Urban Streets

JOHN N. LAPLANTE
Traffic Engineer III
Design and Planning Division
Bureau of Street Traffic
City of Chicago

This paper discusses methods of improving prime direction flow on individual streets. It is limited to those methods that can be accomplished within existing rights-of-way and with minimum street reconstruction. This means either special lane designations, such as reversible lanes, exclusive use lanes, or specific turning and storage lanes, or reversible one-way operation of the entire street during certain hours of the day. All of the methods described are aimed for the ordinary city street, rather than the expressway or special parkway.

REVERSIBLE LANES

The reversible lane is one of the most efficient methods of providing for increased capacity. It can be employed on any street having three or more moving traffic lanes and directional peak volumes occurring at certain periods each day. The directional traffic volume should be at least 3 or 4 to 1 with existing conditions so congested that average speed decreases 25 percent during peak periods. There must also be adequate capacity at the terminals of any proposed reversible lane system.

The major advantage of such a system is that it can add significant street capacity with minimal initial capital costs. It also permits multi-lane operational efficiencies in the peak direction. These efficiencies are primarily due to the increased ability of faster moving traffic to pass slower or stopped vehicles.

A major disadvantage of a reversible lane system can be the reduced capacity and flexibility in the off-peak direction. It can also be quite hazardous if not adequately designated and signed. Such a system may also prove more costly in the long run if it postpones needed capital improvements or if it runs into costly maintenance and daily change-over expenses.

Methods of designation range from permanent overhead or roadside signs to permanent physical barriers with overhead lane signals. The least expensive method is the permanent roadside sign. Such a sign will give the hours of operation and the expected motorist behavior during those hours. This does not, however, provide any positive indication to the unobservant motorist of the time of operation or the specific lanes in which he is to drive. Hanging such signs directly over the affected lanes is somewhat better, but can still be confusing to the less capable driver.

In Detroit, Grand River Avenue has been operated for many years with four lanes in the peak direction and two lanes in the opposing direction during peak periods. The operation consists of large permanent signs hung over the two center lanes every two blocks with the following alternating messages for the inbound traffic: USE BOTH CENTER LANES—7:00 to 9:00 A. M. —Monday thru Friday and KEEP OFF BOTH CENTER LANES—4:30 to 6:30 P. M. —Monday thru Friday. The outbound signs have the times reversed. Before and after studies found that peak direction travel time was cut and that volume in the peak direction increased 41 percent.

Giving these signs interior illumination or making them of neon tubing will give the motorist a positive indication of the times of operation and will be far less confusing. Since they will not be visible during the off-peak hours, they can be made much more eye-catching during the times that they are used. Placing these signs often enough to be always visible to the motorist can run into considerable expense, however, especially if the wording is long or complex.

Using standard lane control symbols in place of words is the preferred method and will cut down on the size of the illuminated sign considerably. The Manual of Uniform Traffic Control Devices has specified a red X over any lane not meant for travel in that direction and a downward pointing green arrow for lanes in which travel is permitted. These signals are being used more and more frequently, and their meaning is becoming accepted by most motorists. They are very easy to maintain and operate, and provide a positive indication of both lane of travel and time of operation. They do have a rather high initial installation cost, and in commercial areas the overhead lane signals tend to get lost in the background lights. They must also be placed far enough away from signalized intersections to avoid being confused with the regular traffic signals.

Chicago has used overhead lane signals on its Hollywood-Ridge system for almost ten years with very successful results. Both streets are four lanes and provide for three lanes in the peak direction. The lane signals are the recommended red X and downward pointing green arrow. The entire system cost $72,000 and is slightly more than one mile in length. Two-way volume increases of more than 50 percent (from 2250 to 3550 veh/hr during the peak hour) were noted on Ridge Avenue. No significant changes in accident experience were noted, and in more than nine years of operation, there has never been a head-on collision involving any of the reversible lanes. Parking is prohibited on both sides, at all times.

Detroit has recently installed a combination sign and signal arrangement over the center lane of Michigan Avenue, a five-lane roadway. The sign can either show a red X with No Left Turn legend, a green arrow with a No Left Turn legend, or no symbol at all with an Only Left Turn legend. This last legend is for off-peak periods and allows the center lane to be used for left turns from either direction. Parking is prohibited at all times. This system has produced volume increases in the peak direction of from 4 to 20 percent in the morning peak period and up to 7 percent in the evening. Travel time during these two periods has decreased 19 and 20 percent, respectively, and average speed is up 23 percent. There has also been an overall accident decrease of 19 percent, although most of this was due to a 93 percent decrease in accidents with parking vehicles brought about by the full-time prohibition of parking. The decrease in non-parking accidents has been 4 percent.

An even more positive designation of reversible lane usage can be obtained through the use of pedestal signs and cones. These signs and cones are manually placed out on the street at the start of each rush period, and are removed when traffic returns to normal. Although there is only a small initial cost outlay, this method involves costly daily maintenance and change-over manpower expense and can be quite hazardous if the cones are not spaced often enough or if a number of consecutive cones gets knocked out of position by passing cars.

Los Angeles was the first city to use reversible lanes during the peak periods, and these lanes are almost completely designated by manually placed signs and cones. The first installation was made in 1928 and there are now approximately thirteen miles of streets using reversible lanes. The total annual operation cost is a little less than $2,000 per lane mile. A study of accident reports reveals in general that the accident rate per million vehicle-miles is much less on these streets than on major streets where lane reversal is not used. Field observations indicate a more satisfactory operation, in terms of smoothness of flow and frequency of stops, and decreased travel times ranging from 1 to 15 min.

Milwaukee used both overhead lane signals and manually placed cones on a six-lane street designated as an interim freeway terminal distributor system. This seven-block stretch of West Clybourn Street was placed in operation in 1963 and has handled two-way traffic volumes of 55,000 veh/day, with as many as 4,000 veh/hr in the peak direction. The data from these five cities are summarized in Table 1. Other successful systems have been installed in Cleveland, Louisville, Memphis, Cincinnati, Arlington, and New York City, where the five-lane Queensborough Bridge uses overhead red and green lane signals.

Permanent physical barriers give the best indication of proper lane usage, but are not usually applicable to normal city streets. On bridges and viaducts, however, where there is no entering or crossing traffic to contend with, this method can be quite useful.

TABLE 1

EXAMPLES OF REVERSIBLE LANES

City	Street	No. of Lanes	Type of Installation	Reported Results
Detroit	Grand River Ave.	6	Overhead signs	Travel time cut. Peak-direction volumes up 41%.
Chicago	Hollywood-Ridge	4	Overhead signals	Two-way volumes up 50%. No increase in accidents.
Detroit	Michigan Ave.	5	Overhead signs and signals	Peak-direction volumes up 4-20%. Travel times down 19-20%. Average speed up 23%. Overall accidents down 19%. Non-parking accidents down 4%.
Los Angeles	13 miles of streets	Varies	Manually placed cones and signs	Accident rate less than streets without lane reversal. Travel times decreased 1-15 min.
Milwaukee	W. Clybourn St.	6	Overhead signals	Interim freeway terminal distributor. Peak direction volumes as high as 4,000 vph.

This usually takes the form of reversible lanes in the center separated from the regular lanes on either side by small curbs or barriers with appropriate signing and channelization at each end. This method is very easy and inexpensive to maintain and operate, but it can be costly to install and is, by its very nature, a much more permanent type of control.

New York City's eight-lane George Washington Bridge with its two-lane physically separated reversible center roadway is an excellent example of this reversible lane technique. Chicago's eight-lane Lake Shore Drive with its three sets of hydraulically operated divider fins is another specialized reversible lane technique that will probably not be applicable to most situations.

SPECIAL LANE DESIGNATIONS

Other special lane designations are left-turn only and right-turn only lanes. These special uses of lanes are quite common, and their efficiency and safety are well established. The most common deficiencies of these types of lane designations are inadequate tapers (should be 20 to 1 on most city streets) and failure to line up through lanes across intersections. Allowing paint markings to deteriorate to the point where they are no longer visible is another deficiency. This has become a common type of improvement, with additional information readily available in the traffic literature.

REVERSIBLE ONE-WAY ROADWAYS

Occasionally, special lane designations or even reversible lanes are not adequate to handle the rush hour traffic in the peak direction. In some situations it may be possible to make the entire street one-way in the peak direction during certain periods of the day. Such an installation has all the advantages of reversible lanes, without the confusion or hazard of opposing lanes of traffic on the same street. However, it does not provide for the off-peak direction at all and can be quite complicated and confusing at the terminals and at intersecting streets.

There are two basic situations where this type of improvement can be applied. The most common is at a specific bottleneck where a reversal of a short street segment of bridge, or the creation of a short reversible roadway segment with no intersecting roadways between the two terminals, will handle the necessary volumes. In either case, some facilities must be available for traffic flowing in the opposite direction. This can be a nearby bridge or a paralleling street or any other logical and convenient traffic rerouting plan. This will require careful planning at the segment terminal and may require expenses for daily maintenance and change-over manpower.

An example of this type of reversible roadway is a two-lane turning roadway in effect at the intersection of Sheridan and Devon in Chicago. The roadway is approximately 300 ft in length and handles a heavy left-turn movement in the morning and the reverse right-turn movement in the evening. It is used in conjunction with a reversible lane system on Sheridan Road, and is designated by cones, pedestal signs and two internally illuminated signs. During non-rush hours it is used as a right-turn only lane. This roadway was installed to handle peak hour turning demands of over 2000 veh/hr and has resulted in a very smooth and improved method of operation.

The other application of the reversible one-way roadway is the reversal of an entire street for a number of blocks during certain parts of the day. Again, provision must be made for the opposing flow on adjacent streets, and the terminals must be adequately signed and channelized. In addition, particular care must be exercised at intersecting streets to prevent motorists from using the street in the wrong direction during times of one-way operation. This can be done with special one-way and turn prohibition signs listing the hours during which they are in effect or with internally illuminated or neon signs that are lit only during the appropriate hours. The regular signs can be quite confusing to the unitiated or less capable driver, while the illuminated signs are considerably more expensive.

One of the best examples of this type of operation is the reversal of 13th Street in Washington, D.C., during the rush hours. This four-lane street, normally a two-way street, is made one-way inbound during the morning rush and one-way outbound in the evening. Blank out neon one-way arrows are used on all cross streets along 13th Street. These radio-controlled flashing red arrows indicate to approaching motorists the direction of travel on 13th Street during the a.m. and p.m. rush hours. At all other times the arrows are dark, thereby indicating two-way operation. This street has been successfully operating as a reversible one-way street for over two decades. It is an excellent example of squeezing out maximum capacity on a relatively narrow and otherwise inadequate city street.

CONCLUSIONS

It is possible to improve prime direction flow on individual city streets without major reconstruction or right-of-way acquisition. The reversible lane can be a very efficient method of providing increased capacity with minimal initial capital costs on any street having three or more moving traffic lanes and directional peak volumes occurring at certain periods each day. However, the use of reversible lanes will reduce capacity and flexibility in the off-peak direction, can run into costly daily maintenance costs, and can be quite hazardous if not properly executed. Most applications of reversible lanes have proved quite successful with sizable increases in traffic volumes, significant decreases in travel time, and no adverse accident experiences.

Where reversible lanes are not capable of handling the rush-hour traffic, it is sometimes possible to make the entire street one-way in the peak direction during certain periods of the day. This avoids the hazard of having opposing lanes of traffic on the same street, but it does increase the confusion at the terminals and intermediate street intersections and drastically affects the off-peak direction traffic capacity.

REFERENCES

1. Dorsey, R. I. The Use of the Off Center Lane Movement in Los Angeles. Traffic Quarterly, Eno Foundation, Vol. 2, p. 291, 1948.
2. Todd, Mansfield M. Reversing Flow in Center Lane of Three Lane Roads. Proc. ITE, 20th Annual Meeting, 1949.
3. Todd, Mansfield M. Effects of Reversible Lane Movement Signalization of Three Lane Highways. HRB Proc., Vol. 30, pp. 346-354, 1950.
4. Watkins, W. F. New Plans for Some Old Streets. Traffic Quarterly, Eno Foundation, Vol. 4, 1950.
5. Traffic Engineering Handbook. ITE, 2nd Ed., pp. 326-329, 1950. (Also 1965 Ed., pp. 559-565.)

6. Dorsey, R. I. Off Center Aids a City Solution. Proc. ITE, 22nd Annual Meeting, 1951.
7. Lyman, E. C. Lane Directing Signals Aid in Solving Traffic Problems. Municipal Signal Engineer, Vol. 16, 1951.
8. Zimmerman, T. W. Reversible Sign Technique. Traffic Engineering Magazine, pp. 415-416, August 1954.
9. Matson, T. M. , Smith, W. S. , and Hurd, F. W. Traffic Engineering, McGraw-Hill Book Company, pp. 302-303, 403, 1955.
10. Rice, T. T. Unbalanced Traffic Flow on Three and Four Lane Streets. Traffic Quarterly, Eno Foundation, Vol. 10, pp. 137, 153, Jan. 1956.
11. AASHO. A Policy on Arterial Highways in Urban Areas. Pp. 208, 229-230, 280, 282, 285, 353-354, and 434, 1957.
12. Bugge, W. A. The Seattle Freeway. Traffic Quarterly, Eno Foundation, pp. 69-79, Jan. 1958.
13. Here's How to Handle Rush-Hour Traffic. Engineering News-Record, Vol. 161, No. 6, pp. 30-34, Aug. 14, 1958.
14. Technical Committee 3F, ITE. A Survey of Off Center Reversible Lane Operational Techniques. Traffic Engineering Magazine, pp. 43-48, Oct. 1958.
15. Technical Committee 3F, ITE. Off Center Lane Movements. Traffic Engineering Magazine, pp. 43-49, Nov. 1958.
16. Forbes, T. W. , Gervais, E. , and Allen, T. M. Effectiveness of Symbols for Lane Control Signals. HRB Bull. 244, pp. 16-29, 1959.
17. Eason, S. D. Reversible Lanes on the Seattle Freeway. Washington State Highways Dept. , 1959.
18. Bugge, W. A. Planning for the Seattle Freeway. ASCE, Los Angeles Meeting, Feb. 1959.
19. Radio Control for Reversible Flow. Traffic Engineering, Vol. 29, No. 5, pp. 16-17, Feb. 1959.
20. Exnicios, T. F. Report on Unbalanced Traffic Flow Operations. ITE, 30th Annual Meeting, Chicago, Illinois, Sept. 1960.
21. McGarthy, D. A Reversible Roadway. Highway Highlights, pp. 8-9, April 1961.
22. May, A. D. , Jr. Squirrel Hill Tunnel Operations Study. Ramo-Wooldridge, Aug. 1961.
23. "Zipper" Funnels Expressway Traffic. Street Engineering, Vol. 6, No. 12, pp. 16-17, Dec. 1961.
24. Hoose, H. T. Peak-Hour Parking Restrictions and Reversible Lanes in CBD. Proc. ITE, 1961.
25. Morse, R. W. Reversible Roadway for Seattle Freeway. N. Y. American Society of Civil Engineers, Proc. , 1964.
26. Armored Train "Zippers" Guard Reversible Lanes. Highway Highlights, pp. 12-13, Jan. 1962.
27. Still, R. C. Four and One-Half Miles of Lane Control Signals. Municipal Signal Engineer, Vol. 27, No. 2, pp. 22-24, March-April 1962.
28. Still, R. C. Continuous Signal Controlled Reversible Lanes. Traffic Engineering and Control, Vol. 3, No. 12, April 1962.
29. Bartelsmeyer, R. R. Reversible Freeway Lanes on the Northwest Expressway in Chicago. Traffic Quarterly, Eno Foundation, Vol. 16, No. 2, pp. 155-172, April 1962.
30. Reversible Lanes Speed Expressway Traffic. American City, Vol. 77, No. 5, pp. 98-100, May 1962.
31. Cottingham, K. E. A Proposed Surveillance System on the Seattle Freeway. Traffic Engineering, Vol. 32, No. 9, pp. 21-24, June 1962.
32. Arnold, S. R. Tidal Flow Traffic. Traffic Engineering and Control, Vol. 4, No. 8, pp. 452-454, 456, Dec. 1962.
33. May, A. D. , Jr. , and Fielder, D. Squirrel Hill Tunnel Operations Study. HRB Bull. 324, pp. 12-37, 1962.
34. Greenberg, J. Preliminary Analysis of the Lincoln Tunnel Changeover Problem. Report of The Port of New York Authority, Tunnels and Bridges Dept. , April 1963.

35. Hoose, H. T. Planning Effective Reversible Lane Control. Traffic Quarterly, Eno Foundation, Vol. 17, No. 3, pp. 408-413, July 1963.

36. Wake, A. G. Reversible Lanes Reduce Congestion at Little Cost. Traffic Engineering, Vol. 34, No. 8, pp. 39-40, May 1964.

37. Hutchison, A. L. Reversible Lane Operation. International Road Safety and Traffic Review, Vol. 12, No. 3, pp. 29-32, Summer 1964.

38. Jennings, S. W. Tidal Flow Working on Albert Bridge. Traffic Engineering and Control, Vol. 6, No. 8, pp. 401-505, Dec. 1964.

39. Gazis, D. C. Optimum Assignment of a Reversible Lane in an Oversaturated Two-Way Traffic Link. IBM Watson Research Center, June 1965.

40. Thorpe, J. D. Off-Centre Street Operation in Melbourne. Traffic Engineering, Vol. 36, No. 11, pp. 26-30, Aug. 1966.

41. Traffic Engineering Handbook. ITE, 1966.

42. DeRose, Frank, Jr. Reversible Center-Lane Traffic System—Directional and Left-Turn Usage. Highway Research Record 151, pp. 1-17, 1966.

43. Mitton, John. Effect and Advantages of the Use of Reversible Street Practices. Proc. ITE, pp. 86-89, 1946.

44. Fencl, R. G. Jackson Boulevard Analysis of Traffic Operations. HRB Proc., Vol. 30, pp. 297-313, 1950.

45. First Aluminum Traffic Control Arches. Civil Engineering, p. 365, June 1951.

46. Traffic Improvement Plan for the Central Business District, Philadelphia, Pennsylvania. Wilbur Smith and Associates, pp. 65-71, 91, 1957.

47. Manual on Uniform Traffic Control Devices. June 1961, pp. 225-228.

48. Bruening, M. E. 6-Lane Street...8-Lane Performance. Traffic Engineering, pp. 16-18, June 1964.

49. Benefit Analysis of Olympic Boulevard Reverse Lane Control. Los Angeles Bureau of Traffic Research Staff Report, June 3, 1965.

Addendum

On 13th Street, N.W., in Washington, D.C., the signs shown in Figure 1 were found to be confusing.

The local police precincts indicated on several occasions that the black and yellow multi-message signs were difficult to read and confusing. When the signing was converted to blank-out type neon indications this confusion was eliminated immediately. A sample of these flashing neon one-way messages with a reversible arrow is shown in Figure 2.

This part-time one-way operation is in effect on 13th Street, N.W., southbound only between 7:00 and 9:30 a.m. and northbound only between 4:00 and 6:30 p.m., Monday through Friday. The balance of the time 13th Street operates as a two-way roadway.

Connecticut Avenue, N.W., is a 60-ft wide roadway with parking normally permitted on both sides of the street. However, during the morning and evening rush hours, Monday through Friday, this major arterial street operates four lanes in the predominant direction of traffic flow and two lanes in the opposite direction. Parking is prohibited during the rush hours on both sides of the street.

The only notification given to motorists concerning this reversible lane operation is a regulatory sign mounted at the curb at the beginning of each block. This black on white rectangular sign merely states "4 Lanes—7-9:30 a.m., 2 Lanes—4-6:30 p.m. Monday through Friday." These signs are over 30 ft to the right of a motorist in the center lane and often times are obscured by buses or trucks in the curb lane.

The pavement markings on this street are a solid white centerline and white stripe lane lines. This arrangement leaves much to be desired during the hours of reversible lane flow. Although exact figures are not available, a number of rush hour traffic

Figure 1.

Figure 2.

surveillance people, and also the police accident investigation units, have reported mishaps relating to this 4 to 2 lane rush-hour operation. Fortunately, records do indicate that no fatalities have occurred in connection with this little publicized unbalanced rush-hour lane operation. The real answer to this problem, of course, is the use of overhead lane control signals which have not been accepted to date.

One-Way Major Arterial Streets

JOHN A. BRUCE

Director of Traffic Engineering

Denver, Colorado

To be successful, all business districts and other traffic generation areas need traffic access, traffic circulation within, and parking or terminal facilities. In past years when traffic flows were lighter the conventional two-way arterial was adequate; but under today's heavier flow conditions, almost all cities are utilizing one-way arterial systems to improve access and circulation. These one-way arterials and one-way grid systems have a record of successful service. It is difficult to imagine the congestion many cities would have today without them. Furthermore, most communities are planning more one-way streets to improve the level of traffic service along their major transportation corridors and in their business districts.

Several reasons may exist for conversion to one-way operation. In general, one-way streets are used because they are more efficient and safer than two-way arterials; thus, they relieve traffic congestion and promote automobile and pedestrian safety.

Improved efficiency and level of traffic service is developed in several ways. One-way streets organize traffic better for improved operation and circulation, allow better progressive signal timing, solve the left-turn problem inherent in two-way arterials, allow better use of multi-turns, develop a more efficient use of street widths, and reduce vehicular and pedestrian conflicts. Through these factors, the capacity of a one-way system is usually considerably higher than a comparable set of two-way arterials; delays are minimized, and travel speeds are increased.

One-way streets are safer because conflicts in the flow pattern are reduced, the one-way direction of traffic eliminates the problem of head-on collisions, and pedestrians can cross one-way streets much easier. Nighttime safety is improved by the elimination of oncoming traffic headlight glare.

ONE-WAY STREETS

Operational Characteristics and Circulation

Unidirectional flow simplifies and organizes traffic better and results in greatly improved operational characteristics for a one-way system, allowing this system to collect and distribute traffic more efficiently. A street should accept traffic from other streets easily and should distribute that traffic to desired destinations including other streets, curb or off-street parking areas, and through curb cuts, to other auto-oriented uses such as drive-ins and service stations. In urban areas, even on crosstown one-way arterials, very little of the traffic is of the "through" type.

Two-way streets have difficulty in distributing traffic, primarily because much of the traffic desires to turn left in the face of the opposing flow which has the right-of-way. Also, parking spaces on the left of a two-way street cannot be reached, and on divided roadways, curb access points on the left are not accessible.

On the other hand, one-way streets distribute their traffic to the left or right with equal ease. Parking spaces and curb access on both sides are open to all motorists. Businessmen often resist one-way operation because they fear the effect of having only one-half of the traffic passing their doors. Yet, it is easy to demonstrate that if motorists are properly directed through public and private announcements, and when motorists have developed experience with a one-way arterial system, businessmen will receive the benefits of the better and safer mobility and access developed by a pair of one-way streets.

Signal Timing

In modern street operation a great deal of emphasis is placed on a smooth flow of traffic controlled by traffic signals. The most efficient, the most accident-free, and the most pleasurable to drive arterial system is the one which maintains a reasonably constant and uniform speed throughout. Stop-and-start driving destroys all three of these attributes.

Two-way streets can provide this desirable smooth flow, if proper spacing of traffic signals can be maintained. All too often, however, signals are required at spacings too close to permit timing that affords smooth flow in both directions. Compromises must be made in the delicate time-distance relationship which governs speed, and the result is a loss of the desired uniform travel speed.

To solve the left-turn circulation problems of two-way arterials, invariably many added left-turn signal phases are installed. These added phases further complicate signal-timing procedures and further restrict the traffic engineer's ability to provide smooth progressive signal timing and flow. Acute signal-timing problems brought about by adverse spacing and multi-phase operation can nearly ruin an otherwise well-designed two-way street.

On a one-way street system there is much less difficulty in obtaining uniform flow and better efficiency because the spacing of signals is no longer a major factor, and the adding of special phases is seldom required. A smooth progression can be provided even with traffic signals every block, such as along a business one-way street or through a grid.

Vehicular and Pedestrian Conflicts, Left-Turn Problems and Multi-Turns

One indication of the accident potential of an intersection is the number of vehicular conflicts. Comparing the intersection of two 4-lane two-way streets with two 4-lane one-way streets, the two-way streets generate 44 possible vehicular conflicts, whereas the one-way streets have only 18 conflict points. This reduction is a major advantage.

Because they cross opposing traffic lanes, left-turn movements on a two-way street cause many points of conflict; therefore, the left-turn movement requires expert motorist judgment unless a special signal phase is provided so that the turn can be made without opposing traffic. Difficulty with left turns from two-way streets is very apparent because of the great number of requests from motorists for left-turn signal phases and the many high-accident locations recorded where left turns are the basic cause.

Left turns from two-way arterials, unless provided with separate left-turn storage lanes, or prohibited entirely, also cause major delays to through lane traffic. Through-motorist irritation leads to unsafe driving practices, such as lane changing and speed limit violations involving motorists trying to catch up with the normal flow set by the signal timing.

One-way streets solve the left-turn problem inherent on two-way streets and even allow a multi-turn design which is difficult to install in two-way operation. Multi-turns in one-way flows must be carefully considered, however, as double turns from a one-way street are a problem if pedestrian volumes in the conflicting crosswalk are moderate to heavy and special WALK phases are not provided. Many cities, however, have utilized double-right and left turns along one-way systems successfully for many years.

Efficient Use of Street Widths

In two-way street design, many streets in areas where congestion occurs have relatively fixed roadway widths and their dimensions do not lend themselves to two equal and usable half-widths for opposing traffic flows. For example, assuming no parking, a street of 34 ft in roadway width with two-way operation is only suitable for two-lane design. In one-way operation, three lanes can be fitted to a 34-ft pavement with an increase in capacity. The same principle applies to other widths which provide an odd number of lanes. More efficient use of existing pavement widths can often be made by designing all lanes in one direction.

Capacity

It has been noted that one-way systems provide better capacity potential because of better operational characteristics, better signal timing, fewer vehicular and pedestrian conflicts, the elimination of the left-turn problem, provision of multi-turn possibilities, and more efficient use of certain street widths. Many references indicate that one-ways improve capacity under various conditions from 25 to 50 percent or more over comparable two-way arterials. This, of course, is a great boon to those responsible for traffic movement in a community. Capacity improvement leads to many one-way street developments as an alternative procedure to expensive two-way street widening projects.

At this point it should be emphasized that the 1965 Highway Capacity Manual (1, p. 325) cautions that the subject of relative efficiencies and capacities of one-way and two-way urban streets has solicited much discussion in recent years. Although early criteria showed substantial benefits in one-way over two-way operation, later interim intersection capacity criteria of the late 1950's showed somewhat contradictory relationships, largely because upgraded one-way systems were being compared with less efficient, unimproved two-way systems. However, the Highway Capacity Manual does concur that one-way traffic flow is more efficient and generally is highly desirable.

Accidents

There are no national statistics concerning the number of accidents on two-way streets versus one-way streets, but there are many indications from cities across the country that accident totals drop after conversion to one-way operation. Reports such as a 23 percent drop in total accidents, and a 62 percent drop in pedestrian accidents in Sacramento, Calif.; 51 percent in Hollywood, Fla.; 50 percent in Raleigh, N.C.; 28 percent in Modesto, Calif.; and 50 percent in Portland, Ore., support the conclusion that accident frequency will be reduced with a properly engineered one-way system (2).

One of the factors involved in a higher accident rate on two-way streets is undoubtedly headlight glare. National statistics show that the nighttime death rate is three times as high as the daytime death rate in urban areas (3). Thus, the use of one-way streets to eliminate nighttime headlight glare, head-on collisions, and left-turn collisions is a very positive step in the direction of reducing accident experience in urban areas.

From the pedestrian standpoint, the one-way street is also much safer. Pedestrians need only look in one direction for vehicular traffic. The platooning of traffic on a one-way street is usually very evident, thus making it quite easy for pedestrians to cross safely during well-defined gaps in flow. One-way street intersections have at least one and sometimes two protected crosswalks where no vehicular turns are made. From the signal-timing standpoint, pedestrians are also aided as excessively long cycles are usually avoided where one-way streets are used. Long cycles cause waiting periods beyond the tolerance of pedestrians, a condition which discourages voluntary observance of traffic controls by pedestrians.

In comparison, two-way arterials are much more difficult for pedestrians to cross because of the basic problems inherent in two-way traffic, e.g., pedestrians must continually look both ways for approaching traffic, adequate gaps in traffic are much less frequent, and the number of conflicts in intersection crosswalks is much greater.

Effect of One-Way Operation on Businesses

In the past, the great majority of businessmen have not favored one-way streets; many still do not. However, in cities today where one-way streets are frequently used as access arterials and CBD grids, disfavor is now at a minimum, as most businessmen realize that business activity is enhanced by the benefits of a properly designed one-way system.

A study conducted in Denver, Colo., in 1964 (4), summarized all available information on the economic effects of one-way streets on businesses. Included where a detailed study of 16th Street in Sacramento, Calif.; a survey by the U.S. Chamber of
Commerce; and a survey by Fresno, Calif. Without excessive detail, it can be said
that business on one-way 16th Street in Sacramento increased nearly 5 percent more
than business on the other streets in the city. The Chamber of Commerce survey
showed that businessmen in 103 out of 134 cities were in favor of one-way operation
after a fair trial. The Fresno survey of merchants associations indicated that 90 percent of the businessmen felt that one-way streets were not harmful to business, and
85 percent would recommend them.

Certainly some types of businesses may be harmed, although probably only tempo-
rarily, by loss of traffic in a certain direction. These are primarily drive-in facilities which previously catered only to the direction of traffic which was eliminated. On
the other hand, many other businesses will certainly increase their trade through the
improved accessibility of one-way street systems.

Effect of One-Way Operation on a Residential Street

When a major arterial through a residential area needs traffic improvement, one-way
system development is often the best answer. Transition construction at the end of a
one-way system can usually be designed and landscaped to fit the neighborhood. The
residential one-ways created for the arterial flow can usually carry the traffic demand
without extensive widening, the use of parking prohibitions, and the loss of street trees.

However, if the added flow capacity must be developed under a two-way arterial
plan, such a design almost always means widening, with the loss of street trees. The
widening usually places moving traffic very close to residences and provides only a
narrow attached sidewalk. This type of design leaves much to be desired and means
less living comfort for those along the arterial.

Certainly, when a one-way couplet is suggested or developed in a residential district, those living along the heretofore little-used residential street will not be benefited by the added traffic. However, those living on the congested two-way arterial
that is to be converted will benefit greatly, particularly in comparison to a two-way
widening project. The overall benefit to the neighborhood as a whole appears to be
better, and the use of one-way street designs for major arterial streets in new subdivisions should be considered.

Other Considerations

There are a few minor disadvantages concerning one-way street flow. These can be
summarized as follows: one-way streets may necessitate additional travel for some
motorists; tourists may become confused with the system; one-way streets may require additional sign posting; emergency vehicles may have more difficulty moving on
a one-way street than a comparable two-way arterial; transit riding habits may be adversely affected, especially if the distance between the one-way streets is great; added
turns along a one-way system may increase pedestrian conflicts unless separate signal
WALK phases are provided; and in a one-way grid or arterial system progressive signal timing may work to the disadvantage of circulating traffic as a block-circulating
motorist generally will have to stop for a red signal at each successive intersection.

The disadvantages, however, are greatly offset by the benefits of one-way flow.

A New York City Department of Traffic publication, "Questions and Answers About
One-Way Avenues," points out that one-way street operation reduces delays in bus
movements caused by congestion, thus giving riders a more enjoyable trip in a smoother
flow of traffic. Also, bus patrons have shorter waits for buses since buses are less
subject to the "bunching up" which occurs in congestion.

The New York report also notes that one-way street flows reduce air pollution from
motor vehicles because of a reduction in stops and periods of acceleration and
deceleration.

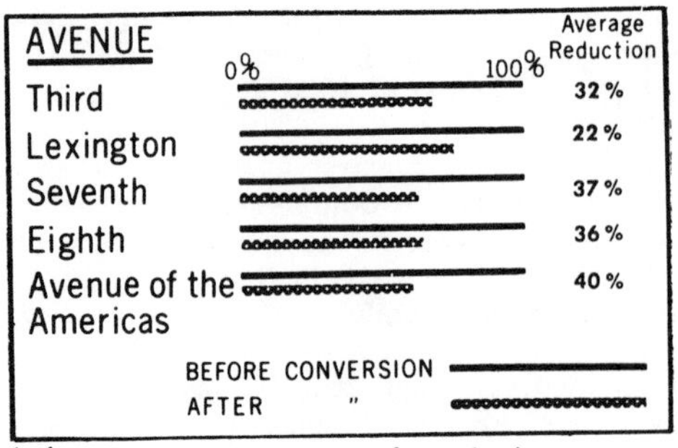

(a) *One-way avenues reduce trip time.*

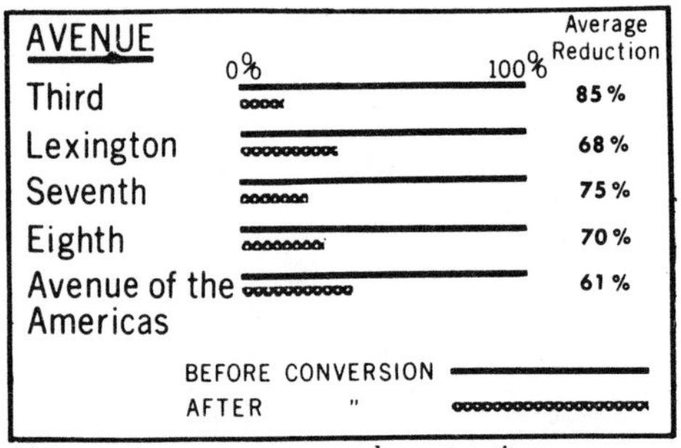

(b) *One-way avenues reduce stop time.*

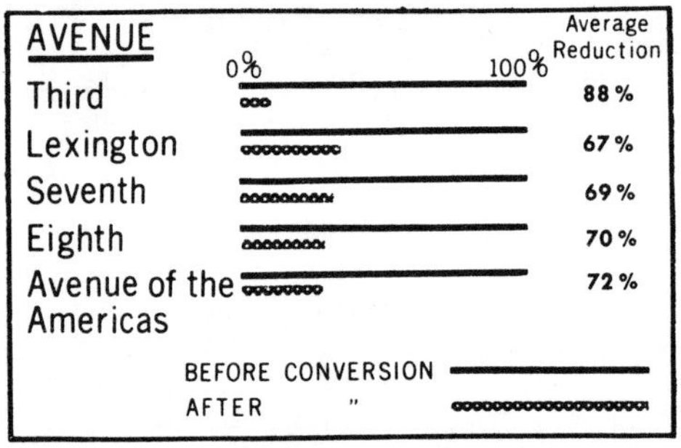

(c) *One-way avenues reduce the number of stops.*

Figure 1.

Future Planning

From the foregoing general discussion, it should be emphasized that the benefits of one-way flow must be considered when future traffic plans are being developed. New business districts, both downtown and along arterials, urban renewal areas, and new subdivisions can certainly use all of the advantages of one-way flows. The benefits can be combined in future planning to provide the most efficient, the safest, the most economic, and the easiest to drive arterial system possible.

ONE-WAY BEFORE AND AFTER STUDIES FROM SELECTED CITIES

New York, N. Y.

The information from New York City has been supplied by Henry A. Barnes, Commissioner, New York City Department of Traffic. The general information comes from a report by the Department entitled "Questions and Answers About One-Way Avenues." The second item is from data sheets concerning a specific study of 5th and Madison Avenues in New York.

General Information Concerning One-Way Avenues. Studies conducted before and after past major conversions have shown the following improvements and advantages gained through one-way operation. Figures shown are minimums. In a number of conversions, specific gains have substantially exceeded the minimums.

Pedestrian accidents reduced	20%
Total trip time reduced	22%
Stopped time reduced	60%
Number of stops reduced	65%
Crosstown delay reduced	40%
Crosstown capacity increased	20%
Bus running time reduced	17%

This information comes from study of 3rd Avenue, Lexington Avenue, 7th Avenue, 8th Avenue, and the Avenue of the Americas. These are major arterial streets carrying traffic through Manhattan. Figure 1 shows (a) the reduction in trip time, (b) the reduction in stop time, and (c) the reduction in the number of stops after conversion to one-way operation.

Before and After Studies of 5th and Madison Avenues. Tables 1 through 4 give the results of an examination of one-way traffic flow benefits achieved on 5th Avenue and Madison Avenue in New York City. Travel time, the number of stops, and the accident experience are studied in detail before and after conversion to one-way operation. Traffic volumes are included for comparison.

TABLE 1

5TH AVENUE—BEFORE AND AFTER CONVERSION (Conversion Date, Jan. 4, 1966)

Location	Month	Avg. Daily Volume	Avg. Trip Time-Min.	Average M. P. H.	Avg. No. of Stops
Washington Sq. to 23rd St.,	June 1966	18722	2.4	19.7	1
0.8 mile	Dec. 1965	15265	4.7	10.2	3
		+23%	-49%	+88%	-66%
23rd St. to 42nd St.,	June 1966	23591	2.9	18.6	1
0.9 mile	Dec. 1965	21725	7.3	7.4	5
		+9%	-60%	+151%	-80%
42nd St. to 57th St.,	June 1966	29965	4.4	9.4	3
0.7 mile	Dec. 1965	26130	7.4	5.7	5
		+15%	-39%	+65%	-40%
57th St. to 138th St.,	June 1966	14953	16.4	14.9	7
4.1 miles	Dec. 1965	11592	22.4	11.0	14.8
		+29%	-28%	+35%	-53%
Total (avg.),	June 1966	19595	26.4	14.8	11
6.5 miles	Dec. 1965	16411	42.1	9.3	28
		+19%	-37%	+59%	-60%

TABLE 2

MADISON AVENUE—BEFORE AND AFTER CONVERSION
(Conversion Date, Jan. 4, 1966)

Location	Month	Avg. Daily Volume	Avg. Trip Time-Min.	Average M. P. H.	Avg. No. of Stops
23rd St. to 42nd St.,	June 1966	12057	5.9	9.2	4.3
0.9 mile	Dec. 1965	11224	7.0	7.7	4.5
		+7%	-16%	+19%	-7%
42nd St. to 57th St.,	June 1966	27277	5.3	7.9	4.5
0.7 mile	Dec. 1965	24136	5.9	7.1	5.3
		+13%	-10%	+11.3%	-17%
57th St. to 135th St.,	June 1966	20090	14.9	16.5	4.8
4.1 miles	Dec. 1965	16341	18.7	13.1	13.3
		+23%	-20%	+26%	-65%
Total (avg.),	June 1966	19808	26.1	13.1	13.5
5.7 miles	Dec. 1965	17234	31.6	10.8	23.0
		+15%	-17%	+21%	-41%

TABLE 3

MADISON AVENUE ACCIDENT SUMMARY (5 Months)

Location	Time	Angle Collision	Rear Ends	Turns	Other	Pedestrian Accidents	Mid-Block Accidents[c]	Total Accidents	Total Injured	Total Killed
23rd St. to	Before[a]	4	6	11	11	11	2	43	19	0
42nd St.	After[b]	4	6	8	13	11	1	42	20	0
43rd St. to	Before	3	10	13	8	5	0	39	24	0
57th St.	After	1	4	3	11	5	0	24	17	0
58th St. to	Before	8	22	18	32	9	15	89	43	0
109th St.	After	9	13	12	13	13	9	60	43	0
110th St. to	Before	8	11	11	16	29	18	75	81	2
135th St.	After	9	11	1	8	3	8	32	21	0
Total	Before	23	49	53	67	54	35	246	167	2
	After	23	34	24	45	32	18	158	101	0
	Change, %	0	-31	-49	-33	-41	-49	-36	-40	

[a]From Feb. 15, 1965 to July 15, 1965.
[b]From Feb. 15, 1966 to July 15, 1966.
[c]Mid-block accidents, those over 100 feet from an intersection, are also listed under their specific category.

TABLE 4

FIFTH AVENUE ACCIDENT SUMMARY (5 Months)

Location	Time	Angle Collision	Rear Ends	Turns	Other	Pedestrian Accidents	Mid-Block Accidents[c]	Total Accidents	Total Injured	Total Killed
Washington Sq. N. to 23rd St.	Before[a]	4	6	6	11	7	1	34	17	0
	After[b]	5	4	11	10	11	0	41	31	0
24th St. to 42nd St.	Before	6	8	15	19	18	4	66	45	0
	After	8	13	16	14	4	2	55	20	0
43rd St. to 57th St.	Before	11	31	14	18	16	6	90	58	0
	After	15	17	10	26	11	2	79	41	0
58th St. to 109th St.	Before	5	17	27	29	9	1	87	40	0
	After	3	14	5	9	11	0	42	29	0
110th St. to 138th St.	Before	14	3	6	7	13	4	43	30	0
	After	7	5	10	14	8	0	44	35	0
Total	Before	40	65	68	84	63	16	320	190	0
	After	38	53	52	73	45	4	261	156	0
	Change, %	-1	-18	-23	-13	-29	-75	-18	-18	

[a]From Feb. 15, 1965 to July 15, 1965.
[b]From Feb. 15, 1966 to July 15, 1966.
[c]Mid-block accidents, those over 100 feet from an intersection, are also listed under their specific category.

San Francisco, Calif.

The following data are from "One-Way Traffic—Its Future in Traffic Operations" by William Marconi, Senior Traffic Engineer, Bureau of Engineering, San Francisco Department of Public Works.

One-Way Streets as Arterials. A very successful application of one-way street operation in San Francisco is to use these streets as arterial routes leading into the Central Business District. One pair of one-way streets feeding the CBD consists of

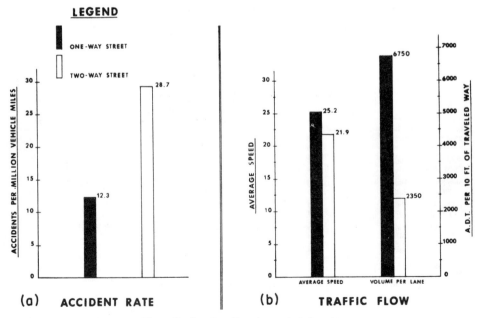

Figure 2. Two San Francisco arterial routes.

TABLE 5

BROADWAY-LINCOLN TRAFFIC VOLUME COMPARISON

Count Locations	Broadway			Lincoln			Combined			Increase (%)
	Two-Way 1963-65	One-Way		Two-Way 1960-63	One-Way		Two-Way 1960-65	One-Way		
		1965	1966		1965	1966		1965	1966	
18th Ave.	12,300	9,200	10,600	5,500	7,900	9,200	17,800	17,100	19,800	11
Colfax	19,800	15,500	17,900	10,500	16,500	17,200	30,300	32,000	35,100	16
14th Ave.	25,700	20,600	28,700	8,800	14,700	17,600	34,500	35,300	46,300	34
8th Ave.	24,000	19,300	24,700	9,900	18,700	16,400	33,900	38,000	41,100	21
3rd Ave.	19,500		25,700			12,700	19,500		38,400	97
Alameda	25,000		22,600			12,200	25,000		34,800	39
Exposition	24,100		17,400			13,700	24,100		31,100	29
Average										33

two streets with 34-ft traveled ways (although an additional lane is added by a parking prohibition in the peak hours) carry almost 50,000 veh/day, and the unidirectional peak-hour flows are 3500 veh/hr. This flow is equivalent to what a four-lane bidirectional freeway would carry. Figure 2 compares the accident rate on two San Francisco arterial routes, a one-way couplet, and the two-way street. The accident rate (Fig. 2a) on the two-way street is 134 percent higher than on the one-way streets. The street cross sections and the neighborhoods they traverse are the same. Off-peak speeds and all-day traffic volume for these streets are also compared (Fig. 2b). Despite the fact that the per lane traffic volume on the one-way streets is 190 percent higher, the traffic movement is almost 4 mph faster. This differential in speed is also maintained in the peak hours of traffic flow.

Denver, Colo.

The information in this section is summarized from an unpublished report by Denver Assistant Traffic Engineers Richard C. Thomas and James L. Brown concerning Denver's Broadway-Lincoln Street one-way arterial system conversion in 1965.

Broadway in Denver has historically been the primary north-south arterial street in the central portion of the city and leads directly to the CBD. Its land use is entirely strip business over the 3.3 miles. Lincoln Street is roughly one-half in strip business use, and it was a secondary arterial street for that length. The other half of Lincoln Street was a residential local street carrying no through traffic.

Traffic Volumes. After conversion to one-way operation, the Broadway-Lincoln system as a whole showed an increase at seven count stations averaging 33 percent. As might be expected, Broadway, the heavier traffic carrier before conversion, shows losses in traffic volume at four of the seven stations, at least in the first year after conversion.

Lincoln Street, considerably the lesser of the two streets to begin with, shows substantial traffic volume increases in the section where it was formerly a secondary through street; and particularly, of course, in the local residential areas where it had no through traffic at all (Table 5).

Accident Experience. A detailed examination of all accidents along Broadway

TABLE 6

BROADWAY-LINCOLN ACCIDENT EXPERIENCE[a]

Intersections	1962	1963	1964	1965	1966
Broadway—8th Ave.	38	42	43	41	53
Broadway—14th Ave.	33	25	44	44	33
Broadway—Colfax	61	55	61	37	28
Broadway—11th Ave.	—b	—b	31	36	27
Broadway—13th Ave.	54	31	46	28	27
Broadway—Speer Blvd.	54	66	70	63	18
Broadway—Alameda	28	30	27	45	18
Broadway—6th Ave.	39	33	20	26	23
Broadway—17th Ave.	32	—b	27	25	22
Broadway—1st Ave.	34	—b	31	21	21
Total	398	357	400	366	270
Avg.				380	270

[a]Decrease over 4-yr average—29%.
[b]Locations not reported as high-accident locations for the years shown. Since the low limit of accidents on the high accident list is usually 25, these intersections have been charged with 25 accidents even though the actual total may have been less.

32

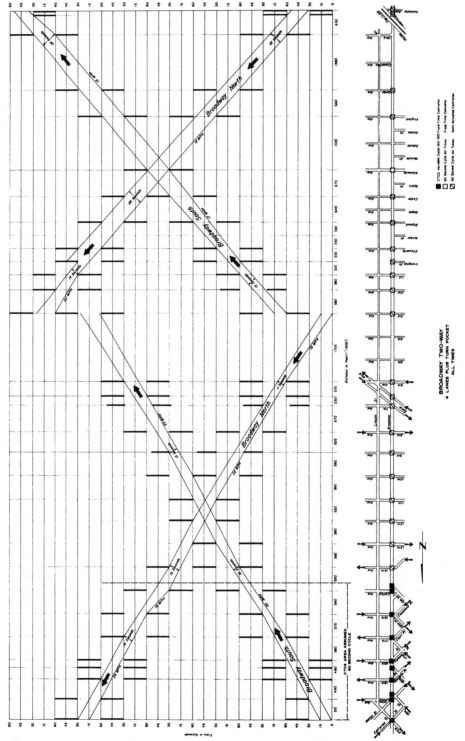

BROADWAY TWO-WAY
4 LANES PLUS TURN POCKET
ALL TIMES

Figure 3.

33

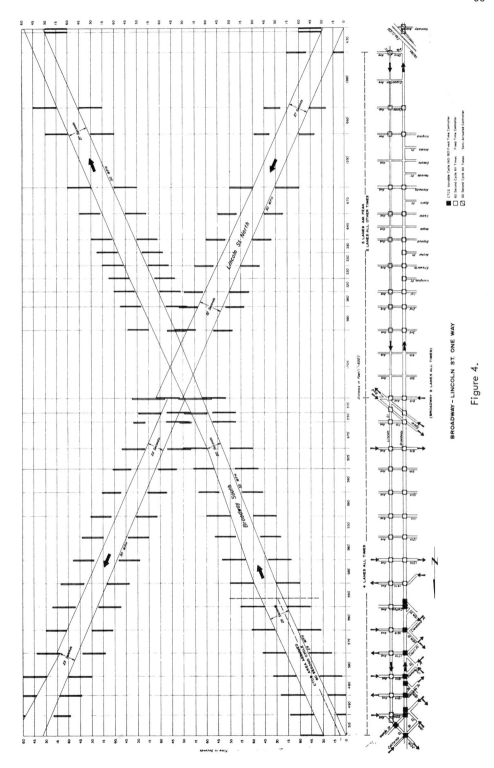

BROADWAY - LINCOLN ST. ONE WAY

Figure 4.

and Lincoln has not yet been achieved, but a study of the ten high-accident locations along Broadway appears to indicate a trend. It should be noted that the average of the seven traffic volume counts on Broadway is the same before and after conversion.

Table 6 illustrates that nine of the ten intersections had a reduction in traffic accidents, when comparing 1966 experience to the average of the preceding four years. The ten intersections together show a 29 percent decrease in accidents.

The one location which shows an increase in accidents has been examined in further detail, and it has been found that nearly half of the accidents reported are occurring between vehicles on the cross street, 8th Avenue.

It is believed that further motorist experience with the one-way system along Broadway and Lincoln Street will result in additional decreases in accidents in the future.

Traffic Signal Timing. Broadway and Lincoln Street before one-way conversion had all of the usual traffic signal problems of major arterial two-way streets. Left turns and left-turn phases presented problems of accidents, congestion, and signal timing as they do on all two-way streets.

Broadway, with four through lanes and continuous left-turn channelization, had traffic signals at such close spacing that the progressive signal speed was in the range of 22 to 25 mph on the northerly two-thirds of the portion later converted to one-way. The through band of signal time equaled only 50 percent of the full green time available to Broadway traffic (Fig. 3).

The southerly one-third of Broadway had different signal spacing and the progressive through band was able to utilize from 50 to 80 percent of the green time available to Broadway traffic. However, the progressive signal speed decreased to 15 to 18 mph.

After conversion to one-way operation (Fig. 4), the traffic signal timing situation showed considerable improvement. In the downtown area, the progressive signal speed is 29 mph, and outside of downtown it varies from 30 to 34 mph. Further, the through band of signal time is able to utilize about 80 percent of the green time available throughout the length of the project. The only exception along the 3.3 miles is at Lincoln Street, Speer Boulevard and 6th Avenue, where the green time available to Lincoln Street is only one-third of the signal cycle because of the required three-phase operation.

Economic Effects. An investigation of the possible effects of one-way operation on retail business is being conducted along Broadway. The facts gathered from a review of sales tax returns a year before and after one-way operation have not yet been fully analyzed; however, the basic conclusion seems apparent.

It has been determined that the more than 300 retail businesses examined along 3.2 miles of one-way Broadway show a sales increase of 12.2 percent comparing 1966 sales to 1964 sales. Over the same period, all businesses in Denver increased their sales by 9.2 percent. Thus, looking only at the street as a whole compared to the city as a whole, Broadway businesses definitely did better in sales.

Different types of businesses, and different sections of Broadway varied quite widely from this overall average. Further, there remains to be made an analysis of the businesses which disappeared during the two-year study. The investigation is continuing and will be reported at a future date.

CONCLUSIONS

The several reports available from cities that studied one-way operation clearly indicate that such operation is a significant method of improving the safety and efficiency of the urban street system. The disadvantages of one-way operation are minor in comparison to the important benefits which can be achieved.

In most one-way designs, capacity is improved, traffic flow is smoother, left-turn problems are solved, pedestrians find fewer vehicular conflicts, and accidents are significantly reduced. In view of these proved benefits, the use of one-way street operation should be considered wherever there is an opportunity for a street improvement project.

Greater attention should be given to the potential use of one-way streets for new developments. Although heretofore the primary application has been in the conversion of existing, parallel, two-way streets, the design of new subdivisions and the through streets serving them should properly include one-way street plans also. The present trend toward non-continuous street design in new subdivisions mitigates against future one-way conversion, thus if there is to be the possibility of utilizing the advantages of one-way operation in the future, they must be planned for in the beginning.

REFERENCES

1. Highway Capacity Manual, 1965. HRB Special Report 87, 1965.
2. Kennedy, Kell, and Homburger. Fundamentals of Traffic Engineering. University of California, Berkeley, 1963.
3. Accident Facts. National Safety Council, 425 N. Michigan Ave., pp. 40, 47, Chicago, 1963.
4. One-Way Street Study, Economic Effects, 1964. Denver Traffic Engineering Division, Denver, Colo., 1964.
5. One-Way Business Streets. U.S. Chamber of Commerce, Washington, D.C., 1954.
6. Carmody, Douglas J. First Year Report on Modesto's One-Way Streets. Street Engineering, Vol. 3, No. 12, Dec. 1958.
7. Second-Year Report: Modesto's One-Way Streets. Street Engineering, Vol. 5, No. 3, March 1960.
8. Crandall, F. B. One-Way Pairs Pay Off on Urban Through Routes. Street Engineering, Vol. 6, No. 1, Jan. 1961.
9. Crandall, F. B. One-Way Routings in Smaller Cities. Traffic Quarterly, Vol. 4, No. 2, April 1950.
10. Before and After One-Way Streets. Dallas Department of Traffic Control, Dallas, Texas, 1957.
11. Eastman, R. C. Ann Arbor Discontinues One-Way Operation of Two Streets. Traffic Engineering, Vol. 21, No. 3, Dec. 1950.
12. Dutton, Noble. The One-Way Grid System in Portland, Oregon. National Safety Council Trans., Vol. 31, 1950.
13. Fowler, Fred T. One-Way Grid System of Portland, Oregon. Proc. ITE, 1952.
14. Kelley, John F. The One-Way Street, Its Effect on Retail Business. California Highways and Public Works, Vol. 32, Nos. 3 and 4, 1953.
15. McCracken, Dwight M. One-Way Streets and Their Values. Traffic Engineering, Vol. 13, No. 3, July 1941.
16. McCracken, Dwight M. Warrants for One-Way Streets and Their Values. Proc. ITE, 1941.
17. McGillivray, R. K. One-Way Traffic System Reduces Accidents and Traffic Congestion. Traffic Engineering, Vol. 15, No. 5, Feb. 1945.
18. One-Way Street Routings on Urban Highways. Traffic Engineering, Vol. 21, No. 9, June 1951.
19. Van Duzer, W. A. One-Way Streets Increase Traffic Flow Without Increasing Accident Ratio and Thus Relieve Rush-Hour Congestion, Etc. American City, Vol. 54, No. 8, Aug. 1939.
20. A Study of Vehicle Traffic and Business Trends "Before" and "After" One-Way Streets in Olympia, Washington. Washington Dept. of Highways, 1952.
21. Traffic Engineering Handbook. Third Edition, ITE, pp. 553-558, 1965.

Addendum

In Peoria, Ill., and in Florissant, Mo., the traffic engineer's office prepared rather grandiose plans for converting all the streets in the CBD to one-way operation. In both instances, these proposals were implemented at one time "in toto" over the objections of the traffic engineer. The results were chaotic even though considerable advance publicity was given to these elaborate one-way street changes.

In Florissant, all of the streets were narrow—in fact, less than 32 ft wide. Both the north-south and east-west streets did lend themselves to one-way coupling. However, when all fourteen streets were changed from two to one-way operation between Sunday evening and Monday morning, the resulting confusion forced a hasty retreat back to two-way operation on all but two streets. As a part of the post mortem it was apparent that a large degree of the opposition resulted from the overnight conversion of all the streets at once and a lack of opportunity for the motorist to become familiar with the proposed one-way system a little at a time.

In Peoria, the story was somewhat the same except the streets were considerably wider, averaging 60 ft. The bus company and some commercial groups in the downtown area were not fully "pre-sold" on the merits of the one-way plan. Consequently, when several of the major streets were converted all at once, these groups fought the change vigorously. The traffic engineer was forced to back off on several of the one-way pairs and had to do a very extensive "second" selling job over a number of years before these streets were again tried as one-way operation. Hindsight would plainly indicate that it would have been far more successful if one or two pairs at a time had been tried instead of disrupting the entire central business district.

Traffic Signs

ROSS T. SHOAF

Assistant City Engineer

City of San Francisco

Dollar for dollar, signs are the least costly of traffic control devices. When properly used, they can provide the lowest cost ratio of sign cost vs accident reduction. Also because of the low cost, the temptation to use traffic signs improperly often causes both an increase in accidents and a disrespect for all traffic control devices.

One might lightly dismiss the subject of traffic signs and their use by merely referring interested persons to the Manual on Uniform Traffic Control Devices, the authority recognized by all professional traffic and highway personnel in the engineering, enforcement and educational fields. However, to understand the role of traffic signs in the safe movement of traffic is to also understand the purpose of signs, what they can do, and what they cannot do. It is only thus, with adequate background knowledge, that the sincere and dedicated person can fully apply the Uniform Manual in causing traffic signs to be installed in a manner that will increase safety and reduce delay.

PURPOSE OF TRAFFIC SIGNS

The principal purposes of traffic signs are summarized in the following:

1. To inform the public of regulations about which they would not otherwise know.
2. To inform the public about driving conditions which are not readily apparent.
3. To inform the public when prima facie conditions are officially altered.
4. To provide the field conditions for routing the public in accordance with information normally found on travel maps.
5. To aid in decision-making with the prime interest being accident and delay reduction.
6. To supplement other traffic control devices.

What Traffic Signs Can Do

As can be concluded from the preceding list, traffic signs can effect the following positive or negative results:

1. Inform the public—mainly the motoring public, but also including the pedestrian and the transit or taxi passenger.
2. Misinform the public—when the information is incorrect or misunderstood.
3. Comfort the semi-informed public—by confirming or correcting information believed to be correct.
4. Disturb and confuse the semi-informed public—when the sign is in conflict with other traffic control devices or is so complicated as to not be readily understood.
5. Create distrust—when signs are incorrectly used.
6. Generate tensions—when needed and sought for information cannot be seen or is seen too late to be useful.
7. Cause accidents as well as prevent accidents, depending upon application.

What Traffic Signs Cannot Do

Traffic signs have many limitations as compared with other traffic control devices; for example:

1. Signs cannot provide a continuous guide through complicated areas and around hazardous locations in the same way as pavement markings can do under normal conditions.

2. Signs cannot be read at the same long distances as can the simpler red, amber and green traffic signal indications.

3. Signs cannot tell the complicated story of proper spacing of motor platoons down a main street which the timing of traffic signals provides without need for telling the story.

4. Signs cannot provide the various degrees of positive barriers that curbs, islands, guardrails and fences provide.

All of these limitations seem obvious, yet traffic signs are used at times with the exception that the very things they cannot do will somehow result from their use.

Traffic signs as a group of traffic control devices are the lowest in cost, but because of the simplicity of their appearance, are much abused. Sometimes they are vandalized by those who pepper them with rifle shots or plaster them with political campaign messages. Often, they are abused by civic and political leaders who misguidedly justify their action with the belief that "even if a traffic sign at a particular location does not do good, such an innocent installation can do no harm"—and it satisfies a constituent for a very low cost!

REGULATORY, WARNING AND GUIDE SIGNS

The following material illustrates from actual experience successful and unsuccessful traffic sign installations on urban and suburban streets. Signs used only with signal operation, one-way operation, reversible-lane operation, curb-parking restrictions and transit operations, are reviewed as to the application of the regulations by others in the Conference and therefore will not be covered in this paper.

Traffic signs are classed in three categories: regulatory, warning and guide. Only a few examples of installations in each category can be cited, but the examples emphasize the need to know the when, where and why of traffic signs.

Stop Signs

STOP signs generally lead all other traffic signs in number requested by the general public. In the City of San Francisco with a population of 750,000 and less than 7000 intersections, requests for STOP signs were received from the general public in 1966 for 110 intersections, of which 25 requests were for additional signs at locations already controlled. Only 20 of the 110 requests were found to warrant installation.

In addition, 27 other intersections where signs were not requested by the general public were found by routine study and investigation to warrant STOP sign installations. Two more installations were ordered by the city fathers over the negative recommendation of engineers and police.

These statistics show that a major problem in connection with the installation of STOP signs is knowing when to say "no."

The following three brief examples of STOP sign installations describe where increased accidents or congestion was experienced.

Example 1. A major city, residential area, secondary feeder street, 3200 ADT with a minor cross street. City council ordered signs stopping the secondary feeder street.

> Results: (3-yr periods) accidents down from 12 (of which 6 occurred
> in one year) to 6 in after period.

But at the next intersection along the feeder street accidents increased; for the same periods:

> Results: accidents increased from 10 to 31.
> Overall Change: 225 percent increase and STOP signs were then re-
> quired and installed at second intersection.

Example 2. Same city, another residential area, minor feeder streets "A" and "B" crossing a minor local street. City council ordered signs stopping feeder street "A."

Results: (3-yr period) accidents down from 8 to 3.

But at feeder street "B" accidents increased and for the same period:

Results: accidents increased from 4 to 24 (calculated 3-yr rate).
Overall Change: 225 percent increase and STOP signs were installed
at feeder street "B" within 18 months.

Studies established that STOP signs at first intersection caused traffic to reroute itself through the second intersection; thus causing the increase in accidents.

Example 3. Complaint made by city council of small town to county traffic engineer that the newly installed traffic signal on the county road and main street of the town was creating congestion. Investigation showed that installation of STOP signs ordered by the city council on the main street within 250 feet of new signals was the cause of the congestion. Signs were removed and congestion disappeared.

STOP signs installed under the warrants of the Uniform Manual will in nearly all cases reduce both accidents and congestion. Favorable installations are so very numerous and well known throughout the nation and in each governmental jurisdiction that they have not been included in this paper.

Yield Signs

YIELD signs, as a regulation, are at the same time both more and less restrictive than STOP signs. They are more restrictive in that they should be used only where there is adequate sight distance and less restrictive because traffic is not required to stop except for cause.

A study of the effectiveness of YIELD signs in San Francisco installed between 1952 and 1965 showed that of 23 installations, 12 produced a significant improvement, 9 showed no significant change and 2 installations significantly increased accidents. Significance for this purpose is defined as a change of an average of one or more accidents per year susceptible to correction by YIELD signs.

Eliminating 3 of the 12 intersections showing an improvement, because of unusual conditions, the 9 remaining intersections produced an average improvement by a reduction from 4.5 to 3.0 accidents per year. Those showing no significant difference varied from 1.9 before to 1.3 accidents per year after. The average periods represented were 4 to 5 years before and 6 years after.

No Left Turn Signs

While to the public STOP signs are best recognized as a traffic control device for reducing accidents, to the traffic official NO LEFT TURN signs are probably considered the more useful all-round control device among traffic signs in reducing both accidents and congestion.

Example 1. At Broadway and Columbus Avenue in San Francisco, right in the heart of the night club area and the crossroads of two major routes into and out of the business and financial section of downtown San Francisco, excessive congestion and accident experience existed with a total intersection volume of 36,000 vehicles daily. The two streets crossed at a flat angle with significant left turns in all four directions but with the two "easy" or flat left turn movements having very heavy volumes.

Studies by the traffic engineer caused him to recommend the prohibition of all left turns. Upon consideration of the necessary legislation by the city council, it was returned to the traffic engineer for reconsideration of changing the then existing two-phase signal operation to three-phase operation which would provide for the major left turns. Because the normal four lanes in all directions and five lanes during peak hours were operating at near capacity, no change was made in signal operation and a 90-day trial of NO LEFT TURN signs was ordered. It was successful and is still in operation.

Results: accidents per year down from 23 to 11, or a reduction of 52
percent.

Capacity was increased an average of 19 percent on all legs (minimum increase was 10 percent).

Travel time improved a minimum of 11 percent for the prohibited left
turners using their new route and between 35 and 100 percent improvement was experienced by other traffic.

Many other outstanding examples of the value of the use of NO LEFT TURN signs
can be found.

Example 2. A state highway route past a state college in a residential area carrying 32,000 vehicles before and 34,000 vehicles daily in the after study.

Results: total accidents for $1\frac{1}{2}$-yr periods down from 23 to 13, a
reduction of 47 percent. Left-turn accidents were down from 12 to 2.

Same state highway route but two different intersections one mile apart, same 1-yr
period, same characteristics and percent cross traffic: Location 1—51,000 ADT, left
turns allowed; and Location 2—54,000 ADT, left turns prohibited.

Results: (1-yr periods) less accidents at Location 2, down from 41
to 15 (left-turn accidents down from 19 to 1).
Overall Change: 66 percent better with NO LEFT TURN signs.

Incidentally, Location 1 (cited for 1959) is still without major improvement and 8
years later, has 59,000 ADT with accidents continuing at 44 to 59 per year. The political strength of a neighborhood shopping area 6 blocks away has been the cause of failure to improve this bad condition.

The placement of traffic signs, particularly regulatory signs, is of extreme
importance.

Example 3. At a downtown intersection of a large city, 42,000 veh/day, extreme
congestion was readily apparent as being caused by left turns. Large (3 by 4 ft) NO
LEFT TURN signs were installed on the near right and far left corners for both directions on one street (the other two left turns already were prohibited at the peak
periods).

Results: (1-yr periods) accidents up from 16 to 32 (calculated rate).

Three months after the original sign installation, two small center islands were
installed containing standard size NO LEFT TURN signs. One year after signs were
installed on the center islands:

Results: (1-yr periods) accidents down from 32 (calculated rate)
to 18.
Overall Change: congestion reduced to normal; volume up 10
percent.

Example 4. Extreme tenacity is also occasionally required to make regulatory
signs work. NO LEFT TURN signs were installed at an intersection of two major
streets in a major community business area, with 33,000 veh/day.

Results: (1-yr periods) accidents down from 31 to 12.
Overall Change: reduction 38 percent.

But the police and traffic engineers almost removed the signs because concentrated
enforcement of a "duck pond"[1] for about a year was required to change the left-turn
habit of the motorists. To wit, one motorist having been tagged by a motorcycle officer standing in plain sight, not only repeated his violation within a half hour, but also
repeated it twice the next day—all with the same policeman on duty.

---

[1]Duck pond: a location where violations are so frequent enforcement officers are not limited in the
number of tickets they can write.

Perhaps the worst thing that can be done is to install an unwarranted regulatory sign. At the request of transit authorities, a city council ordered the installation of peak-hour NO LEFT TURN signs on a major bus route crossing a state highway within the civic center area, with the city hall on one corner. Studies did not support that accidents or congestion warranted the installation. The ADT at this intersection was 52,000.

Both concentrated and sporadic police enforcement proved the location to be a duck pond of violations over a 5-yr period and despite two 3 by 4-ft signs, traffic judges regularly dismissed tags because it was claimed that the signs were not visible. The regulation has now been removed without evidence of adverse operating conditions for transit or the public.

Speed Zone Signs

Speed zone signing is a traffic control device that is not greatly used but, when warranted, is very effective in reducing maximum speeds and increasing minimum speeds. It is a safety device because, by reducing the range of speeds, more motorists drive at more nearly the same speed; thus reducing one cause of accidents—speed differentials.

A second important use of the speed zone signs is to change legally a prima facie speed either up or down when the prima facie speed does not apply to safe operating conditions. This also is used as a safety device which causes a reduction in the range of speeds existing under prima facie conditions.

Example. On a 2-lane highway through a small town with about 8000 ADT, maximum speeds were found to be 80 mph on a prima facie 65 mph roadway. The average critical speed (85 percentile) in the before study was 57.5 and 54.1 at two locations one-half mile apart. After 55 mph speed zone signs were installed, the maximum speed was found to be 70.6 mph and the average critical speeds at the two locations were 51.9 and 55.0, respectively—a reduction of 10 mph in the maximum speed.

A third effective purpose of speed zone signs is to provide a systematic method of gradual speed reduction and speed increase when the prima facie conditions change too quickly for realistic response by all motorists. Again, the primary purpose of speed zoning is to provide practical legal speeds which will encourage all motorists to more nearly approach the same driving speed and thus reduce the range between maximum and minimum speeds.

Warning Signs

The warning sign category includes signs for various crossroads, obstructions, curves of differing degrees of curvature and safe operating speeds and many other conditions about which the motorist must be warned.

The need for such signs is generally quite apparent either from driving the road or from investigation of an accident. The most likely problem to occur in connection with the installation of warning traffic signs is their placement and the use of the companion advisory speed sign when required.

Signs must, of course, be visible. Such a statement seems unnecessary, yet one major city had posted large 2-way arrow signs at the far side of a T-intersection that occurred at the top of a very steep hill. After a bad fatality at one intersection, it was discovered that accidents of a similar nature had taken place at other T-intersections but never in sufficient numbers to indicate the need for special study. The study immediately revealed the need for advance T-Symbol signs. A later check showed a drop in accidents at intersections where treated.

A 35 mph curve at the end of a long tangent serving 40,000 vehicles on a one-way 2-lane road had a high accident experience. A standard curve sign with an advisory speed sign was installed in advance of the curve which was lighted and generally visible to motorists.

Poor vertical and horizontal alignment could not be corrected by the use of signs, but oversized advisory speed signs instead of oversized curve signs and the relocation of the signs a greater distance in advance of the curve emphasized the need for a speed reduction. The change provided more time for the motorist to adjust his speed.

Shape, Color, Reflectivity and Maintenance

Before leaving the subject of regulatory and warning signs, attention must be called to the importance of those sign conditions which experienced traffic engineers and sign personnel accept as routine knowledge. Any one of the subjects—standard shapes and colors, reflectivity for all signs intended for use by the motorist at night, and a high level of maintenance—could in itself warrant a complete paper because of its importance.

One must be content, however, at this time to state flatly that there is a mountain of research and experience available to back up the need for standard shapes and colors, reflectivity and regular high-quality maintenance as specified in the Manual on Uniform Traffic Control Devices available through the Superintendent of Documents, U.S. Government Printing Office, Washington, D.C.

Guide Signs

Normally thought of as directional signs which guide motorists over specific routes and through urban areas, the category of guide signs leading to specific locations of recreation, business and trip generating centers requires as much attention as STOP signs in order to prevent their overuse. In fact, the number of requests in large urban areas is so great that there is need for a strong policy limiting their use in order to keep directional signs from interfering and competing with regulatory and warning signs.

One large metropolitan area will not install a directional sign for a specific center if the location or center can readily be found by use of a city map available at any gas station. They confine their directional signing to general areas such as BEACH, or CIVIC CENTER, and only install signs on the major roads in the vicinity.

Specific locations justify directional signs only when such signs will relieve a problem of congestion or an existing hardship for the motorist.

Street Name Signs

Perhaps the sign most often installed by the traffic engineer and yet generally not thought of as a traffic sign is the street name sign. Street name signs, in the guide sign category, have been used in urban areas since long before the coming of the automobile, and unfortunately, in some localities the same street name signs are still being used.

The faster speeds of the automobile, the greater traffic volumes confronting the driver, and mechanical horsepower which cannot be trained as the horse could, has given the street name sign a far different role from that which it had many years ago. In fact, its role is so changed that it is surprising that so many urban streets and suburban roads have been neglected by lack of upgrading such signs.

There are many different techniques for dressing up the street name sign in a fashion so that it can play its part in modern transportation: larger letters; inclusion of block numbers; same general location for all installations; unobstructed view, location in the same vicinity as traffic signals or other major regulatory signs, double or triple signing at wide or busy locations, and location in advance of intersections when practical for high-speed roads.

A street name sign still has the same simple objective it had in the years before the automobile—to be seen in time to make a safe decision. The only difference is that it must be seen sooner to compensate for high-travel speed and competition for the motorists' attention. Of course, the necessity of being seen in time to make a safe decision applies to all traffic signs whether regulatory, warning or guide.

There is one important difference between the street name signs and all other traffic signs. It is seldom, if ever, that a community has too many street name signs. All other traffic signs have a time and place where they do good and a time and place where they can do harm and should not be used.

CONCLUSIONS

Traffic signs to be successful must first be uniform everywhere the driver goes. The Manual on Uniform Traffic Control Devices is an authoritative document that provides such uniformity. Second, traffic signs must be properly used because they can cause accidents as well as reduce accidents. Persons responsible for the installation of traffic signs should recognize the need to know when, where and why traffic signs should be used.

REFERENCES

1. Manual for Signing and Pavement Marking of the National System of Interstate and Defense Highways, AASHO, Washington, D.C., 1961.
2. Ashwood, J. E. Relative Legibility Distances of Route Numbers and Place Names of Directional Signs. Traffic Engineering and Control, Vol. 5, No. 11, pp. 654-655, 1963.
3. The Lighting of Traffic Signs. Assoc. of Public Lighting Engineers, Technical Report No. 1, London, 1963.
4. Driver Needs in Freeway Signing. Automotive Safety Foundation, 1958.
5. Bauer, H. J. Some Solutions of Visibility and Legibility Problems in Changeable Speed Command Signs. HRB Bull. 330, pp. 60-68, 1962.
6. Burg, Albert, and Hulbert, Slade F. Predicting the Effectiveness of Highway Signs. HRB Bull. 324, pp. 1-11, 1962.
7. Standard Letters for Traffic Signs. California Division of Highways, Sacramento, 1964.
8. Uniform Traffic Control Devices for Canada. Canadian Good Roads Association, Joint Committee on Uniform Traffic Control Devices.
9. Darrell, James E. P. Use and Misuse of Traffic Signs. Traffic Quarterly, Vol. 25, No. 4, pp. 653-663, Oct. 1961.
10. Fitzpatrick, Joseph T. Unified Reflective Sign, Pavement and Delineation Treatments for Night Traffic Guidance. HRB Bull. 255, pp. 138-145, 1960.
11. Forbes, T. W., et al. A Study of Traffic Sign Requirements: Part II, An Annotated Bibliography. Michigan State Univ., Dept. of Psychology, Div. of Engineering Research, 1964.
12. Powers, Lawrence D. Advance Route Turn Markers on City Streets. HRB Proc., Vol. 41, pp. 483-494, 1962.
13. Ricker, Edmund R. Keeping the Motorist on Course. Traffic Engineering and Control, Vol. 4, No. 7, pp. 406-407, 417, Nov. 1962.
14. Rowan, Neilon J. Approach-End Treatment of Channelization—Signing and Delineation. Highway Research Record 31, pp. 57-78, 1963.
15. Schoppert, David W., et al. Some Principles of Freeway Directional Signing Based on Motorists' Experience. HRB Bull. 244, pp. 30-87, 1960.

Addenda

Use of Yield Signs

Experience in YIELD sign use reported from Skokie, Ill., showed that extensive violations of the signs at three locations led to installation of experimental supplementary "information" sign installations. These signs read, "This Means Slow Down and Stop for Cross Traffic." While the widespread use of such non-standard signs is in no way recommended, the results of this experiment showed:

Before:
  Exposure Years, 11.3
  Accidents (right-angle type only), 10
  Frequency per year, 0.89

After:
  Exposure Years, 5.9
  Accidents (right angle), 2
  Frequency per year, 0.34

At three other locations in the same city, traffic volumes and intersection sight distance restrictions indicated replacement of **YIELD** signs with **STOP** control. Results were as follows:

Before (with two-way **YIELD**)
  Exposure Years, 14.5
  Accidents (right angle), 16
  Frequency per year, 1.10

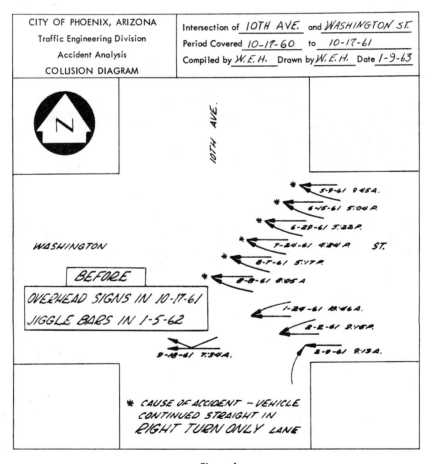

Figure 1.

After (with two-way STOP)
Exposure Years, 3.9
Accidents (right angle), 1
Frequency per year, 0.26

Phoenix, Ariz., Overhead Signs and Jiggle Bars

Washington Street is a major one-way street through downtown Phoenix, Ariz. For some years the major route turned 90 degrees at 10th Avenue. A serious accident problem was identified through the use of accident records. Two hundred lineal feet of jiggle bars and overhead signs were installed at a cost of $520. The before and after collision diagrams (Figs. 1 and 2) show the results. The average daily traffic at this point was approximately 10,800.

Toronto, Ont., Reversal of Stop Signs

Table 1 gives the findings of a Toronto metropolitan area study, relating to accident changes produced by reversal of STOP signs. These were in residential areas, where the signs generally faced the wrong (heavier volume) flow of traffic.

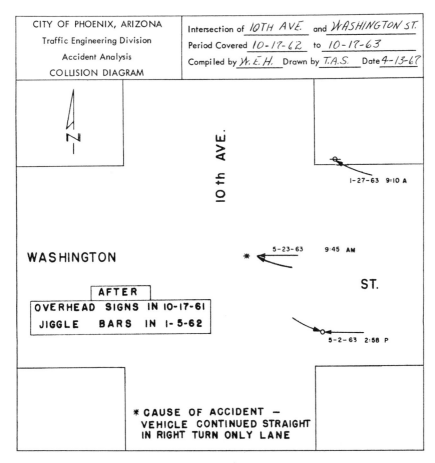

Figure 2.

TABLE 1

REVERSAL OF STOP SIGNS

Intersection	Date Right-of-Way Changed	Accidents per Year	
		Before	After
Alfred and Dudley	Sept. 1964	1	0
Ameer and Regina	Feb. 1965	2	0
Ameer and Baycrest	Feb. 1965	1	0
Byng and Dudley	Sept. 1964	3	1
Doris and Elmwood	Aug. 1965	1	1
Doris and Empress	Sept. 1963	1	1
Doris and Spring Garden	Aug. 1965	1	1
Dudley and Empress	Sept. 1963	2	1
Dudley and Parkview	Nov. 1965	3	1
Empress and Highgate	Sept. 1963	0	0
Empress and Longmore	Sept. 1963	2	0
Hillcrest and Kenneth	March 1964	0	0
Kenneth and Olive	March 1964	2	3
Khedive and Regina	Jan. 1965	1	2
Total		20	11

New Haven, Conn., Removal of Unwarranted Signs

In 1957, two years after the New Haven department was established, a complete inventory of all signs throughout the city was undertaken. (Sign installation has previously been under the police department.) In one middle-class residential neighborhood alone, comprising approximately 15 miles of local streets, by actual count 275 assorted pedestrian signs ("Slow—Children Playing," "Children in Street," etc.) were recorded. There was one grade school in the neighborhood. All streets were constructed to relatively good local street design standards.

Work orders were issued for the removal of all unwarranted and non-standard signs (275)—proper school warning signs were erected for the school at its primary, secondary and tertiary crossing points (some 10 locations), in accord with a planned school safety program. Residential reaction was initially noisy, but full explanations were given in each case and the sign program, as adjusted, remained in effect. Continual review of pedestrian safety provisions in the period 1957 to 1966, in this neighborhood, revealed no pedestrian problem which the former type of signs or placement pattern might have improved. This firm policy of providing pedestrian warning signs only where warranted, has engendered a high level of motorist observance to warning signs.

District of Columbia, Color Coding Route Markers

The color coding of route markers in the District of Columbia was an experimental project carried on in cooperation with the Bureau of Public Roads. This project involved using blue, red, yellow and green US route marker signs for the four cardinal directions. In other words, any US route that proceeded through the District in a northerly direction had all blue signs regardless of whether it was designated as US 1, 29, 50 or 240.

This plan was also believed to have been tried in Arizona. In fact the Arizona State Highway Department Map carried a detailed explanation of this system. Unfortunately, the general public was not fully aware of the trial system used in the District of Columbia. In addition, it is somewhat difficult to educate all the motorists in this area since there are so many millions of visitors to the Nation's Capital each year. After about a year of using the quad-color US route sign-marking system the project was abandoned.

The use of these signs preceded the final decision regarding the use of red, white and blue Interstate markers. Washington's experience just did not justify the continuation of the color-coded system although there still seems to be some sentiment among traffic engineers regarding its use.

Pavement Markings

HARRY B. SKINNER
Executive Director
New Haven Parking Authority
City of New Haven, Conn.

The practice of using markings on the road surface has, rather recently, come into general acceptance throughout the country. This procedure is used for the following purposes:

1. To delineate the so-called pavement centerline, i.e., the longitudinal division of the road which separates the opposite directions of travel;

2. To delineate the intended lane divisions of the road;

3. To delineate the separation of that section of the road intended for normal operating use from the shoulder section—that section of the road for use by vehicles required, for one reason or another, to slow significantly or stop;

4. To delineate the edge of the road—that point beyond which it would not be safe for a vehicle to operate;

5. To define transverse pedestrian crossings of the road;

6. To designate the point at which a vehicle is intended to stop on the approach of an intersection controlled by a stop sign or traffic signal;

7. To mark the approach to a railroad grade crossing;

8. To define the presence of a dangerous obstruction to traffic;

9. To channelize traffic through large, difficult or odd-shaped intersections where the normal operating pattern is not evident to a motorist; and

10. To convey a message to the motorist or pedestrian (normally this practice is used to supplement standard signing for regulatory controls, not to replace signing).

To be effective, pavement markings have to be seen and understood during periods of daylight as well as at night. Most pavement markings are intended to control traffic at night as well as during the daylight hours, therefore, their placement with a night-time reflective material becomes vital. Even in areas with a relatively high level of nighttime artificial illumination the general practice is to place pavement markings with a reflective material.

While operating a vehicle, a motorist's eyes scan the road ahead for a greater percentage of the total time than they scan the roadsides. Therefore, the placement of messages and driving controls for the motorist on the surface of the road is a more logical location than signs along the edge of the pavement. This type of placement has two distinct, and severe, disadvantages: climatic conditions and traffic volumes. In the northern part of the country, where ice and snow cover the pavement surface during part of the year, pavement markings become completely ineffectual during this period. This problem can also become quite severe during a rainstorm in any part of the country, particularly at night. A similar problem exists when handling traffic at such high volumes that it is on a virtual bumper-to-bumper basis. Obviously, if no gaps exist in the traffic stream there is no opportunity to see a pavement marking. Because of these limitations, regulatory traffic controls are practically always displayed on a sign and supplemented through the use of pavement markings. The one major exception is the use of lane directional controls, such as left-hand lane arrow markings. Here it may become too expensive or aesthetically objectionable to specify individual lane operations on overhead signs.

The professional traffic engineers' guide toward uniformity of all traffic control devices, the "Manual on Uniform Traffic Control Devices," recognizes the advantages of pavement markings by outlining, in great detail, the design of railroad grade-crossing markings. This manual also provides for the use of pavement markings for those other purposes previously outlined. At this time, there is a recognized need to survey the pavement marking practices presently employed throughout the country and to establish a uniform practice in the use of pavement markings similar to that which has, to a large extent, been achieved in signing. Several committees of the Institute of Traffic Engineers and the National Joint Committee on Uniform Traffic Control Devices are presently working toward this end.

During the early stages of the development of the nation's highway system the use of portland cement concrete as the construction material created a natural centerline delineation through the use of a longitudinal contraction joint. This joint was normally sealed with a petroleum base mastic compound that created a black centerline marking against the concrete pavement surface. Black impregnants were subsequently added to the cement topping to form a black centerline. With the advent of the extensive use of asphalt as a surfacing material the use of the painted line was developed to define the centerline. The use of this centerlining material substantially reduced the number of head-on accidents, particularly those that occurred at night.

Following the general acceptance of the centerline delineations, lane lines were employed to cut down the number of side-swipe accidents as well as to increase the capacity of multi-lane facilities by keeping traffic contained in well-defined lanes.

In a further effort to reduce accidents, longitudinal demarcations to separate the normal operating lane from the shoulder or pavement edge were developed.

After extensive investigation in Louisiana, it was found that edge lines so significantly moved traffic away from the edge of the pavement that no edge line would be used on two-lane roads less than 24 ft wide (1). On one test section which consisted of a 20-ft wide pavement on a 4-deg curve with a yellow double "no passing" stripe on the centerline, the use of edge lines caused an average encroachment of 0.6 ft over the centerline during daylight hours of operation on the outside of the curve and 0.2-ft encroachment on the inside of the curve.

Investigations also proved that the use of edge markings on a multi-lane divided facility definitely moved traffic in the inside and outside lane to the left. Traffic in the outside lane moved away from the right pavement edge and traffic in the inside lane moved toward the left pavement edge.

A study involving vehicles leaving the roadway on the right along the Merritt Parkway in Connecticut (2) shows that accidents attributable to driver inattentiveness were reduced from 50 during the last year of operation prior to the placement of edge line markings to 29 the first full year of operation after the placement of the markings, and to 26 during the third full year of operation.

This study also showed a tendency for cars to shift to the right, away from the centerline, after the edge line had been placed. This shift averaged 0.12 ft during hours of daylight operation and 0.41 ft during nighttime operation. The accident data available in connection with this study were not sufficiently reliable to prove a substantial reduction. However, the vehicle placement would certainly indicate a safer operation. Placement of the edge line also offered an additional element of security to pedestrians walking along the edge of the pavement. The study also indicated a more uniform speed of operation along the pavement having an edge line, particularly through a horizontal curve section.

An interesting innovation in the use of lane markings has been used in the City of Memphis, Tenn., at the intersection of East Parkway and Poplar. The Parkway north of Poplar, before its recent reconstruction, was a six-lane undivided section (Fig. 1). The Parkway, south of Poplar, was a six-lane divided roadway with a median of approximately a 40-foot width. The result was an approximately 25-ft offset to the left facing northbound traffic. This intersection configuration resulted in an accident frequency averaging 15 "sideswipe" and "fixed object" accidents each year before treatment. After the treatment, the average fell to 9 similar accidents for each year until the intersection was reconstructed, approximately four years ago. The treatment consisted of the placement of 4 by 6-in. plastic strips on 5-ft centers along the projection of the companion lane lines. These projected lane lines were placed along a gentle reverse curve through the intersection. The 4-in. dimension was placed longitudinally to the direction of movement. To overcome the possibility of any misunderstanding by

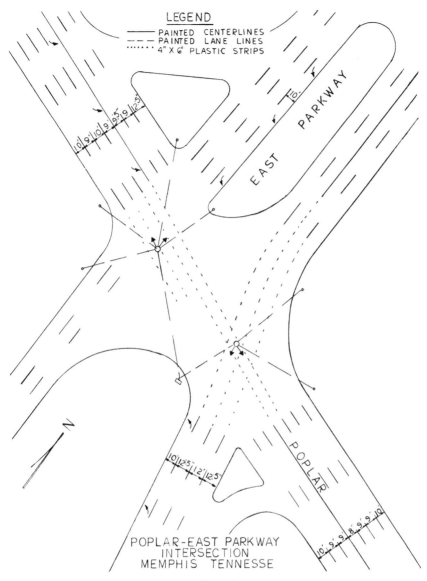

LEGEND
PAINTED CENTERLINES
PAINTED LANE LINES
4" X 6" PLASTIC STRIPS

EAST PARKWAY

TO.

POPLAR

N

POPLAR-EAST PARKWAY
INTERSECTION
MEMPHIS TENNESSE

Figure 1.

cross traffic through the intersection, the 5-ft centers were placed randomly along the
Parkway. The treatment resulted in no discernible pattern to the cross street traffic
on Poplar and the presence of the lane markings through the intersection had no influence on this traffic.

Figure 2 shows a typical program of channelization through a difficult intersection.
The intersection accidents have been reduced from an average of 33 accidents per year
before the treatment to 24 accidents per year after the treatment in spite of an increase
in intersection volume from 30,000 to 34,000 veh/day.

A less impressive, but equally effective, treatment is shown in Figure 3. The accidents have been reduced from an average of 12 each year before the treatment to an

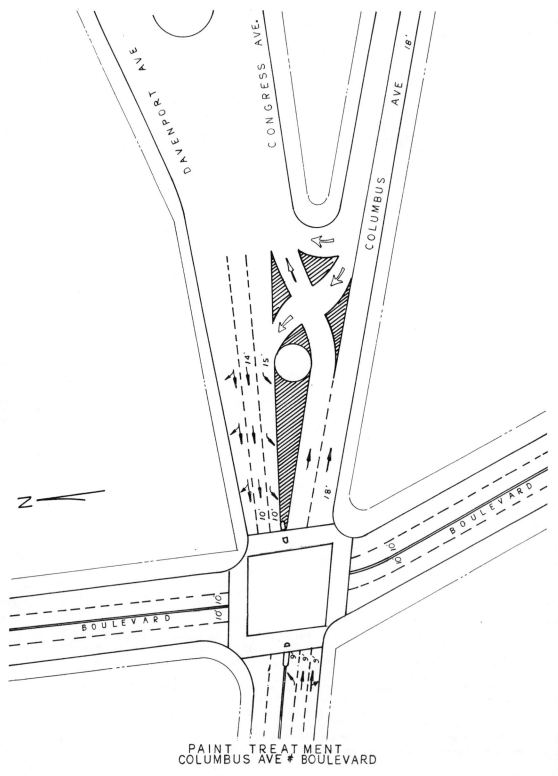

PAINT TREATMENT
COLUMBUS AVE # BOULEVARD

Figure 2.

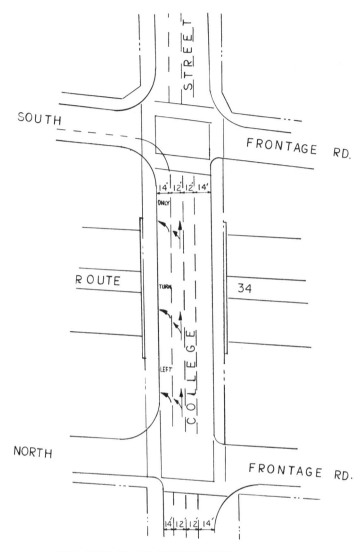

COLLEGE ST. AT FRONTAGE RD.

Figure 3.

average of 10 after the treatment with no significant change in traffic volume. In addition to the accident rate reduction, there is an apparent diminution of congestion and a subsequent increase in efficiency of the intersection.

Another program aimed at reducing accidents was implemented in New Haven, Conn., by painting a special intersection treatment pattern at intersections displaying a particularly high incidence of accidents. This program is employed at the approach to a stop intersection (Fig. 4). During the two years that this program has been in effect, 7 intersections have shown an average of 32 percent reduction in accidents, whereas 2 intersections showed a 63 percent increase in accidents with no significant change in volume nor traffic pattern. The program has been sufficiently effective to warrant

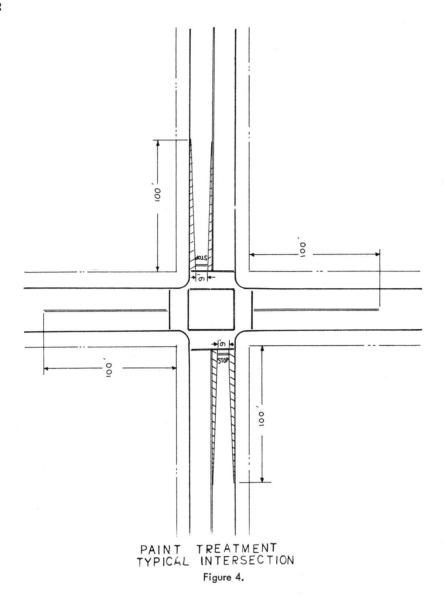

PAINT TREATMENT
TYPICAL INTERSECTION

Figure 4.

repainting this special intersection program each year. Obviously, an uncontrolled use of the program would dilute the effects on the motoring public. Therefore, the city has limited the number of approaches treated in this fashion to 24 approaches out of a total of 1340 approaches to stop signs.

The use of pavement markings to delineate pedestrian crossings is generally accepted. A study of England's zebra crosswalk marking by R. L. Moore of the Road Research Laboratory showed that in the London area an increase in crossing in the prescribed manner for men from 45 to 53 percent after the markings were placed, for women from 63 before to 69 percent after the crossings, and for children from 60 to 81 percent after the placement of the crosswalks. Another Road Research Laboratory study by W. H. Glanville showed that the use of the zebra crosswalk coupled with a pedestrian education program resulted in a 7 percent decrease in pedestrian accidents,

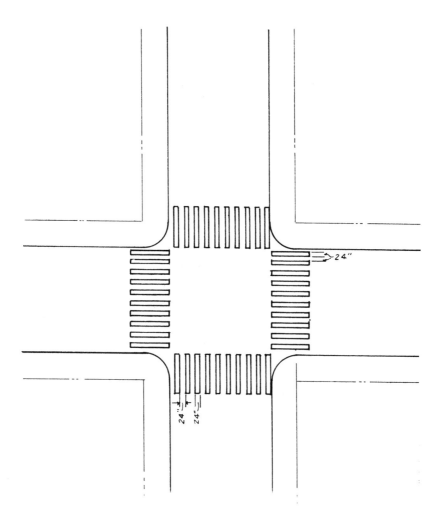

CROSSWALK TREATMENT

Figure 5.

that accidents went down more in towns using the crosswalks than in towns not using them and that accidents fell 8 percent in towns while falling only 2 percent in the rural districts. Figure 5 shows a layout of the zebra-type markings.

Probably the most recent innovation in pavement markings is the use of markings to convey word messages and/or symbols to the motorist. This practice has resulted in a virtually inexhaustible list of messages being passed onto the motorist. Of the more generally accepted practices the word STOP is used probably as frequently as any other message. A study done in England (1) shows that the inclusion of the word "HALT" on the pavement resulted in a 6.7 percent increase in observance to the stop sign and a 1.4 percent decrease in violations of the stop sign. The study also showed a 50 percent reduction in personal injury accidents on all vehicles approaching the intersections after placing the message.

CONCLUSIONS

The use of pavement markings has been unquestionably successful in controlling traffic. This paper has briefly summarized the uses, the limitations and the success of a few of the programs related to the use of such markings. In closing, remember that we live in an urban setting which should be made as attractive and livable as possible. An unrestrained program of painting streets can be just as objectional as a streetscape hidden by an endless row of traffic control signs.

REFERENCES

1. Older, S. J. Effect on Driver of Painting HALT or STOP on the Road at Junctions With HALT Signs. The Surveyor Magazine, March 1960.
2. Williston, Robert M. Effect of Pavement Edge Markings on Operator Behavior. HRB Bull. 266, pp. 8-27, 1960.
3. Planned Pedestrian Program. AAA Foundation for Traffic Safety, 1958.
4. Manual on Uniform Traffic Control Devices for Streets and Highways. U.S. Department of Commerce, Bureau of Public Roads, 1961.
5. Marvin, William L. Vehicle Obedience of Crosswalks and Stop Lines. Unpublished thesis, Yale Bureau of Highway Traffic, 1950.
6. Older, S. J. Driver Behavior at Double White Lines. Traffic Engineering and Control Magazine, Sept. 1962.
7. Rice, Paul W. Effectiveness of Lane Markings on Urban Turning Movements. Unpublished thesis, Yale Bureau of Highway Traffic, 1949.
8. Shepp, A. J., and Lamb, D. R. Shoulder Delineation Markings and Lateral Placement of Vehicles. Public Works, April 1965.
9. Summerfield, Kenneth. Road Markings. Traffic Engineering and Control Magazine, March 1966.
10. Thomas, I. L., Jr., and Taylor, W. T., Jr. Effect of Edge Striping on Traffic Operations. HRB Bull. 244, pp. 11-15, 1960.
11. Carriageway Markings and Edge Lining. Traffic Engineering and Control Magazine, Oct. 1963.
12. Traffic Engineering Handbook. ITE, 1965.
13. Young, W. T. Diagonal Centerlines for Crosswalks. Unpublished thesis, Yale Bureau of Highway Traffic, 1951.

Addendum

EXAMPLE OF PAVEMENT MARKINGS STANDARDIZATION

The Denver, Colorado, pavement markings standards are presented to illustrate techniques employed by this city.

 TRAFFIC ENGINEERING DIVISION OF PUBLIC WORKS

POLICY AND PROCEDURE MEMORANDUM

C. TRAFFIC SIGNS, MARKINGS, AND METERS

No. 8 Pavement Marking   August 30, 1965
                                          Rev. March 2, 1967

I. Purpose

The purpose of this memorandum is to establish the standards for pavement marking, including centerlines, lane lines, crosswalks, stop lines, and pavement messages.

2. Line Marking, Definitions

The terms used in this memorandum in reference to line marking are defined as follows and illustrated in the sketch below:

Outside Lane - a lane which is adjacent to a raised curb or; where curbs do not exist, a lane which is adjacent to the edge of the pavement.

Inside Lane - a lane which is not adjacent to a raised curb, an edge of pavement, or parked vehicles.

Outside-Parking Lane - a lane which is adjacent to parked vehicles and which includes sufficient width to accommodate both a moving vehicle and a parallel parked vehicle.

Inside Turn Lane - a lane which is not adjacent to a raised curb, an edge of pavement or parked vehicles, and which is used to accommodate turning vehicles separate from lanes intended for through traffic.

Outside Turn Lane - a lane which is adjacent to a raised curb or an edge of pavement and which is used to accommodate turning vehicles separate from lanes intended for through traffic.

Pavement Width - the face-of-curb to face-of-curb or, where curbs do not exist, the edge-of-pavement to edge-of-pavement width of the street.

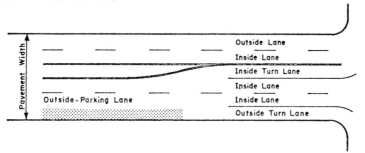

3. Line Marking, Dimensions

The dimensions used in the tables on the pages following the text are developed from what are called Absolute Minimum and Desirable Minimum lane widths. The Absolute Minimum dimensions are the narrowest which should be used in normal practice. If narrower lane widths are used, full usage of those lanes cannot be assumed except under low speed, congested conditions. The Desirable Minimum widths are two feet wider and should be used as the minimum for design. In addition an extra foot has been assigned to Outside Lanes wherever the pavement is wide enough to provide Desirable Minimum lane widths for the remaining lanes.

Type of Lane	Absolute Minimum Lane Widths	Desirable Minimum Lane Widths
Outside Lane	10'-0	12'-0
Inside Lane	9'-0	11'-0
Outside-Parking Lane	17'-0	19'-0
Inside Turn Lane	9'-0	10'-0
Outside Turn Lane	9'-0	11'-0

4. Line Marking, Construction and Use of Tables

The tables on the pages following the text have been created to serve as a guide for the design of lane widths for various combinations of pavement width and parking regulations. They will be useful for both geometric design and pavement marking layout in the field. Unusual conditions will arise which are not shown in these tables, but the principles under which these tables have been constructed can be used to fit those conditions.

The number of lanes in the tables refers to the total of all lanes on the street being designed, including turn lanes, and irrespective of the direction of travel on those lanes. For example, the recommended widths of four lanes on a 40 foot street is the same whether that street is operated with two lanes in each direction or with four lanes in one direction.

The reference to parking in the tables is for parallel parking only. "No Parking" refers to both sides of the street.

Inside Turn Lanes (normally left turn lanes) have been designed so that they remain at absolute minimum width unless there is sufficient pavement width to provide desirable minimum width for the through lanes. Where desirable minimum widths can be achieved or exceeded for through lanes, the Inside Turn Lane is increased to a maximum of 12'-0. In the tables, the Inside Turn Lanes have been shaded for quick identification.

Outside Turn Lanes (either left or right turn) have been designed so that they increase along with through lanes as pavement width increases, to a maximum of 12'-0. In the tables, the Outside Turn Lanes have been shaded for quick identification.

The tables use feet and inches, and the apportionment of five or seven lanes across some pavement widths results in fractions of an inch, since 12 inches is not divisible by five or seven. To avoid this in the tables, and to make the lane dimensions as error-proof as possible, rules of apportioning have been used for pavement widths which are not divisible by five or seven into whole feet and inches. Using these rules, the number of inches apportioned to the five or seven lanes is the same for each lane.

Pavement Width Increments Not Divisible Into Whole Feet and Inches	5 Lanes (Inches Per Lane)	7 Lanes (Inches Per Lane)
1 foot	2 inches	2 inches
2 feet	5 inches	3 inches
3 feet	7 inches	5 inches
4 feet	10 inches	7 inches
5 feet		9 inches
6 feet		10 inches

This system of apportionment of inches introduces errors, but the maximum error of plus or minus two inches in five lane designs and plus or minus three inches in seven lane designs is not significant in terms of the accuracy of pavement marking procedures. The benefits in reducing errors between reading the tables and marking the pavement are expected to outweigh the minor inaccuracies.

In selecting a design where parking is presently permitted, considerable thought must be given to the permanency of that parking.

If there is contemplated the addition of Outside Turn Lanes at some future date, the Outside-Parking Lane dimension in the tables should be abandoned in favor of the combination of the widths of an Outside Turn Lane and an Inside Lane. Similarly, if parking is to be prohibited to provide an additional through lane in the future, the present Parking Lane should be the combination of the widths of an Outside Lane and an Inside Lane. Thought given to these possibilities initially may save a complete re-striping in the future.

5. Line Marking Design

Centerlines in the built-up or urban portions of the City will be either double yellow or solid white in design, according to the standards of the Manual or Uniform Traffic Control Devices. In rural areas where no-passing zones must be established on two-lane highways, the rural system of centerline marking using a dashed white centerline accompanied by solid yellow no-passing lines may be used. Double yellow and solid white centerlines shall be broken at all intersections of city streets and all traffic signal locations not at city streets. Where such centerlines curve or jog through intersections, they may be continued through such intersections in the form of short dashes. Centerlines shall not be broken for driveways unless they are controlled by traffic signals.

Lane lines will be dashed white lines with a ratio of 15 feet of paint and 25 feet of gap. Turn lane lines, or lane lines where lane changing is to be discouraged, shall be solid white, and may be marked double the usual width for added emphasis. Turn lane lines shall be continued through intersections in the form of a solid white line where multiple turns are permitted.

The width of lines used for line marking will normally be about five (5) inches. The space between double yellow lines, or between a dashed white and solid yellow lines, shall be no less than three (3) inches and no more than four (4) inches.

Included in this memorandum are drawings illustrating typical intersection designs and channelization procedures. These should be of value for both geometric design and field layout. Although these drawings show traffic buttons as an optional feature, current policy dictates that these be used at only the most critical locations.

6. Crosswalk Locations

The following types of intersections or locations shall be marked with crosswalks on all legs:

Intersections of Major Arterial Streets with other Major Arterial Streets.

Intersections of Major Arterial Streets with Collector Streets.

Intersections of Collector Streets with other Collector Streets.

Intersections or midblock locations controlled by vehicular or pedestrian traffic signals.

Intersections adjacent to school blocks, and along selected home-school routes.

The exceptions to the above locations will be as follows:

Those intersections where certain crosswalks are omitted to encourage the use of another crosswalk with pedestrian right of way assignment.

Those intersections where all crosswalks are omitted to encourage the use of crosswalks at another location with pedestrian right of way assignment.

Those intersections so rural in nature or so outlying in relation to the built-up part of the city that no pedestrians can reasonably be expected to use the intersection.

Those intersections along parkways or freeways where the inside crosswalks (between the two intersections formed by the parkway or freeway roadways) are omitted because of little pedestrian usage and the need to maintain adequate vehicular storage between these roadways. However, at such locations where pedestrians demonstrate usage of these inside crosswalks, they shall be marked.

7. Stop Line Locations

The following types of intersections or locations shall be marked with stop lines on all approach legs:

a. Intersections or midblock locations controlled by traffic signals.

b. Intersections controlled by school stop sign flashers, but stop lines shall be placed only on approach legs controlled by the flashers.

There are no exceptions to the above locations.

8. Crosswalk and Stop Line Design

Crosswalks and Stop Lines will be white in color. Crosswalks will be ten (10) feet wide as a minimum, but may be wider where wider sidewalks approach the intersection. In the downtown area, crosswalks shall be the width equal to the distance between curb and building (property) line, wherever that distance is paved in the normal manner as total sidewalk. Crosswalks connecting set-back sidewalks will have one line at the back line of the sidewalks and the other ten (10) feet toward the intersection. Crosswalks connecting attached sidewalks will have one line as an extension of the curb line, and the other line ten (10) feet away from the intersection.

Stop lines will be located four (4) feet in advance of a crosswalk where both are called for, creating a two (2) foot clear distance between the stop line and crosswalk line. Stop lines will be located ten (10) feet in advance of a curb line or edge of pavement where crosswalks are not called for. Stop lines will generally be parallel to a crosswalk, but in those instances where medians are more than two (2) feet back of a crosswalk, the stop line should end at that median rather than be parallel to the crosswalk. In addition, in rare instances there will be special conditions where stop lines will be set back from an intersection because of driveway or turning radius considerations.

Crosswalk lines will be twelve (12) inches in width. Stop lines will be twenty-four (24) inches in width.

The drawings attached as a part of this memorandum illustrate typical crosswalk and stop line installations.

9. Pavement Messages

School pavement messages will be white in color. Design and locations will be as noted in the memorandum entitled "School Sign and Marking Installation."

Turning movement messages, consisting of arrows and the word "ONLY", will be white in color. They will generally be located only in lanes which have been continuous for more than a block and which end in mandatory turn lane situations. They may be used in other situations as required.

PAVEMENT MARKING

ILLUSTRATING:

1. Stop line and crosswalk line design for intersections other than downtown exclusive pedestrian phase locations.

2. Centerline and lane line design for conventional pattern and continuous left turn lane pattern.

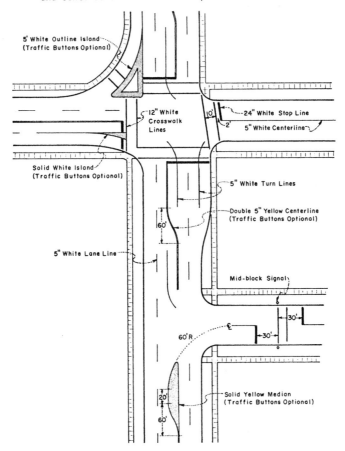

PAVEMENT MARKING

ILLUSTRATING:

1. Stop line and crosswalk line design for downtown exclusive pedestrian phase intersections only.

2. Turn line design for double turns at any location.

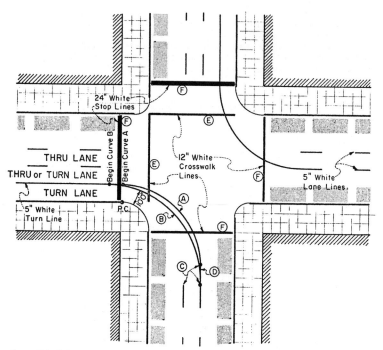

Ⓐ If Turn Lane width is 10'-0 or less, begin radius opposite P.C. of corner radius.

Ⓑ If Turn Lane width is more than 10'-0, begin radius back from P.C. of corner radius so that minimum width of lane is 10'-0.

Ⓒ Begin lane lines at end of radius.

Ⓓ Turn Lane line should intersect the lane line which will provide the Turn Lane with two through lanes going away from the intersection, except where only two through lanes are available.

Ⓔ Line up with curb line.

Ⓕ Line up with property line.

Parking Restrictions and the Curb Lane

DANIEL J. HANSON
Deputy Director for Traffic Engineering
District of Columbia
Department of Highways and Traffic

There is little doubt that the automobile is of great assistance to man in the modern world. However, this same vehicle is of little or no use if there is no place to store the car when he reaches his destination. In early days, when population densities in urban areas were relatively low and life was not so complex, it was usually possible to park a vehicle at the curb near your destination. As population densities increased, however, parking spaces at the curb became far less prevalent.

The need for adequate terminal facilities for highway transport and commercial activities has been recognized for a long time. In fact, it is interesting to note that one of the very first committees appointed in the "new" American Society of Civil Engineers, nearly a hundred years ago, was a committee to study the parking problem in "Lower Manhattan" and make recommendations for its solution. A cartoon of that era shows two men sitting on a park bench surrounded by parked horse-drawn carriages with a caption reading: "Some day we will have horseless vehicles and we won't have to worry about this parking problem."

Curb parking restrictions have been a matter of serious concern for a number of years as evidenced by the following quotations:

> Control of parking at the curb is not the final answer to the parking problem. To have utility, vehicles must be able to load and unload and be stored.
>
> * * *
>
> The average motorist will hesitate to walk much more than two blocks to and from an off-street parking lot or garage. If facilities are to be utilized, they must be placed very close to the motorists destination.
>
> * * *
>
> Parking restrictions are of considerable assistance in keeping road margins clear. Vehicles leaving the parking lane immediately adjacent to a high-speed lane, travel at so low a speed as to be nearly as hazardous as fixed objects. Parked vehicles reduce the sight distance, narrow the effective width and form fixed obstacles on the sides of the road.

These extracts were taken from a publication (1) by Max Halsey in 1941. The subject of this more than 25-year-old text was "Traffic Accidents and Congestion."

Today the automobile has very substantially replaced all other modes of transportation in taking people to and from the places they want to go, except in the very largest urban areas. This certainly should not imply that a majority of traffic engineers agree with this concept. However, it is nevertheless a fact of life today.

This shift from public transit to private automobiles has had a substantial effect on retail activities downtown. As the availability of curb parking spaces downtown diminished, shoppers began to do business farther out from the core of the CBD. Downtown merchants began to establish branches in outlying areas where cheaper land was available for development of large "free" off-street parking areas at these shopping centers.

In an unpublished paper presented at a Traffic Engineering Seminar held in Washington, D.C., in 1965, John Yockey, Vice-President of Woodward and Lothrop Company said his company has eight neighborhood stores in addition to the central store downtown. Nevertheless, the downtown store still maintains 48 percent of the total company business. This would be an indication that although some business activities have declined downtown, this area is still a magnet drawing people despite an obvious lack of curb parking spaces.

Wilbur Smith and Associates made a comprehensive parking study for the Automobile Manufacturers Association in recent years (2). They found that the "Department stores in major cities frequently estimate the value of a parking space as the generator of up to $10,000 in annual retail sales." It should be pointed out that this does not say that the parking space must be at the curb in front of the store. Other studies have been made which illustrate the advantages of curbside parking to adjoining business establishments.

One such study was made by Herbert S. Levinson, of Wilbur Smith and Associates (3). Before World War II, the common location of parking spaces was at the curb. Limited curb space and increased parking demand have reduced on-street parking to somewhat less than 20 percent of the total parking spaces in CBD's. In this respect, Levinson found many interesting facts in his study, such as the following:

> Turnover per curb space is three to seven times higher than for off-street parking spaces.
>
> * * *
>
> Parking durations for curb parkers are consistently less than those for off-street parkers, ranging from only 10 to 50 percent as long.
>
> * * *
>
> Walking distances for curb parkers are considerably less than for off-street parkers.
>
> * * *
>
> Curb parking along arterial roadways, at locations other than the central business district, should never exist at the expense of moving traffic.

This last statement is certainly a most sound principle. In fact, one might even go one step further and severely question the trade-off between a few CBD curb spaces and the valuable curb lane as a means of access to the entire area.

It certainly does not make sense to design and build roads for the purpose of moving traffic and then permit curbside parking to reduce the street's capacity. The Highway Capacity Manual, 1965, indicates that parking at the curb has the effect of reducing the street width by as little as the width of the parked vehicle and as much as 20 ft per lane of parked cars (4, p. 114). In another study, Fred Hurd of the Yale Bureau of Highway Traffic found that mid-block parking at the curb provided a significant increase in the accident expectancy on the entire street.

WASHINGTON, D. C.

An actual case study may be cited, regarding a relatively new curb parking improvement in the Nation's Capital. This study concerns a recently installed rush-hour parking restriction on Pennsylvania Avenue, S.E., near the Capitol Hill area. Pennsylvania Avenue, S.E., connects the U.S. Capitol to adjoining Maryland to the south and east of Washington. During the rush hours, traffic was moving at a level of service of "F", as defined in the Highway Capacity Manual. Most certainly the level of service could never be classified as being better than "E".

The route is an eight-lane roadway, with four lanes in each direction separated by a wide median. Metered curb parking was permitted throughout the day. This restricted the movement of traffic to three lanes in each direction. The street is a very heavily traveled bus transit route, and because of the curb parking, buses were forced to use the second lane from the curb and had to weave in and out of traffic in order to make stops.

Peak-hour traffic in the three traveled lanes was 2300, or roughly 770 vehicles per lane per hour for in-bound traffic during the morning peak hour. The afternoon peak was slightly less when there were only 1940 vehicles during the peak hour or approximately 650 vehicles per lane per hour. The street was posted with a maximum speed limit of 30 mph. Travel time for the critical 1.3-mi section was 3.36 min or a travel speed of 19.1 mph.

In March 1966, parking was prohibited during the rush hours in the direction of major traffic flow only. This restriction extended the 1.3-mi distance on Pennsylvania Avenue, S.E., from 2nd Street and Independence Avenue to the west side of the Sousa Bridge across the Anacostia River at Barney Circle. A "No Standing" restriction was installed on the north side of the street from 7:00 to 9:30 a.m. and on the south side from 4:00 to 6:30 p.m., Monday through Friday.

Conditions six months after the removal of parking indicated a more than 5 percent increase in rush-hour traffic volumes. However, travel time had decreased from 3.36 to 2.47 min. Travel speed had increased over 6.5 miles to 25.7 mph. With the parking removed, buses were found to be using the curb lanes exclusively and trucks in general kept to the right-hand side of the roadway.

The findings after one year of operation include:

1. Reduced rush-hour travel time for cars, 23 percent;
2. Reduced rush-hour travel time for buses, 10 percent;
3. Delays due to stopping, idling and starting were reduced 54 percent;
4. Congestion, measured by traffic density (number of vehicles per mile of roadway), was reduced by over 30 percent; and
5. A saving in incremental travel cost of over 2 cents for each vehicle-mile traveled was accomplished.

This cost savings, when expanded to the total rush-hour travel by motorists, was found to be approximately $56,000 a year. Considering that only 57 percent of the 177 available parking spaces were being used during the rush hours this change has been a sound investment. While there has been an appreciable increase in traffic volume (more than 10 percent), the level of service was also improved to at least level "C". Therefore, the very simple and inexpensive remedy of prohibiting rush-hour parking on Pennsylvania Avenue, S.E., has provided considerable savings to the motoring public.

ATLANTA, GA.

Another recent example of improved street utilization can be found in Atlanta, Ga. Karl A. Bevins, Traffic Engineer of Atlanta, states that a parking regulation along the curb during the p.m. rush hours only has recently made available a third "outbound" lane on Peachtree Road. At the same time several "No Left Turn" regulations were put into effect along a 1000-ft section of Peachtree Road, which presented a critical bottleneck on this major thoroughfare. Changes in the traffic signal sequence from a three-phase to two-phase operation were also implemented as a part of this traffic improvement project in January 1966.

The results of the revised Peachtree Road Operation with the new traffic regulations are as follows:

1. Delays during the p.m. rush period (5:00 to 6:30 p.m.) have been reduced to only an occasional stop due to a "red" traffic signal or a pause for a few seconds behind a left-turning vehicle or a bus which is loading.

2. Outbound travel time during the p.m. rush hour, between the critical section from 14th Street to Lindberg Drive, has been reduced 50 percent.

The time required during the afternoon rush period to travel northbound on Peachtree Road has been reduced considerably. During the p.m. rush period, outbound traffic flow reached a level of 3060 veh/hr for three lanes or 1020 vehicles per lane. The following figures plainly indicate the improvement in street utilization:

Section of Peachtree Road	Time Saved (min)	Improvement (%)
16th Street to Deering Road	10.0 to 3.0	10
Deering Road to Lindberg Drive	8.5 to 5.5	35

This indicates a capacity increase of 58 percent.

The total vehicular volume of traffic moved past the critical Deering Road-25th Street section of Peachtree Road during the maximum 2-hr period has increased 6 percent, from 4040 to 4270 vehicles in the a.m. hours. Likewise a 23 percent increase, from 3160 to 3870 vehicles, has been recorded in the peak 2-hr afternoon period. The maximum rate of flow increased from 2420 to 2590 veh/hr, or 7 percent in the morning. Likewise an increase from 1950 to 2350 veh/hr, or 21 percent, was recorded in the afternoon rush hour.

The Peachtree Road Improvements in Traffic Utilization resulted from the following combinations of changes:

1. No parking 4:00 to 7:00 p.m. on the east side from Colonial Homes Drive to Peachtree Creek.
2. Changing the traffic signal sequence at the intersection of Peachtree Road, Peachtree Hills Avenue and Fairhaven Circle from three to two phase.
3. Prohibiting certain left turns between Spring Street and Deering Road during the period from 4:45 to 6:30 p.m., including turns into or out of driveways and at 2 freeway ramps.

It is apparent that other traffic improvement besides the rush hour no parking restrictions played an important role in this improved street utilization project in Atlanta. There are other similar examples throughout the country where it is very difficult to give total credit to curb parking restrictions since other traffic changes were imposed simultaneously. Several of these exist in Washington, D.C., notably 13th Street, 16th Street and Connecticut Avenue, N.W.

BEVERLY HILLS, CALIF.

Another recent example concerns Wilshire Boulevard in Beverly Hills, Calif. This success story is included in the March 1967 issue of Public Works magazine in an article entitled "Curb Parking Is the Culprit." Public Works Director, Edward E. Tufte states that Wilshire Boulevard is one of the nation's outstanding shopping streets and carries nearly 40,000 veh/day. All curb parking on Wilshire Boulevard, between 7:00 a.m. and 7:00 p.m., was banned on more than a 1-mi section of this street with the merchants' blessing.

Originally, curb parking was allowed, except between the hours of 7:00 and 9:00 a.m. and 4:00 and 6:00 p.m. on this 70-ft wide street. Traffic speeds were exceptionally low and the slowest operation occurred during mid-day when traffic averaged only 11 mph. This reduced vehicular speed resulted mainly from the presence of curb parking. A study indicated that over 40 percent of the total time spent by motorists on Wilshire Boulevard was actually spent standing still.

The following improvements were made on Wilshire Boulevard between April 1963 and August 1965, as reported by Tufte:

1. Revised lane arrangement providing for left turns in the center of the street and three through traffic lanes in each direction.
2. Extension of "No Stopping" regulation in the curb lanes, covering the hours between 7:00 and 10:00 a.m. and 3:00 and 7:00 p.m. with 1-hr parking allowed at other times.
3. Modernizing and interconnecting 18 signalized intersections along Wilshire Boulevard, including the addition of pedestrian "Walk—Dont Walk" indications.
4. Widening the west leg of Wilshire Boulevard.
5. Modernizing and interconnecting the traffic signal equipment at the intersection of Santa Monica Boulevard.
6. Relocation of bus stops from the near side to the far side of intersections.

It is reported that relocation of bus stops improved the intersection capacity approximately 7 percent. In September 1965, all stopping and parking was prohibited on the heaviest traveled section of Wilshire Boulevard between 7:00 a.m. and 7:00 p.m. Although a total of 249 curb parking spaces were removed, amazingly enough, there was little opposition expressed by merchants. Apparently the merchants had been "well sold" in advance concerning the serious impediment to access to their area caused by curb parking.

Briefly the results of the before and after changes revealed the following positive benefits:

1. Overall normal weekday travel speed rose from 12 to 17 mph.

2. Delay to the average driver was reduced from 41 to 24 percent in terms of total travel time.

3. Comparing 1961 and 1965, there was a reduction of 195 reported property-damage accidents, representing an estimated annual savings of about $50,000.

ACCIDENT CONCEPT

It seems appropriate to pursue this accident concept further. Last year there were 31,700 motor vehicle accidents in the District of Columbia. In 5560 or 17 percent of these mishaps, a collision with a parked car was involved. In a 1966 Congressional Record statement (see Addenda), Paul Box indicated that: "Nationally, about 17 percent of all urban accidents, and 4 percent of rural accidents are known to involve parking of vehicles along our streets and highways." This firmly supports our findings in the District, as well as the results shown by Tom Seburn (11).

It certainly cannot be assumed that there would have been over 5000 fewer accidents in the District had all curbside parking been banned. However, studies made in other locations do indicate that the number of accidents can be reduced substantially by eliminating curb parking.

GARDEN CITY, MICH.

An excellent example of this situation is offered in the July 1965 issue of American Highways. A report prepared by the Michigan State Highway Department indicated a reduction of 44 percent in the number of accidents on Ford Road in Garden City in a similar nine-month period before and after curb parking was prohibited (6). This report concludes the following:

1. While total accidents showed significant improvement, the most dramatic reductions occurred in mid-block accidents, those most influenced by curbside parking.

2. Property damage accidents fell 38 percent, from 65 to 40. Total casualties, those hurt or maimed by accidents, plummeted from a high of 63 to a low of 22, a 65 percent drop.

3. In addition to the reduction in accidents and casualties, motorists in Garden City area received an estimated cash savings in excess of $100,000.

4. The savings, compiled by the National Safety Council, reflect repair costs and medical expenses which would have resulted from accidents had there not been any reduction in the accident rate.

CONGRESSIONAL RECORD

One of the most elaborate presentations ever made on this subject can be found in "Streets Should Not Be Used as Parking Lots" which was introduced in the Congressional Record on October 22, 1966, by Congressman Farnsley of Kentucky (7). This discussion by Paul Box covered the curb parking problem, related accident statistics, resulting traffic congestion, and concluded with some very sound principles. This entire article is reproduced in the Addenda to this paper.

SAN FRANCISCO, CALIF.

William Marconi, Senior Traffic Engineer of San Francisco, has found that: "Where block lengths, signals and other factors are similar, it has been demonstrated that the mid-block accident rate is affected by parking. The highest rate occurs where a mixture of parallel and angle parking is permitted. A lower rate occurs with parallel parking only and the lowest rate of all occurs where parking is prohibited."

It cannot be stressed strongly enough that terminal facilities, or parking spaces are as much a part of the highway transport system as are the vehicles and the roadways themselves. It has been clearly demonstrated that a well-built roadway is intended for the purpose of moving vehicles. There is only a limited place on major arterial road-ways for vehicles that are not in motion. The trend is obviously and definitely away from use of the main roadways as a place to park and store vehicles.

Modern zoning ordinances almost everywhere now require adequate off-street park-ing before a new building may be erected. Developers have come to recognize the importance of providing off-street storage facilities for vehicles. For example, Mont-gomery County, Maryland, zoning ordinances (8) require 1.5 off-street parking spaces for every dwelling unit. In the case of high-rise apartments one-half of these spaces must be within the apartment building, either underground or on one or more of the floors of the building.

Similar regulations are currently being employed by numerous governmental agen-cies. In this regard, it would be interesting to canvass all of the large urban areas of the country to compare current off-street parking requirements. It is suggested that such a study should be made.

CHICAGO, ILL.

In 1960, William R. Marston, then Deputy City Traffic Engineer of Chicago, said the following in a Traffic Quarterly article (9):

> One of the more effective traffic improvements that has been applied to our major streets is the rush-hour parking prohibition program. This is one of the lowest cost plans that we have found and results in consider-able increases in speed and safety. We have over 290 curb miles pres-ently so controlled and 160 more are before the City Council for approval. Surveys show that an average of only one car per each retail establishment is parking during the two hours the prohibition is in effect. Many objec-tions to the curb parking prohibition result, of course, but no curtailment of the program has been necessary.

NEW YORK, N.Y.

In a June 1963 American City magazine article (10), Henry Barnes answered some di-rect questions relating to curb parking, as follows:

Question: What conditions do you feel should exist to warrant the removal of on-street parking?

Answer: First, when conditions demonstrate an overwhelming need for moving traffic and, secondly, when the city has provided adequate off-street parking, then curbside meters can be removed without undue hardship to motorists. However, here is a warning—do not allow curbside park-ing to interfere with the traffic movement needs of the street. Streets basically should move traffic, not be parking lots.

Question: Is it possible to increase the traffic volume of outmoded streets without spending a lot of money?

Answer: We slashed dramatically the congestion on two narrow crosstown Man-hattan streets by simply removing the parking on both sides and providing three lanes of traffic during the morning and evening rush hours. Before the introduction of the "Crosstown Roll," motorists made an average of 12.2 stops in the 14-block trip. They now average 8.5 stops and save $5\frac{3}{4}$ minutes despite the fact that improved operating efficiency has at-tracted 17 percent more traffic.

CONCLUSIONS

It is certainly a strong personal hope that the day is not too far distant when all major roadways will be used for the purpose for which they were intended. This is moving people and goods all the way from origin to destination, with ultimate dispatch, a high level of comfort, maximum safety and the highest degree of economy possible. In the opinion of more than one traffic engineer, the day of curb parking on our major arterial streets in urban areas will be short lived.

REFERENCES

1. Halsey, Max. Traffic Accidents and Congestion. John Wiley and Sons, New York, 1941.
2. Parking in the Center City. Wilbur Smith and Associates, New Haven, Conn., May 1965.
3. Levinson, Herbert S. Some Economic Aspects of On-Street Parking. Proc. ITE, 1963.
4. Highway Capacity Manual, 1965. HRB Special Report 87, 1965.
5. Tufte, E. E. Curb Parking Is the Culprit. Public Works Magazine, March 1967.
6. Story by Michigan State Highway Department, American Highways, July 1965.
7. Remarks by Congressman Charles P. Farnsley of Kentucky, presentation by Paul C. Box, Congressional Record, Nov. 21, 1966.
8. Montgomery County, Maryland Zoning Regulations, 1967.
9. Marston, William. Traffic Quarterly, Eno Foundation for Highway Traffic Control, July 1960.
10. Barnes, Henry. Facts and Fallacies of Traffic Engineering. American City Magazine, June 1963.
11. Seburn, Thomas J. Relationship Between Curb Uses and Traffic Accidents. Traffic Engineering, May 1967.

Addenda

Congressional Record

United States
of America   PROCEEDINGS AND DEBATES OF THE 89th CONGRESS, SECOND SESSION

Vol. 112   WASHINGTON, MONDAY, NOVEMBER 21, 1966   *No. 187*

Streets Should Not Be Used as Parking Lots

EXTENSION OF REMARKS
OF
HON. CHARLES P. FARNSLEY
OF KENTUCKY
IN THE HOUSE OF REPRESENTATIVES
Saturday, October 22, 1966

Mr. FARNSLEY. Mr. Speaker, the problems caused by automobile parking along our streets and highways have received entirely too little attention by our citizens, officials, and legislators. Material in the following discussion has been gathered by Paul C. Box, of Skokie, Ill. Mr.

Box has spent over 16 years in traffic engineering work for cities. He testified before committees of both the House and Senate, with respect to public lighting needs. He is chairman of the parking committee of the highway research board, and has been active in studies of parking along our streets for many years.

Mr. Box wishes to emphasize, however, that the viewpoints and conclusions in this discussion are his own, and that he is not presenting the official policy of any organization with which he is associated. The discussion follows:

VIEWS OF MR. PAUL C. BOX

The Problem

The motor vehicle, and most particularly the private passenger car, has brought uncountable blessings to our daily lives. It has increased productivity, and has added immeasurably to our convenience in getting from one place to another. Because of its manifold benefits, and the fact that it represents an essential element of our economy, the automobile and its future progeny are truly here to stay.

The growth in automobile ownership and use has also brought problems, too many of which we have been accepting as necessary byproducts. An obvious element is the so-called parking problem. If we are going to own automobiles, we evidently should at the same time recognize our individual responsibility to provide adequate storage to "stable the beast."

The responsibility rests with the automobile owner at his place of residence. It rests with the businessman at his place of trade, and includes provision of space for both employees and customers or clients. It also rests with the industrial manager in the establishment of parking for employees and visitors. Unfortunately, citizens, and a high percentage of our businessmen, have in the past failed to properly accept their responsibility in this area.

The product of this indifference has been use of our public streets as parking lots. The cost of this attitude is nearly unbelievable when expressed in terms of accidents and added traffic congestion.

Accidents

Nationally, about 17 percent of all urban accidents, and 4 percent of rural accidents are known to involve parking of vehicles along our streets and highways. The number of motor vehicle occupants killed in these accidents is less than a thousand per year. This "low" figure is hardly a cause for complacency, especially if we add the thousands of children that have died in past years as a result of entering the street from behind parked cars.

Our bland acceptance of these tragic accidents, which are preventable, is difficult to understand. The figures are available to any elected or appointed public official. Many are cognizant of the problem, but few have shown the courage to take direct and positive action. At least one example is known, where the residents themselves along an important major traffic route voted two out of three for complete banning of parking along their street. Yet two different groups of elected officials, of opposite political persuasion, separately rejected this popular mandate, and refused to take action despite the alarming parked car accident rate!

Before citing further examples, it is perhaps germane to consider how and why parking is so dangerous when allowed along streets. The first, and major cause of these accidents, is the physical location of the vehicle on the traveled way. It occupies what would otherwise usually be a traffic lane for movement. It is an obstacle in the critical area needed for right turns in and out of side streets, driveways and alleys. Furthermore, this curbside lane is often desperately needed for the added use of straight-ahead traffic. These conditions combine to create a serious conflict.

The second cause of parked car type accidents involves one vehicle leaving the curb parking area. The driver may be directly involved in a collision with one or more moving vehicles, or he may create a rear-end type accident by causing another moving vehicle to abruptly stop in order to avoid impact.

A third cause of parked car accidents involves the driver who stops or slows to enter a parking stall. Both direct and indirect (rear-end and sideswipe type) accidents are caused by such accidents.

A fourth cause is produced by drivers, or passengers of parked vehicles, opening their car doors on the street side. This action also creates direct and indirect types of accidents. Some drivers refuse to consider purchase of automobiles or sports-type cars with center consoles, because this arrangement makes it almost impossible for the driver to slide across the seat, and enter or leave by the proper, curbside door. For many years the courts have leaned toward assessment of accident blame on drivers or passengers who get struck while alighting from the street side of parked cars. Some cities have even passed ordinances assigning primary accident responsibility to such persons.

The fifth type of accident caused by parked cars has already been partially covered, with respect to children who are slaughtered by stepping out from behind parked cars. A similar situation exists with respect to adults entering the roadway from behind parked trucks or buses. To these occurrences must also be added the intersection or driveway accident which occurs, because one or both drivers have their vision blocked by parked cars along the street.

Many of the accidents which have happened in the past, and which occur today, are really caused in part by parked cars, even though this element is never mentioned in the written accident report. It is safe to assume that curb parking is responsible for at least one out of every five accidents that occur in our cities each year.

In order to further examine this problem, we must consider the different types of streets to be found in our cities. A vast difference exists in the accident rate along various streets. Part of this is due to varying volumes of traffic. Thus the minor or side street is quite different in character from the major traffic artery. Similarly, the side street, which is abutted by single family homes, is different from the one with dense apartment development, business or industry. The major traffic route wending through a park, or along a river is not similar to one which bisects a retail area. Streets not only differ in traffic volume, but also in numbers of driveways and curb parked cars, frequency of movement in and out of driveways and parking stalls, and in amount and composition of pedestrians.

Taking first the major traffic route, or arterial street, we find its primary function is defined by the name—it is an avenue for the movement of vehicles. Furthermore, the composition of this vehicular movement is varied to include not only private passenger cars, but also trucks, buses and taxis. In retail or industrial areas, there are also large numbers of pedestrians frequently crossing the roadway.

In addition to the primary function of movement, this type of street is heavily used for access. This simply means that it must normally provide the traveling public with a means of rather directly entering roadside private developments. These developments may be homes, apartments, shops, industries or service facil-

ities. In any event, if one cannot reach these places, they frequently would have no value or utility and thus could not exist in a human-oriented society.

The twin roles of traffic movement and abutting property access are common to practically all city streets and the conventional rural highways. They are equally common to the minor side street. When realistically viewed, however, the side street abutted by homes or small apartment buildings must also act to provide a parking reservoir for unusual demands. It is practical and proper for a large apartment development, business or industry to furnish adequate parking to meet all demands of its clients, employees and customers. We cannot, however, expect the average home owner to supply parking space for more than his own cars, plus one or two visitors. Occasional overflow simply must be met by use of the street.

We then see that the primary function of the minor street is to provide access to abutting property, while a second function is circulation and travel between adjacent blocks and the nearest major traffic routes. Unless homes are built on estate size lots, a third function of the side street is to accommodate overflow parking.

Through the use of intelligent planning, zoning and building regulations, a community can handle its parking problems in two ways. First and most generally accepted is the mandatory provision of adequate off-street parking as part of new building construction, and as part of all remodeling permits. The second approach is to require construction of proper parking facilities for existing buildings. Both of these tools will subsequently be discussed in greater detail.

Failure to enact or enforce adequate local regulations results in a truly second-rate community. The older parts of nearly all our cities, from the smallest farm community to the largest metropolitan center, show the depreciating effects of parking supply neglect.

A four year accident study of some 1200 blocks has been made in one city, which included parked car accident rates along minor streets. Significant findings appeared. Before discussing these in detail, it is desirable to examine the overall accident record of this community, with respect to parked car accidents on all classes of streets. This information is shown for the latest five year period in the following table:

	Number of Accidents	Percent
Major streets:		
Parked car ..	1,174	12
All other	7,795	88
Subtotal	9,969	100
Minor streets:		
Parked car ..	1,083	43
All other	1,427	57
Subtotal	2,510	100
All streets:		
Parked car ..	2,257	18
All other	10,222	82
Total......	12,479	100

When these accidents are related to the mileage of streets in the community on which curb parking occurs, the major streets were found to have a rate of 14 parking accidents per mile per year. The minor street rate was, however, only 1.8 accidents per mile per year. Thus the overall hazard of parking along heavily traveled routes was nearly eight times as great as on minor streets.

The reason for this significant difference is easy to find. The traffic volumes and the degree of parking activity are both much greater, and the probability of accident occurrence is correspondingly higher, on the major traffic arteries. It is therefore clear, that, the first and most urgent activity needed by a community, is to clear parking from its major traffic routes. This should be done on a total basis, and not merely during rush hours to expedite traffic flow. In the cited community, 10 percent of all accidents in the city has been found to occur solely as a result of curb parking on only 6 percent of its total street system!

Turning now to the minor streets, we saw in the Table that 43 percent of all accidents on this class of street was caused by curb parking. If we consider only the midblock accidents (those not involving intersection collisions) we find $\frac{2}{3}$ involve curb parking. A detailed study of these accidents, covering a four year span, found a clear relationship among different densities of land use. [This information is shown in the table on page 71.]

In every case, it can be seen that curb parking is a leading cause of accidents. In this particular study, one short business block was analyzed, where the community had allowed 100 feet of angle type parking along one side of the street in order to service a new post office. The rate caused by the parallel curb and angle parking in this block, expressed on a mileage basis, is 63 accidents per year! This is nearly 20 times the rate on other business type side streets.

This minor example should in itself be grounds to cause the General Service Administration of the U.S. Government to examine its archaic policy of constructing government buildings without provision for customer and visitor parking. Today, the construction of adequate off-street parking for all users of every business building should be the policy of all agencies and levels of government.

Traffic Congestion

On older side streets, with narrow widths and dense curb parking, cities have in many cases been forced to install one-way regulations. Even though the traffic volume on these minor streets is low, vehicles will occasionally meet headon and find no opportunity to pass, if allowed to operate on a two-way basis. One study of side streets found an optimum width of 32 feet, as the one which produced the lowest accident rate with variable degrees of parking in single family areas. For apartment areas, a width of 36 feet is desirable. If the side street is abutted by business or industry, widths of 40 to 48 feet are preferred. Unfortunately, many communities are today still building their side streets at substandard widths.

The provision of proper width is important from the standpoint of avoiding minor street congestion, and allowing better access for emergency vehicles. Since the construction cost of these streets should be borne by the abutted benefited property owner, no general public tax money need be involved.

Along major traffic routes, an entirely different situation exists. Here the large share of traffic is moving to destinations

Density of Land Use	Accidents Per Mile Per Year			
	Curb Parking	Driveways	Pedestrians	Other Types
Single family homes	1.04	0.15	0.13	0.12
Apartment areas	3.10	.45	.25	.52
Business areas	3.50	1.65	.20	.72
Industrial areas	1.15	.95	.04	.20

beyond each individual block. The abutting owner cannot be fairly assessed to provide pavement for such through traffic flows. However, when major traffic routes are allowed to have curb parking, the abutting owner is reaping a personal gain, at the net expense of the general public. He is being subsidized at everyone's expense. Furthermore, this undemocratic arrangement penalizes the owner who does set aside a large share of his land for customer and employee parking. Examples exist where major streets have been widened at great public cost, and rows of stately trees cut down, so that parking lanes can be maintained in addition to the necessary lanes for traffic movement. Occasionally such widening may be warranted, but when it is, the abutting owner should pay for all added costs to provide parking. The public will pay more than enough in the long run, as a result of added accidents and congestion.

The congestion effect of curb parking is not limited to the width of the parked cars. The stopping of a vehicle to park, or the pulling away from the curb, interferes with operation on the adjacent moving traffic lane. In effect, a row of parallel parking along one side of a street takes up the equivalent of some 15 to 17 feet of roadway width.

Angle parking into the curb should never be allowed on any street, unless it is a short, dead end block. The more progressive cities across our country have moved strongly against this vice, and it is disappearing from use. Where still allowed, such parking affects 30 to 40 feet of roadway area on each side of the street. The accident and congestion penalty of this type of parking is simply too great to provide any rationalization for its use. Studies have shown that angle parking produces several times as many accidents, and much greater congestion, than does parallel arrangement.

The tool of rush hour parking restrictions is in widespread use throughout our country. The theory is simply one of providing an added traffic lane, during the hours of heaviest traffic demand. While considerable congestion, and some accidents are thus avoided, thousands of miles of such routes may be found clogged with traffic during other hours of the day. This condition is largely produced by the effect of curb parking which extends beyond the parking lane.

Development of an Action Program

The need for total day and night prohibition of parking along most of our major traffic arteries may readily be observed in nearly all cities. Before it can realistically be banned, however, certain principles must be accepted, which require forthright local action.

Principle No. 1: The functions of a major traffic route are to provide for safe and efficient movement, plus access to abutting property.

Principle No. 2: Curb parking is not a right which is vested with the abutting owner, and he has no legal or moral claim to such usurping of the public way.

Principle No. 3: The cost of allowing curb parking, when measured in terms of accidents and congestion, is an unrealistic and unnecessary burden to place on the public.

Principle No. 4: The continued preservation of residential, business and industrial land uses is imperative to our economy.

Principle No. 5: Parking cannot often be prohibited, until substitute spaces are provided off-street.

Principle No. 6: The leadership for development of such off-street parking must come from the local governments.

Principle No. 7: The cost of providing these parking facilities should be borne by the benefited property owners.

72

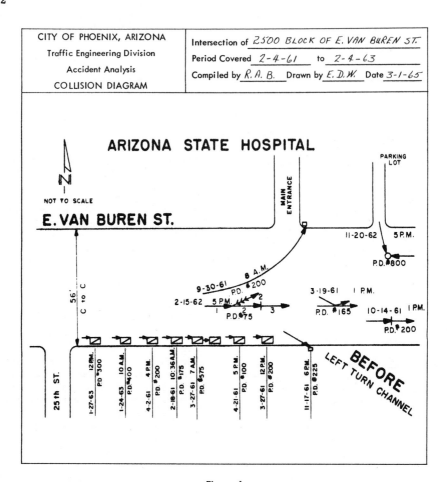

Figure 1.

Congressional Record (continued)

Principle No. 8: The location of parking facilities must be such as to minimize walking distance, which frequently implies wrecking older buildings near the center of each block of congested areas.

Principle No. 9: The development of such parking programs will frequently be fought by all affected owners, and powerful political pressures will be brought to bear to block the work.

Principle No. 10: Elected and appointed officials must exhibit both courage and farsightedness, to conceive, execute and maintain the policy.

The implications in adoption of these Principles are varied. In many cases our cities lack the enabling legislation, and new laws are needed at the state

levels. Such laws should allow the local community to condemn property, and assess benefited owners, for provision of all types of parking on all types of land, including residential, business and industrial. They should allow development of local parking authorities where needed to handle problems of central business areas. They should allow the establishment of street parking permit fees in dense residential areas, where the money thus collected is put into a fund for construction of local parking lots. The laws should, in short, encourage and assist local government in solving the problems.

At the state level, the legislators should strongly support their highway commissions and departments, in denying use

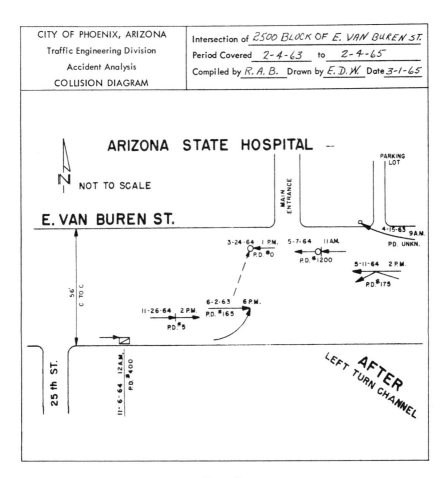

CITY OF PHOENIX, ARIZONA	Intersection of *2500 BLOCK OF E. VAN BUREN ST.*
Traffic Engineering Division	Period Covered *2-4-63* to *2-4-65*
Accident Analysis	Compiled by *R. A. B.* Drawn by *E. D. W.* Date *3-1-65*
COLLISION DIAGRAM	

Figure 2.

Congressional Record (continued)

of state funds for highway or street work of any kind, along routes which have curb parking allowed. They should not allow use of local shares of motor fuel or road user gas tax funds by communities on routes with curb parking.

At the national level, legislators should not approve funds for construction of public buildings, unless these developments include provisions for adequate off-street parking to serve all users of the building. In a similar fashion, Federal funds should be denied to states for use in construction or maintenance of highways with parking.

These are strong statements, because positive action is needed. They are in-

tended to promote concepts, and not to develop detailed policy. In practice, of course, consideration must be given to individual conditions. There are exceptional cases, which are recognized even in our laws against murder. We do, however, desperately and urgently, need to first understand, and secondly to cope with, our parking problems at all levels. The conditions are worsening at an alarming rate, but there is no simple nor painless remedy. The disease of parking on our major streets and highways can only be cured by positive and continued action, and with the support of a majority of our citizens.

MADISON, WIS.

A typical parking layout for parallel parking at the curb on high volume streets of Madison, Wisconsin, is attached. This method of marking parking stalls is new to Madison. It is not to be confused with "paired" parking, a system which has been in use in many cities for the last few years.

A no parking area of from 9 to 11 ft between each parking stall is marked on certain heavy traffic streets. In this way, a motorist can enter a vacant curb stall by using a

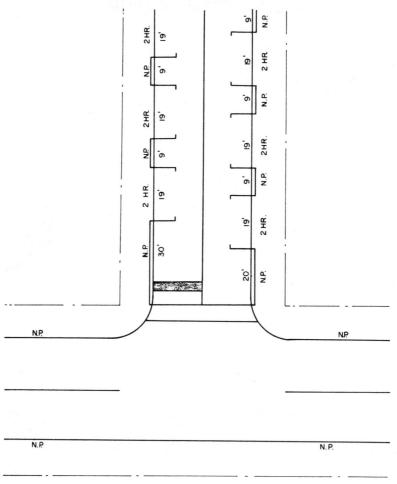

Figure 3. Typical parking layout.

total of 36 to 40 ft for the maneuver. In this way, the vehicle is driven into the stall and then is backed into the proper parking space. When leaving, the vehicle is backed into the space to its rear and then enters traffic without making any other maneuver.

These markings have been a material benefit for heavy moving traffic and also they have eliminated many delays on streets with bus routes. Bus drivers have commented many times on the decreased delays to traffic in the moving traffic lanes because of this particular type of marking.

Exclusive Bus Lanes

JOHN N. LAPLANTE
Traffic Engineer III
Design and Planning Division
Bureau of Street Traffic
City of Chicago

A method of providing added capacity in the peak direction on streets with heavy bus volumes is by the use of exclusive bus lanes. Although this does not always provide added capacity for trucks or passenger vehicles, it does permit more efficient bus service. This can make bus travel more attractive, thereby increasing the number of people who ride the bus rather than drive. Such lane usage can be either full-time or part-time and is usually restricted to streets where a lane of buses would carry as many people as a lane of automobiles. It must not interfere with necessary traffic movements or access to street frontage.

The most obvious advantage of the exclusive bus lane is its ability to improve bus speeds substantially through the most congested areas. It can also help to reduce congestion by separating the slow-moving and frequently stopping buses from the rest of the through traffic. Although it is relatively inexpensive to install and maintain, it does require continual enforcement to prevent misuse of the lane by unauthorized cars and trucks. Another possible disadvantage is the fact that it usually reduces the number of moving lanes available to the rest of the traffic. If the curb lane is used, it can make right turns difficult and street access loading zones impossible during the hours of operation. If one of the center lanes is used, it will greatly facilitate right turns, but it can create pedestrian hazard zones in the bus loading areas. On two-way streets such a lane will make left-turn maneuvers rather difficult.

Special-use lanes can be designated either by signs over the exclusive lane or next to the lane on light poles or pedestals. These signs will usually be supplemented by distinctive paint markings and special messages painted directly on the pavement. In center lane operations, pedestrian safety islands are usually delineated in the middle of the street. These islands should offer some physical protection to the waiting passenger, particularly if the bus lane is in effect all day long. Whether the lane is in effect all day or just during rush hours, successful operation requires constant and fair police enforcement and a good program of public relations.

EXPERIENCE IN CITIES

Exclusive bus lanes have been installed in many cities. Chicago has had considerable success with its 7-block long Washington Street bus lane in the heart of the Loop. Washington Street is a five-lane one-way street, and the exclusive bus lane is the center lane. It is designated by special pavement markings and pedestal signs, and most of the passenger loading zones have protective railings and splash guards along the outside of the zone. The Chicago Transit Authority has reported a speed-up in transit operations from 14 to 28 percent.

Rochester, N. Y., uses a 2-block exclusive bus lane during the evening rush hours only. A saving of 30 minutes loading time in the peak 2-hr period is reported.

An 8-block stretch of Baltimore's one-way Cathedral Street uses an exclusive bus lane during both the morning and evening rush periods. The city has experienced a 17 to 22 percent speed-up of transit travel and a 39 percent speed-up of other traffic.

Atlanta's Peachtree Street was reconstructed for 4 blocks, adding one more lane (from 4 to 5) and designating the curb lane for buses only during the rush hours. Buses were speeded up 4 percent in the morning rush and 33 percent in the evening, while general traffic was speeded up 110 and 61 percent, respectively.

TABLE 1

EXCLUSIVE BUS LANES

City	Streets	Description	Time	Results
Chicago, Ill.	Washington Street (one-way)	7 blocks long, one lane in center of 5-lane street	All day	14-28% speed-up in transit operations after 5 months
Rochester, N.Y.	Main Street	Initially one block, later extended from Plymouth to Goodman	4-6 p.m.	Saving of 30-min loading time in peak 2-hr period
Baltimore, Md.	Cathedral Street (one-way)	8 blocks long	7:30-10 a.m. 4-6 p.m.	17-22% speed-up of transit travel; 39% speed-up of other traffic
Atlanta, Ga.	Peachtree Street	4 blocks of northbound lane; at the same time, street was changed from 4 to 5 lane operation	7-9 a.m. 4-7 p.m.	Buses speeded up 4-33%; general traffic speeded up 61-110%
Birmingham, Ala.	Third Avenue	8 blocks long	7-9 a.m. 4-6 p.m.	40% decrease in accidents involving transit vehicles; 27.7% decrease in bus travel time; 29% decrease in auto travel time; gain of 394 parking hours per day downtown
Peoria, Ill.	Adams and Jefferson Streets	Adjacent one-way arteries, 4 blocks each	3-6 p.m.	25% speed-up in transit service; 10% speed-up for other vehicles

Birmingham's Third Avenue has an exclusive bus lane for eight blocks every morning and evening rush period. A 40 percent decrease in accidents involving transit vehicles, a 27.7 percent decrease in bus travel time, a 29 percent decrease in auto travel time, and a gain of 394 parking hours per day in the downtown area are reported.

In Peoria, Ill., Adams and Jefferson Streets are adjacent one-way arteries. Both have used exclusive bus lanes during the evening rush hours only. A 25 percent speed-up in transit service and a 10 percent speed-up for other vehicles have resulted.

Data on results of exclusive bus lanes are summarized in Table 1. Additional information can be obtained from the American Transit Association.

CONCLUSIONS

Exclusive bus lanes have been installed in many cities with varying degrees of success. These special-use lanes improve bus speeds substantially through the most congested areas, but they do require continual enforcement to remain effective and reduce the number of moving lanes available to the rest of the traffic. The cities summarized in Table 1 are only those cities that have been relatively successful with their use of exclusive bus lanes.

REFERENCES

1. Rainville. Transit—The Traffic Engineer's Opportunity. Traffic Engineering, pp. 15-19, 39, June 1958.
2. Reserved Transit Lanes. Traffic Engineering, pp. 37-40, July 1959.
3. Traffic Considerations in Planning of Central Business Districts. Traffic Engineering, Report of ITE Project Committee 6D, pp. 40-43, June 1964.
4. Traffic Engineering Handbook. Pp. 565-568, 1965.

Addenda
PHOENIX, ARIZ.

Figure 1. Recessed bus bay, Phoenix, Ariz.

Figure 2. Recessed bus bay, Phoenix, Ariz.

78

DENVER, COLO.

The "skip-block" bus stop design in downtown Denver was installed to provide a bus stop for each block, taking into account the mandatory right-turn lanes every other block in the one-way grid. A schematic drawing of the downtown area (Fig. 3) shows the skip-block bus stops and double-turn locations. Two stops in one block are provided, but no stops in the following block because of the mandatory-turn lane in the following block. However, the net effect is to provide one stop per intersection, alternating near side and far side locations.

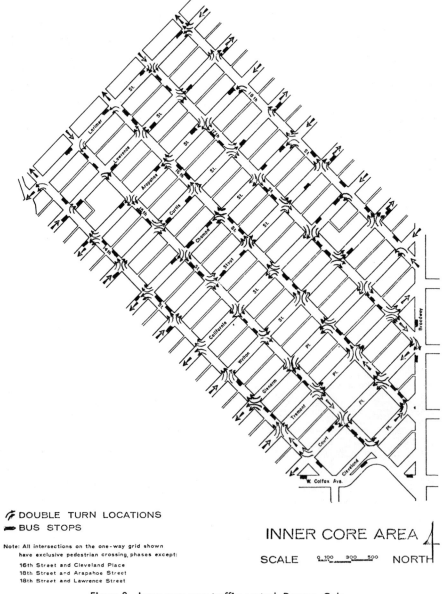

x> DOUBLE TURN LOCATIONS
► BUS STOPS

Note: All intersections on the one-way grid shown
  have exclusive pedestrian crossing phases except:
  16th Street and Cleveland Place
  18th Street and Arapahoe Street
  18th Street and Lawrence Street

INNER CORE AREA

SCALE   0 100   300   500   NORTH

Figure 3. Inner core area traffic control, Denver, Colo.

WASHINGTON, D.C.

In Washington, D.C., a number of streets are paved with asphalt and a concrete bus bay is provided. The real answer to preventing creeping or slippage in a bus stop area is the construction of a concrete slab. Figures 4 and 5 show typical bus bays in the District of Columbia. Figures 6 and 7 are before and after photographs of a recessed bus bay.

Figure 4. Bus bay, Washington, D.C.

Figure 5. Bus bay, Washington, D.C.

Figure 6. Before bus bay construction.

The following description tells the complete story on the Pennsylvania Avenue, S.E., plan. Actually the key to this program was the elimination of curb parking during the peak hour only in the direction of major traffic flow. This in fact made the curb lane available for the heavy bus operation. No special signs or pavement markings were required since the sheer volume of buses makes the curb lane practically an exclusive bus lane.

Figure 7. After bus bay construction.

IMPROVING QUALITY OF TRAFFIC FLOW

Pennsylvania Avenue, S.E., from the U.S. Capitol to Anacostia River is an important thoroughfare serving downtown Washington. Originally buildings along the Avenue were row houses for single-family occupancy. Land has been rezoned for a community business center class. Many of the old row houses have been converted to offices and small businesses. A few have been retained for residential property. In most cases, people live on the second and third stories. There are two theaters, one or two supermarket-type stores, several gasoline stations, a bank or two, and a school or two along the Avenue. But for the most part the buildings are still of the original construction with narrow frontages along the street.

The street consists of two 38-ft roadways separated by a wide planted median. Each roadway was marked for four traffic lanes. The total length is 1.3 miles.

Situation in 1965

By summer 1965, traffic congestion had become so bad that people were complaining to District officials. Complaints were sufficiently numerous to warrant a special study by the Bureau of Traffic Engineering and Operations.

Traffic volumes did not seem overly great. There had been little change in volumes for several years. Counts indicated some 34,000 veh/day for traffic moving in both directions. The worst tie-ups were occurring between 7:00 and 9:30 a.m. and 4:00 to 6:30 p.m. Traffic moved orderly and without delay during the balance of the day. Traffic during the morning and afternoon rush periods (westbound from 7:00 to 9:30 a.m. and eastbound from 4:00 to 6:30 p.m.) amounted to 4200 and 3700 vehicles, respectively.

The posted speed limit was 30 mph. Average overall speed was found to be under 20 mph for each of the periods of peak-traffic flow. Throughout the balance of the day traffic moved along at around 28 mph.

Regulated parking spaces had been laid out as requested by businessmen and residents to serve their needs. A total of 177 marked bays was provided along the north curb line for westbound traffic and along the south curb line for eastbound traffic. These spaces had time limits imposed to permit and encourage turnover parking. This timing made 442.5 vehicle-hours of parking available for the morning and afternoon peak periods, if properly used. By actual count, it was found that these spaces were being used to only 57 percent of capacity. The greatest number of vehicles parked along the curb on one side of the street in the whole 1.3 miles at any one time was 78. These were found in the eastbound roadway one afternoon between 4:00 and 6:30. There were times during the morning peak period of traffic flow, when no more than 13 vehicles were parked in the curb lane for westbound traffic. Yet, these few vehicles were reducing the effective width of the roadways from four to three lanes. As a result, traffic, inbound and outbound, was backed up each morning and afternoon.

Recommend Remedial Changes

A review of facts collected revealed that (a) over 20 percent of the total traffic in 24 hours was crowded into three lanes, 5 hours a day, and (b) elimination of parking, in the direction of major flow, only $2\frac{1}{2}$ hours in the morning and afternoon, would provide an additional lane for traffic.

Parking in the direction of major flow was prohibited Mondays through Fridays. This regulation was promulgated on February 23, 1966. To compensate for the lost parking spaces additional parking regulations were instituted on neighboring side streets. Four free lanes were made available for movement of traffic in the direction of major flow during peak periods in place of the three lanes for movement and one for parking previously in use.

Situation in October 1966

The only changes made in conditions on Pennsylvania Avenue, S.E., were those pertaining to inbound traffic in the morning and outbound traffic in the afternoon for Mondays through Fridays. All studies were designed to measure before and after effects

TABLE 2

NUMBER AND COST OF ACCIDENTS
ON PENNSYLVANIA AVENUE, S. E.[a]

Severity of Accident and Type of Collision	Unit Cost[b] ($)	1965		1966	
		Number	Total Cost ($)	Number	Total Cost ($)
Property damage only:					
Rear-end	600	3	1,800	8	4,800
Side-swipe	400	13	5,200	17	6,800
Personal injury:					
Rear-end	1,800	3	5,400	3	5,400
Pedestrian	2,400	3	7,200	1	2,400
Total		22	19,600	29	19,400

[a]Between 2nd and 15th Streets, in the direction of major traffic flow (westbound from 7:00 to 9:30 a.m. and eastbound from 4:00 to 6:30 p.m.), Mondays through Fridays, March through September.
[b]Source: Washington Area Motor Vehicle Accident Cost Study, 1966.

as applied to these two periods of time. A systems effectiveness study was made to evaluate quality.

1. There was a slight increase in traffic volume: inbound 7:00 to 9:30 a.m., 4400 vehicles and outbound 4:00 to 6:30 p.m., 3900 vehicles.

2. Overall travel time was reduced by 23 percent.

3. Delay due to stopping, idling and starting was reduced by 54 percent.

4. Congestion, measured by traffic density (vehicles per mile of roadway) was reduced by 29 percent.

5. Travel cost was reduced by 23 percent for a net saving of $56,000.

D. C. Transit Company made a study of overall travel time of their buses. Removal of the parked vehicles at the curb resulted in a reduction of bus travel time of 10 percent.

Accident experience before and after the changes indicates there was no significant change. The only accidents that could have been affected by absence or presence of vehicles parked at the curb are those happening along the roadway. Collision types would be rear-end, side-swipe, parked vehicle or vehicle maneuvering to park, fixed object or pedestrian. Since parking of vehicles on the Avenue has no influence on traffic in the cross streets, angle collisions in the intersections were eliminated from the study. The study period was March through September 1966. To be consistent, accident records for the same months in 1965 were reviewed. Metropolitan Police reports indicated there were 29 accidents in the specified collision types. This is seven, or nearly one-third, more than occurred in 1965. When analyzed in the light of severity and cost (Table 2), this difference is really not significant.

CONCLUSIONS

Vehicles parked at the curb on Pennsylvania Avenue, S.E., from 2nd to 15th Streets, during a.m. and p.m. periods of peak traffic flow:

1. Caused undue congestion in inbound and outbound traffic;

2. Slowed traffic down to under 20 mph in a 30-mph zone;

3. Caused delay in transit vehicles maneuvering around parked vehicles to get to bus stops at the curb.

Removal of parking in the direction of major flow had the following effects:

1. Reduced travel time for all traffic 23 percent;

2. Reduced travel time for transit buses over 10 percent;

3. Reduced delays due to stops, idling and starts by 57 percent;

4. Reduced congestion by 33 percent; and

5. Generated an annual saving to rush-hour users of $56,000.

This saving indicates users of the Avenue, during the rush hours only, were paying at the rate of up to 90 cents per vehicle-hour for people to park freely at the curb, in the direction of major flow, throughout the morning and afternoon peak flow periods on Mondays through Fridays.

New Traffic Signals
Their Effect on Street Utilization

THOMAS E. YOUNG
City Traffic Engineer
Cincinnati, Ohio

The average citizen appears to be convinced that the solution to any traffic problem, involving vehicular or pedestrian right-of-way, is a traffic signal. On the other hand, every city traffic engineer has probably stated that, a traffic signal at A street and B street will increase accidents and delays, if the location does not "meet the warrants," or if intuition tells him it should not be installed. He may or may not have factual data to support the statement.

Will the installation of a traffic signal increase or decrease accidents and/or delays? The answers depend on the intersection, the traffic pattern, the previous traffic control, and the traffic signal installed. Even the most superficial investigations will show that accidents and delays have decreased following some traffic signal installations, and have increased following others. The real problems are to identify the physical and traffic characteristics under which signals will produce improvements in accidents and delays, and those under which undesirable results will occur. Answers to these problems could shed real light on traffic signal warrants, and should also aid in improving design standards for traffic signal installations.

Accident record data are available for before and after studies of most traffic signal installations. Delay studies are much less common, and unless made in advance, there is no practical way to recreate before information. In any case, there are so many factors and variables beside the signal installation which affect the comparative results, that a rigorous statistical analysis of accident and delay studies at a large number of intersections is difficult.

It is possible, however, to study the effects of new signals on street utilization by means of group studies of intersections to determine if general patterns can be found. Also, case studies can be made at intersections where significant changes have occurred in either accident records, delays, or both. The remainder of this paper will consist of reports of two such group studies, followed by a number of case studies at individual intersections with which the author has had experience in Cincinnati.

While assembling and preparing data for this paper, the author learned of the report prepared by Paul C. Box for the Signal Committee, NJCUTD, "Assembly, Analysis and Application of Data on Warrants for Traffic Control Signals," which is an exhaustive study of pertinent data most of which are directly applicable to this paper. His report also includes a bibliography of 264 references. With that report as background, this presentation will be limited to the unpublished studies from Cincinnati.

ACCIDENTS AT INTERSECTIONS
BEFORE AND AFTER SIGNALIZATION, 1950-1957

In 1959, a study was made by the Cincinnati Division of Traffic Engineering of accidents occurring before and after signalization at 152 intersections where traffic signals were installed during the years 1950 to 1958. The study was quite general in nature, being a comparison of the average number of accidents per year for the five years immediately preceding signalization, against the average number of accidents per year for the period from the installation date through 1959. The comparisons were made in three categories: (a) all accidents; (b) injury and fatal accidents; and (c) pedestrian injury accidents.

No attempt was made to evaluate changes in traffic volumes or patterns, to compare accident rates, nor to evaluate fulfillment of traffic signal warrants. It also was not practical to evaluate previous deficiencies which might have existed in the stop sign control, such as poor stop sign location, or visibility obstructions which could have been eliminated. Design adequacy of the signal installation also was not evaluated.

In general, the before traffic control at the intersections consisted of stop signs for the cross or side street, although there were a few (less than 10) four-way or all-way stops. The signals were installed according to standards of the time, using overhead, far side mountings, dual indications on major approaches, and pedestrian signals where required. At all intersections where progression problems existed, and/or where side street volumes were very low, coordinated semi-actuated controllers were installed. Most of the few isolated locations were actuated unless minimum volume warrants were met. Signals installed later in the study period were generally designed to higher standards than the earlier ones.

The study did not include locations where major physical reconstruction had taken place, but many of the signalization projects did include intersectional channelization. The results of the study were as follows:

All accidents after signalization:
    Yearly average increased at 102 intersections
    Yearly average decreased at 23 intersections
    No significant change at 27 intersections
All injury and fatal accidents after signalization:
    Yearly average increased at 58 intersections
    Yearly average decreased at 24 intersections
    No significant change at 46 intersections
Pedestrian injury or fatal accidents after signalization:
    Yearly average increased at 30 intersections
    Yearly average decreased at 32 intersections
    No significant change at 90 intersections

This study obviously showed no general advantage of traffic signal control as an accident prevention measure and, in fact, indicated that it was much more common for accidents to increase after signalization although there were some dramatic improvements at individual intersections. The picture was somewhat better with respect to accidents resulting in injury or death and pedestrian accidents, but still gave no support to signalization as a general safety measure.

The few locations identified as four-way or all-way stops before signalization showed no significant difference in pattern from the remainder of the group.

ACCIDENTS AT INTERSECTIONS
BEFORE AND AFTER SIGNALIZATION, 1959-1964

In 1967, a study was made in Cincinnati of 32 intersections, comparing accidents in the calendar years immediately before and immediately after the year in which the signals were installed, as a starting point. The results of this initial comparison were as follows:

All accidents after signalization:
    One year total increased at 10 intersections
    One year total decreased at 22 intersections
All injury and fatal accidents after signalization:
    One year total increased at 7 intersections
    One year total decreased at 14 intersections
    No significant change at 11 intersections
Pedestrian injury and fatal accidents after signalization:
    One year total increased at 2 intersections
    One year total decreased at 6 intersections
    No significant change at 24 intersections

This study shows far more favorable results from signalization than did the earlier study, with respect to accident reduction. The reasons for this improvement are not

TABLE 1

SIGNALIZED INTERSECTIONS—BEFORE AND AFTER STUDY, APRIL 1967

Intersection	Total Before (1 yr)	Total After (1 yr)	Total Change	Inj/Fatal Before	Inj/Fatal After	Inj/Fatal Change	Approach Lanes Major Street	Approach Lanes Minor Street	Warrant 1 Volume	Warrant 2 Interruption	Warrant 3 Pedestrian Volume	Warrant 4 Progressive Movement	Warrant 5 Preventable Accident History	Warrant 6 Combinations
Stanton and Taft	25	3	-22	2	0	-2	2	1	892/100	892/100a	/	OK	20a	
Burton, Greenwood and Reading	25	10	-15	5	3	-2	3-2	1	1671/81	1671/81a	1671/45	Poor	NA	
Harrison and Westwood	22	8	-14	2	0	-2	3-2	2	1221/344a	1221/344a	1221/64	OK	1	
Eastern and Kellogg	17	6	-11	0	0		2	2	1022/310a	1022/310a	1022/194	NA	7a	
Eastern and Linwood	10	3	-7	2	0	-2	2	2	665/289a	665/289a		OK	1	
Eighth and Trenton	11	4	-7	1	0	-1	2	1	490/94	490/94	490/86	Poor	3	
Race and Thirteenth	14	8	-6	1	0	-1	2	1	391/237	391/237	391/174	OK	5a	
Clifton and Warner	8	4	-4	0	2	+2	2	1	444/113b	444/113	444/61	OK	5a	
Edwood, Faircrest and North Bend	6	2	-4	4	0	-4	2	1	957/106	957/106a		OK	2	
Grand and Warsaw	11	7	-4	0	1	+1	1	1	439/101	439/101		OK	NA	
Kennedy and Woodford	9	5	-4	1	0	-1	2	1	256/119	256/119	256/15	NA	NA	
Montgomery, Orchard and Robison	7	3	-4	2	2		1	1				OK	NA	
Overlook and Rapid Run	10	6	-4	1	0	-1	2	1	262/132	262/132		NA	5a	
Hamilton and Knowlton	6	3	-3	0	0		2	1	883/54	883/54	883/72	Poor	1	
Ludlow and Middleton	5	2	-3	0	0		2	1	771/83	771/83a	771/20	OK	NA	
Argus and North Bend	7	5	-2	1	0	-1	2	1	957/136b	957/136a		OK	0	
Eastern and St. Andrews	4	2	-2	1	3	+2	1	1			/	Yesa	1	
Evans and Gest	4	2	-2	1	1		2	2	450/227b	450/227		NA	0	
Madison and Victory Parkway	25	23	-2	1	0	-1	2	1	1139/510a	1139/510a	/	OK	NA	
North Bend and Savannah	6	4	-2	0	0		2	2	792/196a	792/196b		OK	3	
Banning, Belmont and North Bend	9	8	-1	1	0	-1	2	2	666/69	666/69		OK	4	
Center Hill and North Bend	2	1	-1	1	1		2	1				NA	0	
Eastern and Hazen	1	2	+1	0	1	+1	2	1	635/46	635/46		OK	0	
Glencross, Mitchell and Tower	1	3	+2	1	1		2	1				OK	0	
Eastern and Wenner	1	3	+2	1	2	+1	2	1	538/114	538/114		Yesa	0	
McHenry and Westwood Northern	4	6	+2	1	1		2	2				NA	0	
Highland and Ringgold	3	6	+3	0	0		1	1				OK	0	
Linwood and Paxton	0	5	+5	0	1	+1	1	1	576/36	576/36		OK	0	
Froome, Gray and Winton	3	9	+6	1	0	-1	3	1	571/116b	571/116b	571/6	NA	0	-a
Herschel and Linwood	5	12	+7	0	1	+1	2	1	706/92	706/92		OK	4	
Baltimore and Westwood Northern	7	18	+11	0	2	+2	2	2	452/62	452/62		NA	2	
1961 MUTCD Warrants: One Lane									500/150	750/75	600/150		5	
Two Lanes									600/200	900/100	600/150		5	

a Warrant met.
b 80% of warrant.

TABLE 2

DELAY DATA EDWOOD AND NORTH BEND

Street	Approach Time	Volume		Avg. Delay Per Vehicle (sec.)		Total Delay (veh-hr)	
		1960	1967	1960	1967	1960	1967
SB Edwood	A. M. [a]	323	352	25. 15	28. 17	2. 25	2. 75
	P. M. [b]	167	172	20. 06	35. 2	0. 93	1. 73
NB Edwood	A. M.		29		20. 7	0. 20[c]	0. 17
	P. M.		17		37. 0	0. 25[c]	0. 18
Side Street	A. M.					2. 45	2. 92
total	P. M.					1. 13	2. 66
EB North Bend	A. M.				18. 1[d]	0[c]	3. 39
	P. M.				29. 3[d]	0[c]	1. 54
WB North Bend	A. M.				12. 7[d]	0[c]	0. 75
	P. M.				14. 5[d]	0[c]	2. 17
Main Street	A. M.					2. 45	4. 14
total	P. M.					1. 13	3. 71
Grand total	A. M.					2. 45	4. 89
	P. M.					1. 13	3. 71

[a] 7:00 to 9:00 a.m.
[b] 4:00 to 6:00 p.m.
[c] Estimated.
[d] Per delayed vehicle.

entirely clear, with possibilities being improved signal design standards, different application of warrants, and better geometric treatment in connection with signalization. In any case, further study of these intersections, the conditions leading toward their signalization, and the design problems involved seemed warranted.

All intersections were installed to current standards which are considerably higher than in the earlier study, and included all overhead vehicular signals and dual indications for all approaches with volumes greater than 3,000 veh/day. Every intersection in the group included pedestrian signals and all but one is traffic actuated. Two of the intersections were four-way stops before signalization.

Table 1 shows the intersections with an evaluation of preinstallation data versus the numerical and specific warrants for pretimed signals in Section 3-D of the 1961 Manual On Uniform Traffic Control Devices.

Although this evaluation is by no means conclusive, it does show a pattern of support for the present warrants with respect to the effect of signalization on accidents. Of the seven intersections having accident reductions of six or more after signalization, all but one met fully one or more of the standard warrants. Of the three intersections meeting the accident experience warrant, each showed a significant reduction in accidents.

Conversely, of the ten intersections showing an increase in accidents following signalization, only two met any semblance of warrants. One of these, Eastern and Wenner, was warranted only on a very marginal progressive movement basis. The other met, marginally, the 80 percent warrants for volume and interruption to continuous traffic.

The study gave very little support to the idea that unwarranted signals, per se, will increase accidents, since there were nine intersections meeting none of the standard warrants, where accidents did decrease to some degree after signalization. The study results, and investigation of the intersections involved, suggest that significant increases in accidents after signalization occurred at locations with serious design problems, or serious deficiencies in signal design, or both, and were largely independent of warranting conditions. Such design problems might well include severe approach grades, approach grades or alignment resulting in inability to provide adequate advance signal visibility, and unsatisfactory location for progressive signal timing.

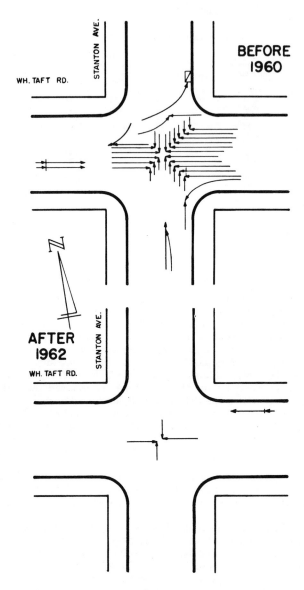

Figure 1.

CASE STUDY—ACCIDENTS AND DELAYS
BEFORE AND AFTER SIGNALIZATION, NORTH BEND AND EDWOOD

General Data

The intersection of North Bend and Edwood was signalized in 1962 from two-way stop control, following a long history of citizen requests. North Bend Road is a major cross-town arterial route, 4 lanes wide. Parking is prohibited during rush hours and is so light at other times that all four lanes are generally available and used. Edwood Avenue is a two-lane roadway, with one approach being a collector-type thoroughfare and the other approach a "no outlet" entrance to a small residential area. The

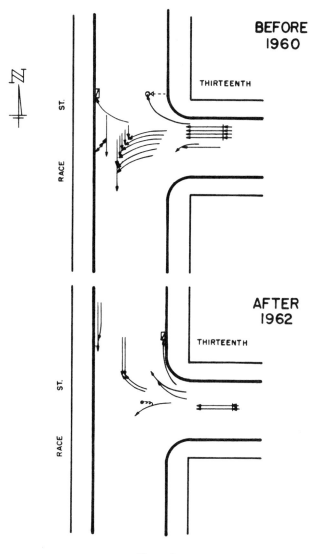

Figure 2.

intersection is level, nearly at a right angle, and visibility is excellent. At the time of signalization, the 1961 MUTCD interruption of continuous traffic warrant was just met, with eighth highest hour volumes of 957 vehicles from both directions on North Bend and 106 vehicles from the higher approach from Edwood.

The signal is semi-actuated and is the end signal of a coordinated system including six other signals. The cycle length is 60 sec, with the cross-street minimum 9 sec and maximum 17 sec.

Accidents

Reported accidents were 6 in 1961 (before signalization) and 17 in the 3-yr period from 1963-1965 (after signalization). There was some increase, as might be expected, in

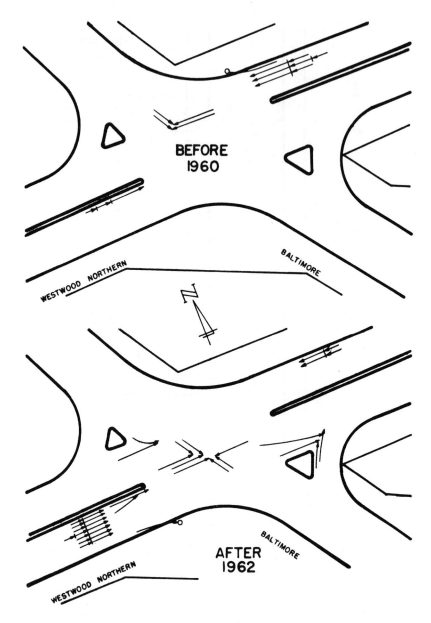

Figure 3.

rear-end and side-swipe accidents, and a decrease in certain miscellaneous types. There was one right-angle accident in 1961 (before) and two in the 1963-65 (after) period. There were no injuries or fatalities, and no pedestrians involved in any of the accidents before or after. It is concluded that signalization did not result in a significant change in accident experience at this intersection.

Delays

Delay studies for four peak hours were made on Edwood, in 1960, two years before signalization, and on all approaches in 1967, five years after signalization. The results cannot be compared directly because of significant volume increases on both streets, and the 1967 studies lacked an hourly separation, covering the two-hour periods of 7:00-9:00 a. m. and 4:00-6:00 p. m. Table 2 gives the results of the two studies.

Total delays were greater after signalization on every approach for which before data were available. The increase on the side street was minimum during the morning rush hour, when side street volumes were at a maximum. Delays on each major street approach varied directly with the volume, but delays on the westbound approach were substantially smaller than on the eastbound approach, apparently because of the progressive timing and platooning effect. It can be assumed that nearly all signalized delay on the major street is an increase over the two-way stop conditions, although there is some error in this due to left-turn delays, and friction from side street entry into minimum gaps. The results seem generally consistent with the work of Paul Box.

Results of this study support the conclusion that for an intersection just meeting the interruption warrant, delays will be substantially increased on all approaches by signalization. The increased delay on the minor street will be proportionately greater at lower volume levels, while the increase on the major street will be proportionately greater at peak volume levels.

Although delays at this intersection were substantially increased by signalization, there is a major difference in the apparent acceptability to the public of delays under signalized conditions, as compared to two-way stop conditions, particularly on the minor street. The knowledge that an opportunity to move within a reasonable time is provided seems to make a higher level of delay acceptable to the public under peak-volume conditions, although we have no actual evaluation of this factor.

CASE STUDIES—ACCIDENTS BEFORE AND AFTER SIGNALIZATION

Stanton Avenue and Taft Road

This is a right-angle cross intersection with four lanes on the major street, Taft Road, and two lanes on the minor street, Stanton Avenue. Taft Road is a major cross-town arterial, which legally and physically is two-way, but paired with a parallel street to form, for signal timing purposes, a one-way couplet. Signals on Taft are progressively timed for westbound traffic, and the signal installed at Stanton in 1961 was semi-actuated and coordinated in this westbound progression. Volumes on Taft show the effect of the signal system and are substantially heavier westbound. Stanton is a neighborhood collector street. The intersection met the interruption warrant when installed in 1961. Buildings and shrubbery limit visibility of approaching westbound traffic when entering from Stanton.

In 1960, there were 25 reported accidents, 18 of them right angles, of which 12 involved eastbound traffic on Taft. In 1962, after signalization, there were only three accidents, as shown in Figure 1. The 1963-65 average was 7. 3 per year. There were only three right-angle collisions in the four years after signalization.

Unexpectedly, however, a serious pedestrian accident problem developed after signalization, with seven such accidents in three years. Three involved failure of a turning driver to yield right-of-way, while four involved signal violations, two by drivers and two by pedestrians. There were no pedestrian accidents the year before signalization.

While the pedestrian problem is not readily explained, this intersection seems to be an example of one well adapted to signalization, meeting interruption and accident experience warrants, at which highly satisfactory accident reduction results were produced by signalization. The visibility restriction seems to have been an important factor in the unsatisfactory accident record under two-way stop control, and proved largely correctable by well-designed signals.

Race and Thirteenth Streets

Race and Thirteenth Streets is an example of an intersection meeting the accident experience warrant only, at which signalization produced good results in accident reduction.

The intersection is a level, T-type, with Race the north-south major and Thirteenth the minor street from the east. Race Street becomes one-way southbound starting at Thirteenth, and Thirteenth Street is one-way westbound. The intersection is on the fringe of downtown Cincinnati, and the signal installed in 1961 is pretimed, and coordinated on both approaches on the downtown signal system. Pedestrian volumes are very heavy, and were a major factor in the decision to signalize the intersection.

There were 14 accidents in 1960, as shown in Figure 2. After signalization, there were 8 accidents in 1962 and a total of 14, or 4.67 per year, for the next three years, a substantial improvement.

Baltimore Avenue and Westwood Northern Boulevard

Signalization of this isolated, oblique angle, cross intersection located on a hillside, was a catastrophe. Westwood Northern, the major thoroughfare, approaches the intersection from the west on a steep upgrade of 9 percent, cresting with a hump 100 ft west of the intersection. The east approach is on a curving 8 percent downgrade. Westwood Northern is a four-lane facility with a 2-ft wide raised median strip. Baltimore is 36 ft wide, generally two lanes, but on the signal approach is used for two approach lanes in each direction.

It was felt that the previous four-way stop control was inappropriate on a major thoroughfare, and two-way stop control was not practical because of the restricted visibility to the west. Therefore, although no standard warrants were met, a semi-actuated signal was installed in 1961.

In 1960, there were seven accidents (including two angle collisions), and no injuries. In the four years following signalization, there were 83 accidents, an average of 21 per year, including 10 injury accidents. There were eleven right-angle collisions, and a very large number of rear-end, side-swipe and turning movement accidents.

The approach grades and alignment at this intersection, coupled with high approach speeds, created difficult design problems, which obviously were not solved in the original signal installation. Deficiencies included inadequate approach visibility of the eastbound signal indications, inadequate yellow intervals for the prevailing speeds, poor signal visibility for southbound Baltimore. It may also be that a fully actuated operation would have reduced the frequency with which groups of vehicles on Westwood Northern are stopped, as compared with the semi-actuated operation. The one-year before-and-after accident diagram is shown in Figure 3.

It is hoped that corrective measures will bring the accident hazard at this location under control. It also emphasizes the importance, first, of careful signal design where operating problems are present, and second, of monitoring accident records carefully so that a situation such as this one does not go uncorrected for four years.

CONCLUSIONS

The foregoing studies are by no means conclusive. However, the author believes that data suggest the following points for consideration and discussion:

1. Signalization is not, per se, a reliable accident reduction measure.

2. Signalization is most likely to produce an accident reduction when standard warrants are met, and is most likely to produce a significant increase in accidents where signal control is unwarranted.

3. Notwithstanding, a well-designed traffic signal installation need not produce a significant increase in accidents even at locations where signalization is completely unwarranted, unless special design problems are present.

4. Where serious accident increases do occur following signalization, the problem can usually be traced to design problems and signal design deficiencies, unrelated to presently established warrants.

5. Restricted visibility of approaching traffic is an important factor in intersectional right-of-way control not directly covered in present warrants, and an important design factor in signalization regardless of warranting conditions.

6. Signalization will substantially increase intersectional delay at the volume levels provided in the 1961 MUTCD warrants.

7. A delay warrant for signalization appears to be desirable. However, it should take into account the varying acceptability to the public of different levels of delay under different traffic control conditions.

REFERENCES

1. Box, Paul C. Assembly, Analysis, and Application of Data on Warrants for Traffic Control Signals. Signal Committee, National Joint Committee on Uniform Traffic Control Devices, 1967. (Lists 264 references on this subject.)
2. Kuemmel, David A. A Study of Delay and Accident Characteristics of Four-Way Stop and Signalized Intersections in the City of Milwaukee. Unpublished thesis, University of Wisconsin, 1960.

Addenda

NEW HAVEN, CONN.

Flashing Signals Overnight

In 1962 New Haven installed a radio interconnected, pre-programmed, multi-dial multi-offset signal system. In programming the 24-hr 7-day operations, 8 of the 90 total CBD locations were set up for "overnight flash" from 1:00 a. m. to 6:00 a. m. weekdays, and 2:00 a. m. to 7:00 a. m. weekends. Two years later, routine accident reco review revealed a tendency toward severe inter-angle accidents at 4 of the locati during the overnight flash period. The number of accidents in nighttime operation was not alarming—averaging about 2 each location yearly over 24 months. However, the staff had immediate concern with the severity involved for downtown locations. Sight distance deficiency combined with prevalent motorist behavior in passing through flash locations was determined to be the cause. Four locations were programmed back to 24-hr fixed-time operation, and 4 were retained for overnight flash, according to the following criteria:

1. Motorist observance (in New Haven) of flash locations (red on minor, amber on major) is generally satisfactory during daytime, but markedly poor at night, especially during the midnight to 6:00 a. m. hours.

2. Where intersection sight-distance is deficient (as is generally true in downtown areas) observance is a vital necessity. The 4 locations experiencing severe accidents, in all cases, were deficient in sight distance.

3. Volume studies indicate most downtown intersections did not warrant fixed-time signal operation in the so-called overnight period. However, the considerations of item 2 are the primary guidance for establishing overnight flash.

4. Overnight flash is a motorist convenience and is desirable where conditions allow such operation. Some back-up device, possibly a "blank out" type stop sign, which could be activated during flash to supplement the red approach, may be necessary where motorist observance rates are unsatisfactory to permit use of flash alone. (It is interesting to note that the "old type" signal lens had STOP etched across the face of the lens.)

4:00 P. M. Signal

This is a factory location, with four pedestrian and vehicle surges daily. Traffic through the intersection is unidirectional other times. The signal is programmed to operate fixed time for the four periods, about 30 min each, weekdays only. The signal has favorable geometric relationships to other signal locations, and the factory population is steadily increasing. After fixed-time operation, the signal reverts to flashing operation. In effect, the programming plan provides signal control when volume conditions warrant such control, and flashing control is effected when volumes drop below warrants.

WASHINGTON, D. C.

The 1965 Accident Summary for Washington, D. C., indicates 163 locations with fifteen or more reported accidents. This figure increased to 190 locations in 1966. In 1965, 148 or 90 percent of these high accident locations were signalized intersections.

A summary of the work by Mike Flanakin in connection with the Bureau of Public Roads project of "Accident Experience as Related to Regular and Flashing Operation of Traffic Signals" follows. In addition, news releases which were used in connection with the conversion of a large group of signals from nighttime flashing to full 24-hr color operation are also included.

Accident Experience as Related to Regular and Flashing Operation of Traffic Signals

Results of an investigation in Washington, D. C., indicate that, under the studied conditions and from a traffic standpoint, regular signal operation is safer than flashing operation. A group of 162 traffic signals in the District of Columbia was changed from flashing operation in the early hours of the morning to full color operation. Accident experience at those locations, corresponding to the hours involved, was analyzed for periods of five months before and after the change. The same analysis was conducted with other groups of intersections where no change was made and compared with the first analysis. The purpose was to determine which overall trends compensate each other, and eliminate the effect of variables other than the change in signal operation.

The results showed that total accidents diminished significantly by about 40 percent at the locations where signals were changed from flashing to full colors and during the hours of the change. Those accidents represent approximately 2 percent of the total traffic accidents in Washington, D. C.

About 60 percent fewer angle collisions occurred after the change was made, while all personal injury accidents were down by more than 50 percent. Also, the severity of the accidents was less after the change was made.

Action of the Board of Commissioners

The Board of Commissioners, D. C., on March 21, 1967, approved a recommendation from the Director of Highways and Traffic that 79 existing traffic signals in the city be placed on full 24-hr color operation.

This recommendation was based on a recently completed two-year study that involved an analysis of nighttime accident experience in relationship to full color and flashing operation of traffic signals. Results of this study have indicated that certain types of signalized intersections, such as exceptionally wide streets, roadways with median strips, and locations where approach speeds are relatively high, lend themselves to 24-hr color operation, and that the conversion from flashing to full color will materially reduce the number and severity of nighttime accidents at certain signalized intersections.

Some of the main arterial streets included in this change-over from flashing operation between 1:00 and 6:00 a. m. to full color operation are Wisconsin Avenue, N. W., 16th Street, N. W., Constitution Avenue, N. E., and South Capitol Street. Each of these major traffic arteries carries in excess of 30,000 veh/day.

The proposal approved by the Board had the prior endorsement of the Traffic Division of the Metropolitan Police Department and the Citizens' Traffic Board.

The Department of Highways and Traffic, D. C., estimated that approximately two months would be required to complete the proposed conversion, and when completed, 440 out of 1,000 signalized intersections in the District of Columbia would be in full color operation.

BETHANY, OKLA.

Experience with flashing operations in small cities during the night hours has resulted in few accidents, as shown by the following data concerning four signalized intersections in Bethany, Okla. (population 20,000), on US 66.

Intersections 1 and 2 are in a small CBD-college area. The other two are $\frac{1}{2}$ mile and $1\frac{1}{2}$ miles west of the CBD in heavily developed residential areas. All flash amber on US 66 and red on cross streets from midnight until 6:00 a.m.

1. US 66 and College Avenue

    Traffic volumes (24 hour) are approximately 3000 veh/day on College Avenue and 24,000 veh/day on US 66.

    Accident Experience (2 years):

Total reported accidents	19
Property damage accidents	15
Injury accidents	4
Accidents between midnight and 6:00 a.m.	0

2. US 66 and Asbury Avenue

    Traffic volumes (24 hour) are approximately 2800 veh/day on Asbury Avenue and 23,000 veh/day on US 66.

    Accident Experience (2 years):

Total reported accidents	18
Property damage accidents	16
Injury accidents	2
Accidents between midnight and 6:00 a.m.	0

3. US 66 and Rockwell Avenue

    Traffic volumes (24 hour) are approximately 8400 veh/day on Rockwell Avenue and 20,000 veh/day on US 66.

    Accident Experience (2 years):

Total reported accidents	28
Property damage accidents	19
Injury accidents	9
Accidents between midnight and 6:00 a.m.	3

4. US 66 and Council Road

    Traffic volumes (24 hour) are approximately 4000 veh/day on Council Road and 16,000 veh/day on US 66.

    Accident Experience (2 years):

Total reported accidents	38
Property damage accidents	19
Injury accidents	14
Fatal accidents	1
Accidents between midnight and 6:00 a.m.	0

Signal Modernization

A. F. MALO

Director
Department of Streets and Traffic
City of Detroit

It is generally recognized that traffic signals have a profound influence on traffic flow. They automatically assign right-of-way to the various movements necessary at intersections, and thereby affect every individual in the traffic stream, including pedestrians. In the age when signals were first put into use, their design was simple and uncomplicated. but they adequately handled the comparatively light and slow-moving traffic of the times. The normal installation was a single four-way solid head on a span wire or pedestal in the center of the intersection, or corner-mounted signals either on two diagonal corners or on all four corners of the intersection.

Traffic in most cities has reached volumes at or approaching the capacity of the normal intersection. The traffic stream is made up of all types of vehicles including many passenger automobiles, large trucks, and buses, representing different sizes and operating characteristics. Streets and intersections must operate at peak efficiency in order to move such traffic. Controls must be modern and efficient, and signal visibility must be perfect. The efficient and safe movement of traffic through the intersection, therefore, generally requires signal indications in the driver's line of vision, unobstructed by large vehicles, and undisturbed by a background of advertising signs. Special turn indications or lane control might be required, and at wide or boulevarded streets, advance greens and lagging ambers and reds might be indicated. For safe intersection clearance, an all-red period in addition to normal amber may be required.

In urban areas, pedestrians are an important part of the traffic problem and must be considered in the signalization of intersections. Pedestrian signals, therefore, frequently constitute a part of modern traffic signal installation.

Signal modernization at individual intersections has been accomplished at varying scales in numerous cities. Modernization projects at individual intersections have included both controller and visibility improvements. Improvements in visibility might include the installation of additional heads, the relocation of heads, or the placing of the units on mast arms or span wires over the traffic lanes to replace or supplement curb-mounted signals. The location of heads over the lanes of travel place the indications in the line of sight of the driver. They eliminate to a great extent the possibility of large trucks and buses obscuring from view the low-mounted corner signal. On business streets, the visibility of corner signals is often reduced by a background of numerous brightly lighted advertising signs.

Modernization of controls may include the replacement of an obsolete controller with a modern fixed-time or actuated controller with detectors in the intersection. Arrows controlling individual movements such as right and left turns have been effectively employed. Special timing sequences and the use of all red periods to clear wide intersections have reduced accidents.

Most controller or visibility modernizations tailored to the needs of the intersection have generally proved safer and more efficient. Before-and-after studies provide evidence to back this statement. Although many improvements have been made without measuring the results, some studies are available which prove the benefit of modern traffic signal installations. Examples in this paper are the results of studies comparing conditions before and after the installation of modern signals and controls.

The signal visibility modernization program for the City of Detroit included primarily the installation of over-the-road indications, generally installed on mast arms mounted diagonally from the near right and far left corners and with the faces in line with the

TABLE 1

ACCIDENTS BEFORE AND AFTER MODERNIZATION, DETROIT, MICH.

Location	Date of Modernization	Before (1955)					After (1960)				
		Angle	Ped.	Rear End	Other	Total	Angle	Ped.	Rear End	Other	Total
Boston-Dexter	Dec. 1958	18	—	4	1	23	1	—	1	1	3
Calvert-Linwood	July 1958	4	—	2	2	8	2	—	2	2	6
Chalmers-Charlevoix	Jan. 1958	13	1	3	2	19	2	—	3	2	7
Charlevoix-Grand Blvd.	Feb. 1958	4	—	10	3	17	1	—	6	1	8
Charlevoix-Van Dyke	Feb. 1958	8	1	—	2	11	3	—	2	5	10
Chene-Ferry	April 1958	14	—	12	4	30	1	1	4	2	8
Chicago-Fourteenth	May 1958	10	—	4	1	15	3	—	2	2	7
Clairmount-Twelfth	May 1958	6	1	9	9	25	3	1	12	6	22
Conner-Kercheval	Jan. 1958	5	—	5	2	12	1	—	1	2	4
Conner-Vernor	Feb. 1958	7	1	5	2	13	3	—	7	3	13
Elmhurst-Fourteenth	May 1958	2	—	4	3	9	—	1	1	2	4
Elmhurst-Linwood	June 1958	12	2	10	6	30	—	2	7	2	11
Ferry-Russell	April 1958	4	1	13	19	37	—	—	3	5	8
Grand Blvd.-Kercheval	Feb. 1958	12	—	6	6	24	3	—	4	4	11
Grand Blvd.-Mt. Elliott	March 1958	12	1	11	9	33	3	—	17	10	30
Grand Blvd.-E. Vernor	June 1958	11	1	13	2	27	6	—	3	3	12
Kercheval-McClellan	Jan. 1958	10	—	7	4	21	2	1	3	1	7
Kercheval-St. Jean	Feb. 1958	4	3	4	2	13	3	—	5	2	10
Kercheval-Van Dyke	Feb. 1958	8	1	2	3	14	4	1	8	4	17
Twelfth-Webb	Aug. 1958	5	—	3	11	19	2	—	6	2	10
Total		169	13	127	91	400	43	7	97	61	208
Percent change							-75	-46	-24	-33	-47

approach to the signal controls. Such intersections might have, in addition, corner installations of standard heads or "Walk—Don't Walk" signals, or a combination of the two. Each location is tailored to the needs of the intersection. On December 31, 1961, there were 1,334 signalized intersections in Detroit, 1,152 operated by the city and 182 operated by the county. All of these were modernized. Pedestrian "Walk—Don't Walk" signals are provided at 300 locations operated by the city, and at 36 locations operated by the county. Twenty representative locations were chosen for a before-and-after study of accidents at these modernized intersections. Before modernization, none of these locations were equipped with over-the-roadway signal indications. After modernization, the approaches on the major streets were equipped with two overhead indications and each approach on minor streets with at least one overhead indication. The analysis is given in Table 1. From the data, the following accident reductions were calculated:

Right-angle - 75 percent
Rear-end - 24 percent
Pedestrian - 46 percent
Other types - 33 percent
Overall - 47 percent

TABLE 2

PEDESTRIAN ACCIDENTS AT TEN LOCATIONS IN THE CBD BEFORE
AND AFTER INSTALLATION OF WALK-DON'T WALK SIGNALS, DETROIT, MICH.

Location	Date of Installation	1958		1960	
		Pedestrian Accidents	Violators	Pedestrian Accidents	Violators
Woodward-Montcalm	Jan. 1959	—	—	2	1
Woodward-Columbia	Jan. 1959	3	1	1	1
Woodward-Elizabeth	Jan. 1959	—	—	—	—
Woodward-Adams	Jan. 1959	4	2	2	—
Woodward-Park-Witherell	June 1959	—	—	1	1
Woodward-Clifford-John R	July 1959	3	2	1	1
Woodward-Grand River	July 1959	2	1	—	—
Woodward-Gratiot-State	June 1959	3	2	2	—
Washington Blvd.-Grand River	Oct. 1959	1	1	—	—
Washington Blvd.-Clifford	Sept. 1959	—	—	—	—
Total		16	9	9	4
Percent change				-44	-56

98

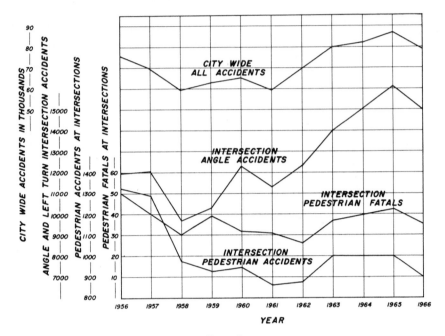

Figure 1.

Probably the most significant figure in this analysis is the reduction in the most serious type of accident—the right-angle. The reduction in right-angle accidents accounts
for 65 percent of the total reduction at these locations. The analysis indicates that the
modernization of traffic signals has achieved the desired results from the safety standpoint; not reflected in this study is the greater convenience and comfort for the driver.

The modernization of signals in the CBD included the equipping of the majority of the
locations with Walk—Don't Walk pedestrian signals. To measure the results of this program, ten of the locations with the highest pedestrian volume were selected, and pedestrian accidents before the installation of the signals were compared with the number
of accidents after the installation. Also studied was the number of pedestrian accidents
occurring while a pedestrian was walking against a red or Don't Walk signal. Table 2
indicates a reduction from 16 pedestrian accidents before to nine pedestrian accidents
after, or a reduction of 44 percent. Better observance of the Don't Walk signal as
compared to the normal red indication was indicated by the reduction from nine accidents
occurring before to four pedestrian accidents after installation, or a reduction of 56
percent. The results of this study indicate, at least on a sample basis, the results
achieved with pedestrian signals. A subsequent study of 60 locations before and after
the installation of Walk—Don't Walk signals included all of the CBD installations
(40 locations), plus 20 at other locations. There was a similar result with 57
before and 29 after or a 49 percent reduction in total accidents, and of those involving
violations, a reduction from 22 to 8, or 72 percent. These results substantiated the
findings of the previous study.

On January 1, 1951, there were 70 intersections equipped with pedestrian signals,
most of which were at school crossing locations. Between January 1, 1951, and December 31, 1965, 280 additional intersections were equipped, including most intersections within the CBD, intersections of wide streets and high pedestrian volumes, some
school crossing locations, and newly signalized intersections with street widths in excess of 40 ft.

During the 10-yr period 1956 through 1965, the city-wide total accident picture showed a generally upward trend (accidents were down in all categories in 1966). There were 16 percent more accidents occurring in 1965 than in 1956. During the same period, the trend of intersection right-angle and left-turn accidents was definitely upward. The 1965 total was 47 percent higher than the 1956 total for these categories. The intersection pedestrian accident picture, however, showed a definite downward trend with the 1965 total being 25 percent less than the 1956 total (Fig. 1). It is felt that a definite relationship exists between the reduction of pedestrian accidents and the more extensive use of pedestrian signals. This may be contrasted with the increase in total accidents, right-angle and left-turn accidents at intersections. Discretion used in determining locations for pedestrian signal installation, judicious enforcement of the punitive pedestrian signal ordinance, and adequate public information on the subject have apparently improved pedestrian safety.

The Wayne County Road Commission installs and operates signals at 706 locations in Wayne County, 192 of which are in the City of Detroit. At isolated locations in the built-up suburban areas, the county installed single, four-faced signals on span wires in the center of the intersection. As traffic increased, the single indication was insufficient and many locations were modernized by adding additional indications or by other means. At the intersection of Allen Road and Eureka Road in Wyandotte (Figs. 2 and 3), the installation of a second set of signal faces for each direction reduced accidents from a total of 12 in the year before to seven in the year after installation, or approximately 41 percent reduction. Two of the after accidents were side-swipes on which signal control would ordinarily have no effect. The greatest reduction was in rear-ends, which reduced from four to none, indicating better visibility approaching the intersection.

A similar improvement at the intersection of Farmington Road and Five Mile Road (Figs. 4 and 5), in the center of Livonia showed a reduction in total accidents from 7 to 4, or 43 percent. In this case, the right-angles which reduced from 2 to none showed the greatest reduction.

A third location, similarly modernized, at Allen Road and Sibley Road (Figs. 6 and 7) near the City of Riverview, showed a reduction in accidents from 8 to 5, or 38 percent. Right-angles in this case were reduced from 5 to 3.

At the intersection of East Outer Drive, a boulevarded street with a wide divider and three moving lanes in each direction, and Conant Avenue, a four-lane undivided street in Detroit (Figs. 8 and 9), signals were modernized to provide two indications for each approach including double indications on Conant on each side of the center island. This improvement resulted in a reduction in total accidents from 36 to 29, but right-angle accidents which were a problem in two quadrants before reduced from 15 to 2, or 86 percent. The right-angle accidents were all far-side-of-the-island accidents before modernization. The installation of far-side island indications were the major factor in reducing right-angle accidents.

At the intersection of Inkster Road and Joy Road (Figs. 10 and 11), bordering Dearborn Heights and Livonia, accidents increased to a total of 35 for a 1-yr period. This intersection is equipped with two complete four-face installations on span wires over the intersection. Volumes are heavy on all approaches, all turns are allowed, and turning movements are comparatively heavy. This intersection was modernized by the introduction of a 1-sec, all-red interval after each phase. The results were surprising. Total accidents reduced from 35 to 11, or approximately 70 percent. Turning accidents reduced from 12 to 7, rear-end from 11 to 3, and right-angle from 9 to 1. The additional second evidently has provided the additional time required to clear through and turning traffic from the intersection.

The City of Detroit has also had favorable results with the use of all-red periods. A typical example is the intersection of Larned and Mt. Elliott (Figs. 12 and 13). Larned is a one-way street originating in the CBD, dead-ending about three miles east at Mt. Elliott. At this point, drivers use Mt. Elliott to reach other major arteries continuing east into the residential areas. Right-angle accidents were reduced by the use of an all-red period. During the base with a 60-sec cycle, the all red is 1.2 sec. During the peak with a 70-sec cycle, this is extended to 1.4 sec (2 percent of the total cycle).

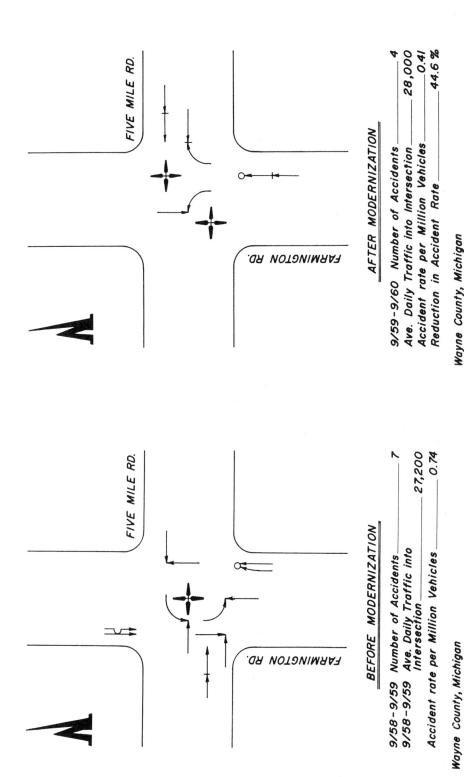

FIVE MILE RD.

FARMINGTON RD.

AFTER MODERNIZATION

9/59-9/60	Number of Accidents	4
	Ave. Daily Traffic into Intersection	28,000
	Accident rate per Million Vehicles	0.41
	Reduction in Accident Rate	44.6 %

Wayne County, Michigan

Figure 5.

FIVE MILE RD.

FARMINGTON RD.

BEFORE MODERNIZATION

9/58-9/59	Number of Accidents	7
9/58-9/59	Ave. Daily Traffic into Intersection	27,200
	Accident rate per Million Vehicles	0.74

Wayne County, Michigan

Figure 4.

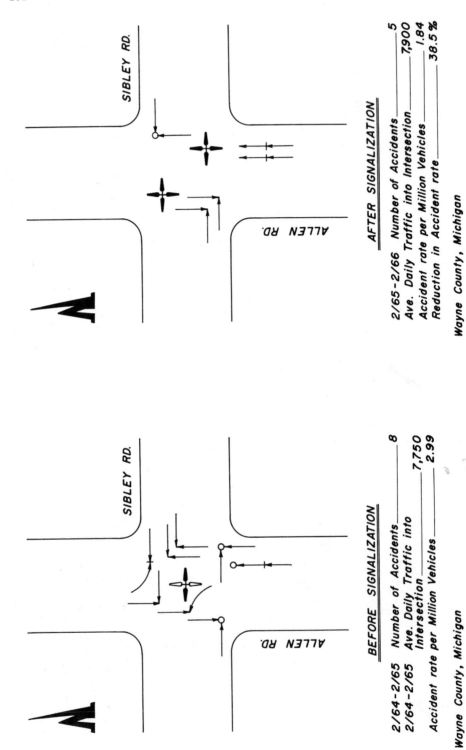

SIBLEY RD.

ALLEN RD.

BEFORE SIGNALIZATION

2/64 - 2/65   Number of Accidents _____ 8
2/64 - 2/65   Ave. Daily Traffic into
                Intersection _____ 7,750
Accident rate per Million Vehicles _____ 2.99

Wayne County, Michigan

Figure 6.

SIBLEY RD.

ALLEN RD.

AFTER SIGNALIZATION

2/65 - 2/66   Number of Accidents _____ 5
             Ave. Daily Traffic into Intersection _____ 7,900
             Accident rate per Million Vehicles _____ 1.84
             Reduction in Accident rate _____ 38.5%

Wayne County, Michigan

Figure 7.

103

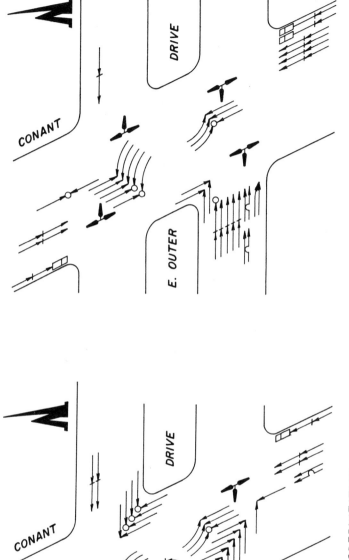

CONANT

DRIVE

E. OUTER

AFTER MODERNIZATION

4/60-4/61 Number of Accidents —————— 29
Ave. Daily Traffic into Intersection —————— 47,900
Accident rate per Million Vehicles —————— 1.78
Reduction in Accident rate —————— 21.6%

City of Detroit, Michigan

Figure 9.

CONANT

DRIVE

E. OUTER

BEFORE MODERNIZATION

4/59-4/60 Number of Accidents —————— 36
4/59-4/60 Ave. Daily Traffic into
Intersection —————— 46,500
Accident rate per Million Vehicles —————— 2.27

City of Detroit, Michigan

Figure 8.

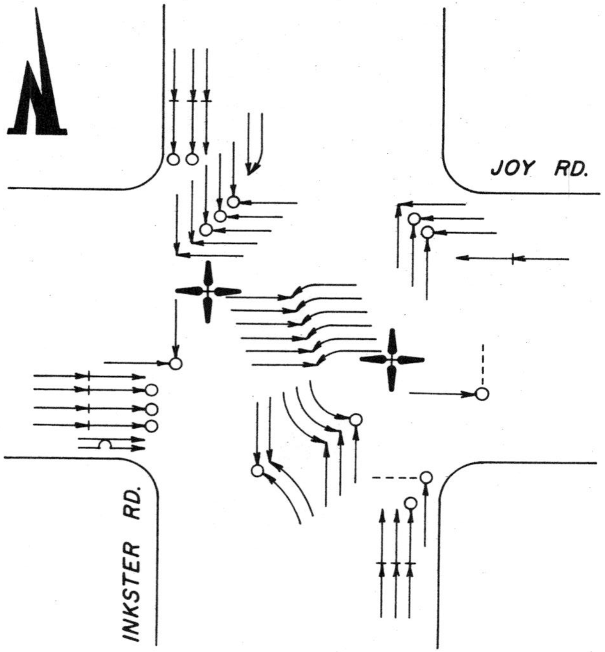

104

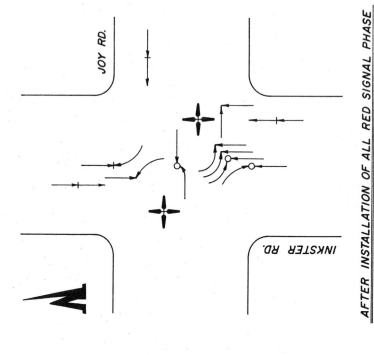

JOY RD.

INKSTER RD.

N

AFTER INSTALLATION OF ALL RED SIGNAL PHASE

2/65-2/66	Number of Accidents	11
	Ave. Daily Traffic into intersection	33,900
	Accident rate per Million Vehicles	0.94
	Reduction in Accident rate	69.0 %

Wayne County, Michigan

Figure 11.

JOY RD.

INKSTER RD.

N

BEFORE INSTALLATION OF ALL RED SIGNAL PHASE

2/64-2/65	Number of Accidents	35
2/64-2/65	Ave. Daily Traffic into Intersection	33,300
	Accident rate per Million Vehicles	3.04

Wayne County, Michigan

Figure 10.

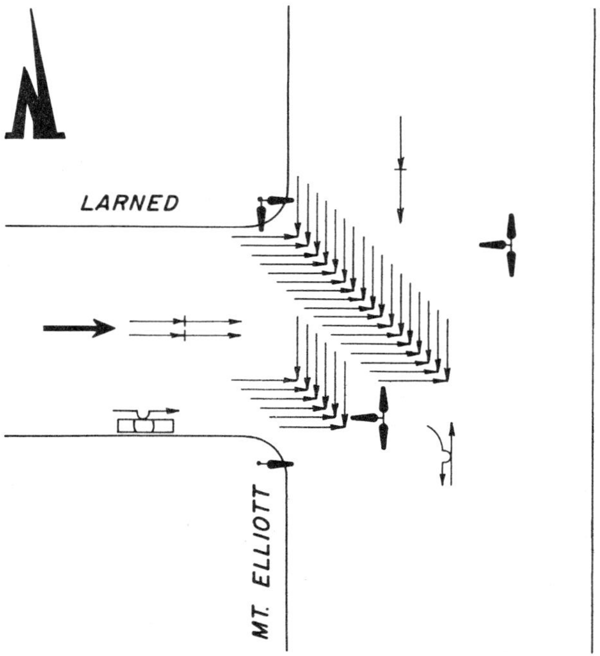

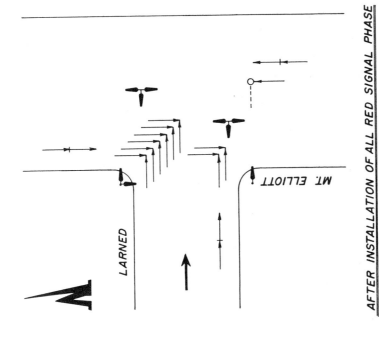

AFTER INSTALLATION OF ALL RED SIGNAL PHASE

1959 → 1962 Number of Accidents — 12
1962 Ave. Daily Traffic into Intersection — 12,150
Accident rate per Million Vehicles — 2.90
Reduction in Accident rate — 58.4%

City of Detroit, Michigan

Figure 13.

BEFORE INSTALLATION OF ALL RED SIGNAL PHASE

1959 Number of Accidents — 28
1959 Ave. Daily Traffic into Intersection — 11,800
Accident rate per Million Vehicles — 6.98

City of Detroit, Michigan

Figure 12.

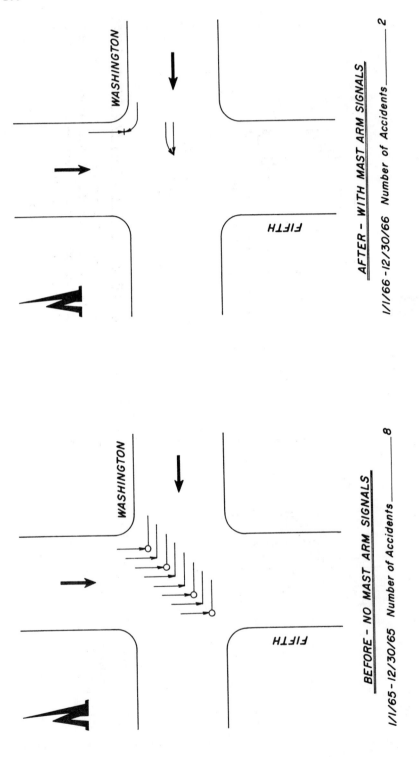

AFTER - WITH MAST ARM SIGNALS

1/1/66 -12/30/66 Number of Accidents————— 2

City of Phoenix, Arizona

Figure 15.

BEFORE - NO MAST ARM SIGNALS

1/1/65 - 12/30/65 Number of Accidents————— 8

City of Phoenix, Arizona

Figure 14.

Total accidents reduced from 28 to 12 with right-angles reducing from 23 to 8, or 35 percent. Some of the difficulty at this intersection results from the fact that southbound traffic on Mt. Elliott can see not only the signal at Larned, but also the one at Jefferson not more than 300 ft beyond Larned. A possible change in timing is being studied in an effort to further reduce the number of right-angle accidents.

The Division of Traffic Engineering of the City of Phoenix experienced a reduction in accidents at an intersection after the installation of mast arms to supplement far side corner indications. The traffic engineer describes the improvement somewhat as follows:

> Traffic signals in the downtown area of Phoenix are double indication, far right and far left. Both Washington and Jefferson Streets are 68 ft wide with a 52-ft width on all crossing streets. Because of the width of these one-way streets and the volumes of traffic, we have felt that mast arms were highly desirable for these east-west streets. Subsequently, at the intersection of 5th Avenue and Washington, 20-ft mast arms with 8-in. indications were installed which provide a total of 4 indications. The accident diagrams (Figs. 14 and 15) are for 1965 prior to the mast arms, and the accident diagram for 1966 is the after period. The number of accidents decreased 8 to 2 and right-angle accidents were entirely eliminated in the after year. We subsequently made accident analyses of all intersections that are signalized on Washington and Jefferson between 5th Avenue and 4th Street. Throughout this distance, the speed limit is 25 mph. The number of accidents for the year 1966 is given in Table 3. About 52 percent of the accidents are susceptible to correction by improvement of the signal indications. Using these data, we were able to procure funds for the coming year to install mast arm indications facing all Washington and Jefferson traffic throughout the area. In about 18 months, we should be ready to make a one-year after study.

The results recorded by Phoenix parallel those resulting from the same type of modernization in Detroit which experienced a 75 percent reduction of right-angle accidents for 20 representative locations. It is apparent that the installation of overhead indications providing improved signal visibility reduced significantly those accidents susceptible to correction with modern traffic signal control.

The Department of Traffic in the City of Los Angeles has reported on the results of various types of signal modernization. At seven isolated intersections where existing signals were up-dated to provide greater visibility and better control, a before-and-after study indicates a reduction in total accidents from 103 to 52, or almost 50 percent. Right-angles show a 75 percent reduction. Details for each intersection are shown in Table 4.

The Bureau of Traffic Research of the Department of Traffic has furnished a staff report on accident frequency comparison at three high-accident locations. The summary report is quoted vertabim as follows:

Introduction

> In 1960 a list of high accident frequency locations was prepared from data recorded during the 18 month period January 1, 1959, to June 30, 1960. A detailed study in 1960 of the top 50 locations resulted in traffic signal and control modifications.
>
> This report summarizes the effect of these changes on accidents at three locations in the Hollywood Area of Los Angeles.
>
> The intersections (including approaches) selected for "before" and "after" accident studies were:
>
> 1. Sunset Boulevard and Highland Avenue (location "A")
> 2. Sunset Boulevard and LaBrea Avenue (location "B")
> 3. Hollywood Boulevard and Gower Street (location "C")
>
> Data for the "after" study was recorded during the 18 month period January 1, 1964, to June 30, 1965.

108

TABLE 3

WASHINGTON-JEFFERSON ACCIDENT STUDY IN
DOWNTOWN PHOENIX, ARIZ.
(January 1, 1966 to December 31, 1966)

Street	Type of Accident	Total	Accident of Correctable Type (%)
(a) Intersecting Washington Street			
4th Street	12 Angle 1 Rear-end (6 Injury)	13	92
3rd Street	1 Turning 4 Angle (1 Injury)	5	80
2nd Street	1 Turning 1 Pedestrian 1 Rear-end (2 Injury)	3	0
1st Street	2 Pedestrian 1 Turning (2 Injury)	3	66
Central Avenue	7 Angle 2 Rear-end (2 Injury)	9	80
1st Avenue	3 Angle 5 Turning 1 Pedestrian (3 Injury)	8	50
2nd Avenue	2 Turning 1 Pedestrian (1 Injury)	3	0
3rd Avenue	4 Turning	4	0
Total	4 Rear-end 26 Angle 14 Turning 4 Pedestrian (17 Injury)	49	53
(b) Intersecting Jefferson Street			
5th Avenue	6 Angle 2 Turning (3 Injury)	8	75
3rd Avenue	3 Turning 7 Angle (4 Injury)	10	70
2nd Avenue	None		
1st Avenue	2 Angle 1 Turning (1 Injury)	3	66
Central Avenue	5 Angle 3 Rear-end (3 Injury)	8	62
1st Street	2 Angle 4 Turning 1 Pedestrian (4 Injury)	7	28
2nd Street	2 Turning	2	0
3rd Street	3 Turning 1 Rear-end 1 Pedestrian 3 Angle (2 Injury)	8	37
4th Street	3 Turning 2 Angle 1 Pedestrian (3 Injury)	6	33
Total	27 Angle 3 Pedestrian 18 Turning 4 Rear-end (20 Injury)	52	52
(c) Totals of Washington and Jefferson Streets			
	32 Turning 53 Angle 8 Pedestrian 8 Rear-end (37 Injury)	101	52.5

TABLE 4
EFFECTS OF TRAFFIC SIGNAL MODERNIZATIONS ON ACCIDENT REDUCTION, LOS ANGELES, CALIF.

Location	Before Modernization					After Modernization				
	RA	LT	RE	Other	Total	RA	LT	RE	Other	Total
1st St. and Mission Rd.	5	4	5	9	23	4	1	1	2	8
1st St. and Virgil Ave.	7	2	0	0	9	3	4	1	1	9
6th St. and Central Ave.	3	0	2	1	6	1	1	1	3	6
15th St. and Alameda St.	6	0	3	2	11	0	0	1	2	3
67th St. and Western Ave.	11	0	1	3	15	0	1	2	1	4
Century Blvd. and Vermont St.	7	0	13	2	22	1	4	4	4	13
LaBrea Ave. and Wilshire Blvd.	10	1	6	0	17	3	1	4	1	9
Grand totals	49	7	30	17	103	12	12	14	14	52

Purpose

The purpose of this study was to determine to what extent modifications in traffic signals and controls influence accident frequency. It was also intended to show if specific changes reflect reductions or increases in certain types of accidents.

Conclusions

In general, the traffic signal and control modifications made in 1960 appear to have reduced accident frequency within intersections. Accidents on the approaches to the three intersections have increased.

On the approaches where mast arm indications were installed or had been in place, rear end collisions increased much more rapidly than on those which do not have mast arm indications.

However, right-angle accidents showed a much greater reduction at the two intersections where mast arm indications were installed on all approaches than at the intersection which has mast arm indications on the major street only.

A considerable reduction in left turn accidents occurred at those locations where special left turn signal phases were installed.

Pedestrian accident data for the two locations where pedestrian signals were installed showed one accident "before" and two "after" for both locations. This was considered to be an insufficient number to draw conclusions concerning the effect of pedestrian signals on the frequency of accidents involving pedestrians.

Since improved street lighting was installed in conjunction with traffic signal modifications, no relation between accident frequency and street lighting alone could be determined.

As the traffic signal modifications varied for each location the extent of the modification and the accident reductions or increase by type and total follows:

Before and after traffic volume data are also included.

The details for each intersection are given in Tables 5, 6, and 7. Right-angle accidents show a significant reduction where mast arm indications were installed on all approaches. The report shows a considerable reduction in left-turn accidents occurring at those locations where special left-turn signal phases were installed.

A more complicated modernization accompanied by rechannelization is contained in a report obtained from the Montana Highway Commission. The location is the intersection of Helena, Montana and Lyndale Avenues in the City of Helena. A plan of the intersection before and after is shown in Figures 16 and 17. The description of the intersection and the completed modernization project is as follows:

The before installation by the City of Helena consisted of near-right and far-left signal indications post-mounted 8 ft high. Signal controller equipment was fixed time with railroad preemption. Cycle length was 50 sec split

TABLE 5

TRAFFIC CONTROL CONDITIONS, LOS ANGELES, CALIF.

Before January 1, 1959, to June 30, 1960	After January 1, 1964, to June 30, 1965

(a) Sunset Blvd. and Highland Ave. [a]

1. Two-phase fixed-time signal.	1. Actuated left turns for Sunset Blvd.
2. No left turns from Highland Ave. (3:00 p. m. -6:00 p. m.).	2. No left turns from Highland Ave. (7:00 a. m. -7:00 p. m.).
3. Highland Ave. off-centering during a. m. and p. m. peak hours.	3. Highland Ave. off-centering during a. m. and p. m. peak hours.
	4. Four-way mast arm indications.
	5. Pedestrian signals.
	6. Mercury luminaires installed in conjunction with mast arm signals.

(b) Sunset Blvd. and LaBrea Ave. [b]

1. Two-phase, fixed-time signal.	1. Two-phase, fixed-time signal.
2. Mast arms for Sunset Blvd. only.	2. Mast arms for Sunset Blvd. only.
3. No pedestrian signals.	3. No pedestrian signals.
	4. Three-second all-red interval following LaBrea Ave. green.

(c) Hollywood Blvd. and Gower St. [c]

1. Two-phase, fixed-time signal.	1. Two-phase, fixed-time signal.
	2. Four-way mast arm indications.
	3. Pedestrian signals.
	4. Mercury luminaires installed in conjunction with mast arm signals.

[a] 24-hr volume entering intersection: before, 80,870; after, 74,870; change, -7.44 percent.
[b] 24-hr volume entering intersection: before, 65,760; after, 67,760; change, +3.04 percent.
[c] 24-hr volume entering intersection: before, 36,500; after, 41,670; change, +14.16 percent.

TABLE 6

SUMMARY OF INTERSECTION AND APPROACH ACCIDENTS BY
TYPE AND SEVERITY, LOS ANGELES, CALIF.

Type	Prop. Damage		Injury		Fatal		Total		Change in Total (%)
	Before	After	Before	After	Before	After	Before	After	
(a) Sunset Blvd. and Highland Ave.									
Left-turn	10	2	9	6	0	0	19	8	-58
Right-angle	8	0	8	2	0	0	16	2	-88
Rear-end	9	11	8	11	0	0	17	22	+29
Side-swipe	6	3	2	1	0	0	8	4	-50
Pedestrian	0	0	1	1	0	0	1	1	0
Other	1	3	2	0	0	0	3	3	0
Total	34	19	30	21	0	0	64	40	-38
(b) Sunset Blvd. and LaBrea Ave.									
Left-turn	3	4	6	2	0	0	9	6	-33
Right-angle	6	1	3	4	0	0	9	5	-44
Rear-end	4	10	5	8	0	0	9	18	+100
Side-swipe	2	5	0	1	0	0	2	6	+200
Pedestrian	0	0	3	1	0	0	3	1	-67
Other	4	3	0	5	0	0	4	8	+100
Total	19	23	17	21	0	0	36	44	+22
(c) Hollywood Blvd. and Gower St.									
Left-turn	3	3	3	5	0	0	6	8	+33
Right-angle	5	2	6	5	0	0	11	7	-31
Rear-end	2	4	4	3	0	0	6	7	+17
Side-swipe	3	1	0	0	0	0	3	1	-67
Pedestrian	0	0	0	1	0	0	0	1	—
Other	4	2	0	0	0	0	4	2	-50
Total	17	12	13	14	0	0	30	26	-13

TABLE 7

ACCIDENT FREQUENCY BY TYPE AND LOCATION, LOS ANGELES, CALIF.

Type of Accident	Intersection			Approach		
	Before	After	Change	Before	After	Change
(a) Sunset Blvd. and Highland Ave.						
Left-turn	19	8	-11	0	0	0
Right-angle	14	2	-12	2	0	-2
Rear-end	2	2	0	15	20	+5
Side-swipe	1	1	0	7	3	-4
Pedestrian	1	0	-1	0	1	+1
Other	1	0	-1	2	3	+1
Total	38	13	-25	26	27	+1
(b) Sunset Blvd. and LaBrea Ave.						
Left-turn	6	6	0	3	0	-3
Right-angle	6	5	-1	3	0	-3
Rear-end	2	2	0	7	16	+9
Side-swipe	0	1	+1	2	5	+3
Pedestrian	2	1	-1	1	0	-1
Other	0	0	0	4	8	+4
Total	16	15	-1	20	29	+9
(c) Hollywood Blvd. and Gower St.						
Left-turn	6	8	+2	0	0	—
Right-angle	10	7	-3	1	0	-1
Rear-end	2	1	-1	4	6	+2
Side-swipe	1	0	-1	2	1	-1
Pedestrian	0	1	+1	0	0	—
Other	0	1	+1	4	1	-3
Total	19	18	-1	11	8	-3

50-50. Montana Ave. traffic proceeding south had only a YIELD sign to guide it in crossing the Montana-Lyndale traffic, as did the traffic turning left from Lyndale Ave. onto Helena Ave. to cross Montana Ave. This resulted in considerable congestion at the intersection with accompanying hazard due to restriction of sight distance.

The intersection improvement consisted of rechannelization and installation of new traffic signals. Three strain poles support signals on span-wires. This leaves the islands clear of signal poles which might be a physical and sight-restricting hazard. Double indication was used for each approach except that additional pole-mounted signals provide sight distance for the Montana-Lyndale Ave. approaches which are on a curve. The signals on the northeast corner of the intersection are mast-arm mounted. Actuated pedestrian signals provide indications for pedestrians crossing the street.

The signal controller is three-phase traffic actuated with loop detectors on each approach. Signal timing includes a 3-sec yellow and 3-sec all red following each green interval. Montana-Lyndale is the major movement and is left on recall. There is a railroad preemption which, after appropriate yellow intervals, locks the controller onto the Montana-Lyndale green indication and illuminates a NO LEFT TURN sign for Lyndale Ave. traffic approaching the traffic from the west.

The before and after improvements show a reduction in accident rate of 48.3 percent for 1966, the first full year of operation.

It is sometimes impossible to properly signalize a complicated intersection without proper channelization to guide traffic through the intersection. The intersection described in the foregoing was improved by the combination of both signalization and channelization. The after study shows a substantial decrease in accidents and there is little doubt that the intersection operates more efficiently than before.

112

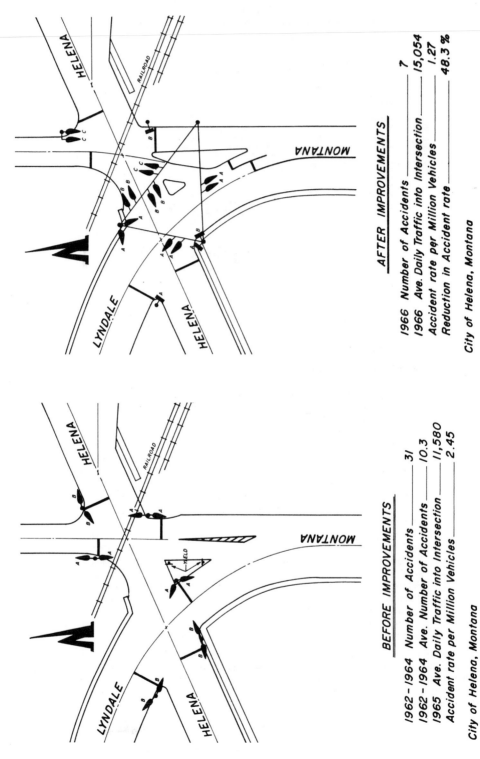

BEFORE IMPROVEMENTS

1962-1964 Number of Accidents —————— 31
1962-1964 Ave. Number of Accidents ——— 10.3
1965 Ave. Daily Traffic into Intersection ——— 11,580
Accident rate per Million Vehicles ——— 2.45

City of Helena, Montana

Figure 16.

AFTER IMPROVEMENTS

1966 Number of Accidents —————————— 7
1966 Ave. Daily Traffic into Intersection ——— 15,054
Accident rate per Million Vehicles ——— 1.27
Reduction in Accident rate ——— 48.3 %

City of Helena, Montana

Figure 17.

CONCLUSIONS

The examples of traffic-signal modernization described in the foregoing indicate that modern signal controls tailored to the needs of traffic can improve the efficiency of intersections and reduce accidents. It is obvious that improved visibility is a major factor in accident reduction. The introduction of mast arm or overhead signals in every case resulted in reduced accidents. Observations have shown that the use of all red periods by Wayne County and the City of Detroit has been successful. Unfortunately, the examples cited are the only ones available with before-and-after experience. There should also be more studies indicating the value of special left-turn signal phases. The one cited by Los Angeles indicated a considerable reduction in left-turn accidents as a result of such an installation.

Detroit is committed to a pedestrian signal program using the incandescent Walk—Don't Walk indication. Each year, major streets are being equipped with such signals at intersections warranting such protection. It is felt that the use of the words Walk—Don't Walk has had an effect on observance by the pedestrian of all type signals throughout the city.

Pedestrian signals properly observed, especially on wide streets, not only benefit the pedestrian, but also expedite the movement of vehicular traffic. Detroit uses the flashing Don't Walk which is the clearance period timed to normal walking speed. Properly observed, this eliminates pedestrians from the crosswalk when the green appears for the intersecting street. This eliminates considerable delay but unfortunately before-and-after studies have not been made to measure this effect accurately.

Addenda

PHOENIX, ARIZ.

A study of accident records demonstrated a need for mast arms. These were installed at a cost of $2,000. The before and after collision diagrams (Figs. 18 and 19) present the remarkable reduction in accidents which this action achieved. Washington Street is one-way and carries approximately 15,000 cars a day at this location.

114

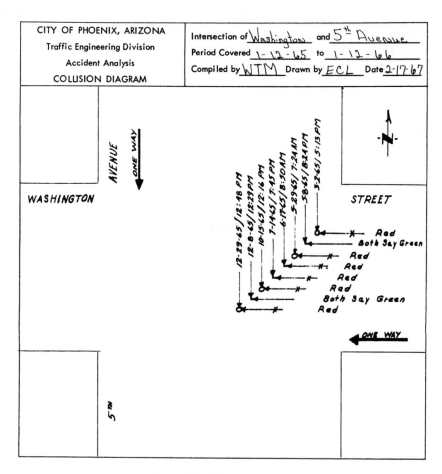

CITY OF PHOENIX, ARIZONA
Traffic Engineering Division
Accident Analysis
COLLISION DIAGRAM

Intersection of Washington and 5th Avenue
Period Covered 1-12-65 to 1-12-66
Compiled by WTM Drawn by ECL Date 2-17-67

WASHINGTON   AVENUE   ONE WAY   STREET

12-29-65/12:48 PM
12-8-65/18:29 PM
10-15-65/12:16 PM
7-14-65/7:45 PM
6-17-65/8:50 AM
5-29-65/7:2 AM
5-8-65/8:24 PM
3-2-65/5:13 PM

Red
Both Say Green
Red
Red
Red
Red
Both Say Green
Red

ONE WAY

5TH

Figure 18. Before mast arms.

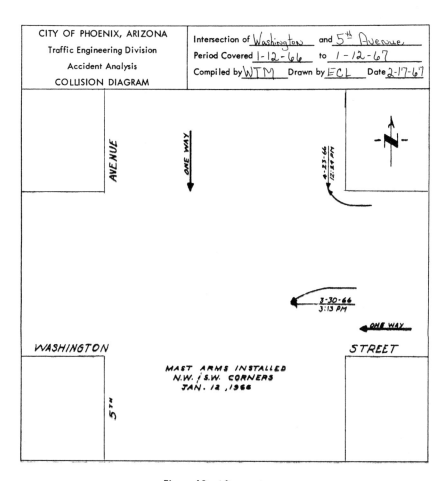

CITY OF PHOENIX, ARIZONA	Intersection of Washington and 5ᵗʰ Avenue
Traffic Engineering Division	Period Covered 1-12-66 to 1-12-67
Accident Analysis	Compiled by WTM Drawn by ECL Date 2-17-67
COLLISION DIAGRAM	

Figure 19. After mast arms.

WASHINGTON, D. C.

The system originally developed in Washington provided that whenever a Walk message appeared it represented an exclusive walk interval for pedestrians. When it was decided to convert some of these pedestrian signals to semi-exclusive or share the green intervals, the following system was used: (a) the green ball vehicular indication appeared for both cars and pedestrians when it was legal to walk, (b) the pedestrian signal indication was dark until it was time to provide a clearance interval, at which time the Don't Walk was lighted, (c) the Don't Walk stayed on during the balance of the green vehicular indication, yellow clearance and red interval, and (d) the Don't Walk was blanked out at the beginning of the next green.

Several of these signals were formerly in operation near the Matomic Building on H Street, N. W. The following news release spells out the changeover and gives a description of the flashing Walk operation currently used at locations where a semi-exclusive interval is in use.

* * *

The District of Columbia, a pioneer city in the protection of pedestrians, has been the installation of new flashing Walk signals at numerous intersections in the downtown area. Where traffic volumes do not warrant a complete separation of pedestrians and vehicles, the flashing Walk signal will be used to advise pedestrians when to cross. The new devices will flash a white Walk signal to pedestrians while vehicular traffic signals will permit motorists to turn providing they yield to pedestrians in the crosswalk.

Deputy Director for Traffic Engineering and Operations of the D. C. Department of Highways and Traffic, Daniel J. Hanson, feels that the distinctive white Walk and portland orange Don't Walk indications are an important step in providing pedestrians with their own color combination. Red pedestrian signal faces now in use will be phased out of service over several years as a part of this new pedestrian safety program.

The Don't Walk pedestrian signal indication tells a pedestrian when not to step off the curb. H Street, N. W., between 14th and 18th, was the site chosen for installing the new devices. Intersections along I, L and M Streets are also scheduled for similar installations.

When the program is complete there will be two standard pedestrian signal indications in the District of Columbia. A steady Walk indication will signify a vehicle-free pedestrian crossing. A flashing Walk light will be used only at intersections where traffic is permitted to turn providing motorists yield to pedestrians.

ST. LOUIS, MO.

The City of St. Louis has a unique situation related to walk signals. The walk signal as used in St. Louis, with the designation WALK, has always meant that the pedestrian had exclusive use of the crosswalk—there would be no interference from vehicles. Therefore, when upgrading signals, particularly on one-way streets, using pedestrian indications, and in order not to conflict with the WALK policy, the "Walking Man" symbol was used. At the present time, there are approximately 40 intersections with this type control.

There are other locations where St. Louis would like to use this indication; however, the city has been somewhat hesitant because it is not in the Uniform Manual.

Route Signal Systems

ELLIS C. HENRY, JR.
Traffic Commissioner
City of St. Louis

It is quite obvious that a vehicle traveling along a given route can move faster if the electric signals are adjusted so that each signal turns green as the vehicle approaches. However, the setting of the electric signals cannot be based just on the speed limit of that particular street section or route.

The physical features of a traffic route affect the speed at which a vehicle can be expected to move. Signal offset timing adjustments are necessary to compensate for the following features:

1. Horizontal and/or vertical curves which are such that visibility is obscured and/or vehicle operation is affected.

2. Poor geometric design, including inadequate lane widths, lateral clearances, medians, left-turn storage and channelization, which has an adverse effect on vehicle operation.

3. Irregularly or poorly spaced signalized intersections which make it impractical to provide coordination for two-way traffic flow.

4. Poorly located signal indications which affect driver response and ability to move conveniently along the route.

There are also other factors affecting the travel speed of the vehicles which must be considered when timing offsets are established:

1. The percentage of commercial vehicles and buses and their inability to accelerate and maintain a uniform speed, thereby reducing the overall operating speed of all vehicles.

2. Traffic volumes and directional flow characteristics during peak traffic hours. Operating speeds vary directly with the traffic density. High density, midblock frictions, and lack of adequate capacity, particularly at signalized intersections, are general reasons for reduced speeds along any route. The City of St. Louis uses, on most of its pre-timed signal system routes, three offsets and/or cycle splits: (a) offsets to favor inbound traffic during the morning peak traffic period, (b) offsets to favor outbound traffic during the afternoon peak traffic period, and (c) offsets to provide a minimal amount of delay for both directions of traffic flow along the route during the normal period or traffic period other than morning and afternoon peak traffic periods.

3. An underlying consideration in signal coordination is accident potential. When a motorist, leaving or passing through an intersection with the green indication is confronted with an amber at the next intersection, the resulting indecision creates a potential for either rear-end or right-angle accidents, depending upon the action taken by the driver.

DISCUSSION

Before and after studies have been conducted on several route-systems in St. Louis. These studies have entailed speed and delay measurements, accident experience, and volume comparison. Traffic movement along the three route-systems discussed here has been improved by the use of better coordinated signalization and the addition of signalized intersections. However, the number of accidents per year has generally increased on all route-systems.

TABLE 1
NORTH GRAND AVENUE

Item	Year		Change (%)
	1962	1967	
Average trip time, min and sec:			
A. M. —southbound	10 5	9 13	-8. 6
Normal—southbound	9 41	9 51	+1. 7
Normal—northbound	10 40	7 53	-26. 1
P. M. —northbound	11 17	8 38	-23. 5
Average overall speed, mph:			
A. M. —southbound	17. 3	18. 9	+9. 3
Normal—southbound	18. 0	17. 7	-1. 7
Normal—northbound	16. 3	22. 1	+35. 6
P. M. —northbound	15. 4	20. 2	+31. 2
Average delay, min and sec:			
A. M. —southbound	3 2	2 15	-25. 8
Normal—southbound	3 2	2 40	-12. 1
Normal—northbound	2 47	1 17	-52. 8
P. M. —northbound	3 39	1 57	-46. 6
Volume, ADT	21, 000	25, 000	+16
Accidents at intersections	201[a]	233[b]	+16

[a] 1963.
[b] 1966.

North Grand Avenue

The North Grand Avenue route-system (Forest Park Boulevard to West Florissant Avenue) is approximately 2. 9 miles long and consists of three basic roadway sections varying in width from 50 to 80 ft.

The 50-ft wide section is 1. 5 miles long, and runs through and north of a highly concentrated midtown commercial, shopping, and office district having relatively high traffic generation. It contains 14 signalized intersections which are closely spaced, preventing coordination for traffic progression in both directions. At heavy left-turn locations, the street surface has been divided into five lanes to provide a left-turn slot. Parking is restricted in these areas.

The second section, where the width varies from 56 to 80 ft, is in a light commercial area (the wider portion of this street section formerly served as the principal ingress and egress to the old Sportsman's Park sports stadium). This section is 0. 3 mile in length and contains three signalized intersections.

The third section, 76 ft wide, serves a residential and light commercial area, is 1. 1 miles in length, and contains three signalized intersections. All of the intersection approaches provide three lanes with painted left-turn slots.

The original "Speed and Delay" studies for this area were conducted in 1962, when all of the signalized intersections were pre-timed. Since that time, five signalized intersections have been added. Three of the added signalized intersections are of the traffic-actuated type and contain a background cycle which is used during peak traffic hours to maintain synchronization. These three signals replaced four-way stop intersections, which were in effect at least part-time on normal weekdays. The other two intersections are pre-timed signals and were established to improve traffic flow and pedestrian movement across North Grand Avenue. No significant roadway changes took place during the study period. Signal indications along the route were improved at many locations by the addition of mast arm signal indications. Signalization along this street is uniform, with far-right, far-left indications.

Table 1 gives trip time, speed, delay, volume and accident data for North Grand Avenue. While traffic volumes and accidents have increased, the average travel time has generally decreased. The decrease in travel time and delay can be attributed to signal timing changes, improved visibility, and the addition of signalized intersections, as shown in Figure 1.

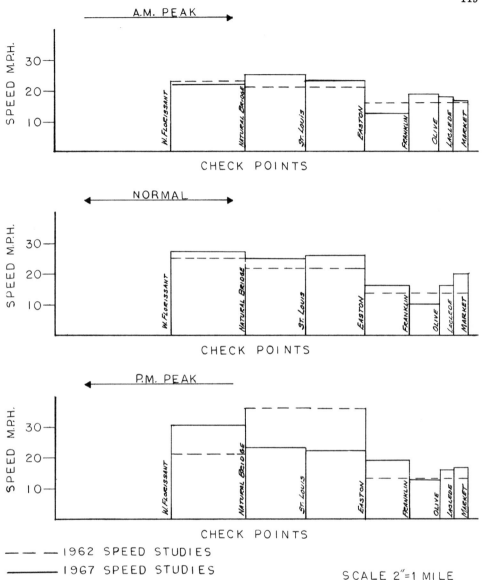

Figure 1. Average speed between check points, Grand—north.

McCausland Avenue

The McCausland Avenue route-system (Daniel Boone Expressway to Arsenal Street) encompasses a distance of approximately 1.33 miles and consists of two roadway sections.

The first section is 40 ft wide and is located in a residential area. Peak-hour parking restrictions permit the use of the entire roadway surface which is marked for four lanes of traffic. The section is approximately 0.87 mile long and has three signalized intersections.

TABLE 2

McCAUSLAND AVENUE

Item	Year		Change (%)
	1962	1967	
Average trip time, min and sec:			
A. M. —northbound	3 29	3 27	-1. 0
Normal—northbound	3 29	4 1	+15. 3
Normal—southbound	3 41	3 7	-15. 4
P. M. —southbound	3 59	3 53	-2. 5
Average overall speed, mph:			
A. M. —northbound	22. 8	23. 1	+1. 3
Normal—northbound	22. 8	19. 8	-13. 2
Normal—southbound	21. 6	25. 6	+18. 5
P. M. —southbound	20. 0	20. 5	+2. 5
Average delay, sec:			
A. M. —northbound	21	22	+4. 8
Normal—northbound	28	56	+50
Normal—southbound	23	18	-21. 7
P. M. —southbound	48	48	0
Volume, ADT	22, 000	23, 000	+4
Accidents at intersections	51[a]	71[b]	+39

[a] 1963.
[b] 1966.

The second section is 70 ft wide, with two 33-ft wide driving areas and a 4-ft wide median; it serves a light commercial area. It is approximately 0. 46 mile long and contains three signalized intersections.

Off-peak hour or normal period signal coordination is not maintained along McCausland Avenue, since five of the six signalized intersections are traffic actuated. However, background cycles are used during peak morning and afternoon periods to provide signal coordination during these periods. These background cycles were added during the period between the two speed and delay studies.

From the time of the 1962 studies, until the present studies were conducted, no new intersections were signalized and no significant roadway changes were accomplished along the McCausland Avenue route-system (Table 2). Figure 2 shows speed variation.

North Kingshighway Boulevard

The North Kingshighway route-system (Lindell Boulevard to West Florissant Avenue) encompasses a distance of approximately 3. 75 miles and consists of two roadway sections.

The first section is 60 ft wide and serves the West End hotel complex, several churches, residences, light commercial area, and a large department store. This section is 1. 25 miles in length and contains eight signalized intersections.

The second roadway section is composed of two driving areas, each approximately 27 ft, separated by a parkway median of 50 ft. This section is 2. 5 miles in length and contains eight signalized intersections. This section includes a volume-density signalized intersection at the full-diamond interchange with the Mark Twain Expressway. This volume-density signalized intersection voids any coordination with the one pre-timed signalized intersection to the north.

No significant roadway changes have been made along Kingshighway Boulevard during the study period. Three new signalized intersections have been added—all actuated with background cycles for peak-hour operation. One of the three signals replaced a part-time stop sign, and one a four-way stop intersection. Extensive signal indication improvement work has been accomplished, such as changing from near-right signal indications to uniform far-right indications, and addition of mast arms. Data for this route are given in Table 3. If adjusted for difference caused by two intersections where it was necessary to allow left-turn movements (previously not allowed), the accident data would be 166 and 208 and the percent change 25. 2. Figure 3 shows speed variation.

Additional accident data are given in Table 4. After installation of the progressive timing systems, accidents generally increased. However, with only one exception (Kingshighway signals), these accident increases were less than the overall city average change.

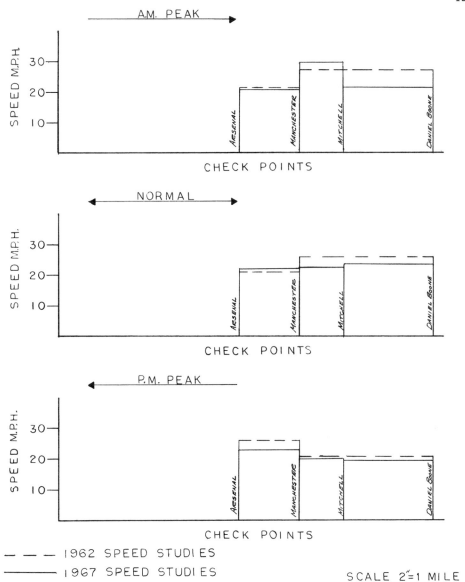

Figure 2. Average speed between check points, McCausland—south.

Table 5 summarizes data on newly signalized locations along the routes. While none of the intersections are truly high-accident locations, the trend on Kingshighway was an increase in accidents, while no statistically significant changes were noted on Grand Avenue.

METHODS OF INTERCONNECTION

After a route-system has been established, some method must be provided to insure that the proper relationship between signalized intersections is maintained. In St. Louis, two methods are used.

TABLE 3

NORTH KINGSHIGHWAY BOULEVARD

Item	Year		Change (¢)
	1962	1967	
Average trip time, min and sec:			
A. M. —southbound	11 56	13 4	+9. 5
Normal—southbound	12 26	11 10	-10. 0
Normal—northbound	12 34	12 0	-4. 5
P. M. —northbound	13 33	11 52	-12. 5
Average overall speed, mph:			
A. M. —southbound	18.9	17. 2	-9. 0
Normal—southbound	18. 1	20. 2	+11. 6
Normal—northbound	17.9	18. 8	+5. 0
P. M. —northbound	16. 6	19. 0	+14. 5
Average delay, min and sec:			
A. M. —southbound	2 54	3 34	+21. 6
Normal—southbound	3 1	2 38	-12. 7
Normal—northbound	2 50	2 28	-13. 0
P. M. —northbound	4 9	2 33	-38. 5
Volume, ADT	28, 000	31, 000	+10. 7
Accidents at intersections	166[a]	254[b]	+53

[a]1963.
[b]1966.

Non-Interconnected Offsets

This system depends on the power company to furnish constant frequency electric service, and St. Louis has had considerable success with this system. Of course, power failures can destroy a signal offset timing program. If this occurs over a large area, a great deal of time may be required to retime the system.

The major traffic arterials where this system is used are patrolled daily, and secondary streets are checked a minimum of twice each week. To minimize the amount of

TABLE 4

ACCIDENT SUMMARY

Location	Before 1963	After 1966	Change (¢)
(a) North Grand Avenue			
Signalized intersections	201	233	+16
Non-signalized intersections	64	52	-19
Between intersections	48	51	+6
All accidents	313	336	+7
(b) North Kingshighway Boulevard			
Signalized intersections	166	254	+53
Non-signalized intersections	105	135	+29
Between intersections	78	75	+4
All accidents	349	464	+33
(c) McCausland Avenue			
Signalized intersections	51	71	+28
Non-signalized intersections	16	22	+37
Between intersections	23	16	-30
All accidents	90	109	+21
(d) City-wide Accidents (approx. 700, 000 population)			
All locations	15, 248	21, 347	+40

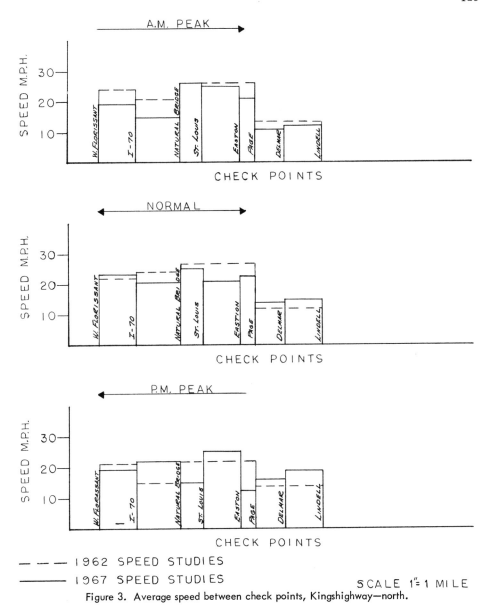

Figure 3. Average speed between check points, Kingshighway—north.

deviation, the city uses master cycle dials located in the radio room, with all signal timing referenced to these master cycle dials via the two-way radio in the electrician's truck.

Direct Wire Interconnect

St. Louis has underground ducts available which can be used in many locations to provide direct-wire interconnection. Single conductor wires in the required number are pulled where needed to provide the interconnection. This is usually 5 to 7 wires, depending on the number of functions to be controlled.

TABLE 5

ACCIDENT RELATED TO INSTALLATION
OF NEW SIGNALS

Location	Before Signalization 1963	After Signalization 1966
(a) North Kingshighway Boulevard		
Cote Brilliante Ave.	5	10
Maffitt Ave.	3	9
Penrose Ave.	5	9
Total	13	28
(b) North Grand Avenue		
Franklin-Enright	15	12
Bell Ave.	9	7
Cook Ave.	10	8
North Market St.	14	16
Hebert St.	7	9
Total	55	52

There are other methods of interconnection which sometimes are feasible because of the great distance to be covered and/or the expense of installing underground cables. A radio interconnect system requires the installation of a base radio transmitting station near the master controller and a receiver at each local controller to receive instructions. A leased telephone system uses telephone pairs leased from the telephone company. It usually requires complicated tone-phase systems to transmit and receive the needed information between the master and the local controller.

CONCLUSIONS

Traffic flow along a traffic route-system can be expedited if the traffic signals are adjusted to provide a coordinated system with timing at each signalized intersection adjusted to minimize delay.

To provide maximum efficiency, some type of interconnect or offset relation should be provided and maintained, to insure the proper relationship of signalized intersections along the route at all times.

Addenda

PHOENIX, ARIZ.

Phoenix made an extensive study in comparing costs of radio, telephone lease line, and city-owned line. The cheapest installation was found by use of lease telephone interconnect. Cost data are given in the following 1962 material obtained from Charles E. Haley, City Traffic Engineer of Phoenix.

Interconnection of Traffic Signals, Re: Agreement With Local Telephone Company

The Division of Traffic Engineering, after extensive study, recommends the City of Phoenix enter into an agreement for interconnection of all the traffic signals with the local telephone company. The purpose of providing the single pair of telephone wires to each signal is to electrically interconnect the traffic signals so that the time relationship between signals will be maintained for progressive traffic movement.

At the present time the majority of signals must be checked manually each week. An employee of the electrical division must spend approximately a full day each week checking these signals. Because of power failures signals can be out of synchronization for as much as a weeks time. By interconnecting electrically, better transportation and service to the public will result. Interconnection is also the first step in the modernization of the traffic signal system. Through interconnection, by installing a computing-type of control system, we can send information out to individual controllers adjusting the amount of green time and their relationship one with another depending upon the traffic flow. This, however, is the next step in the modernization of our signal system and will require additional monies in the future.

The cost for this service, which is in the 1962-63 budget, is:

1. First year capital outlay $4600 (one time cost)
2. Tariff for remainder of budget year $3700
3. Tariff for each additional year $5700

The Division compared these costs with the costs of other methods of interconnect; i. e., city-owned and installed wire and radio interconnect. City-owned and installed wire would cost twice as much as leasing from the telephone company, interconnection by radio would cost three times as much as leasing this service from the telephone company. These prices quoted by the telephone company are considerably less than prices quoted in previous years. We understand this is a national reduction in price as the telephone company is energetically seeking leased wire business for data transmission.

The installation of a complete electric interconnect system is the first step in the creation of a completely electronically controlled, traffic sensitive, modern, flexible type of traffic signal system.

* * *

Agreement

The City Council of the City of Phoenix has authorized the City Manager to enter into an agreement with the telephone company for the purpose of providing telephone wire service to interconnect traffic signals in the City of Phoenix.

The agreement, which was negotiated and agreed upon as to form and content by both parties, is as follows:

The company agrees to furnish and maintain one pair of telephone wires to each signal location requested by the City of Phoenix according to the following terms:

Construction

No new construction will be required of the telephone company. The maximum overhead run from the company terminal facility to the City of Phoenix signals will be 180 feet. If spans of greater length are encountered, the City of Phoenix will furnish and install the necessary poles. Service runs will be made by the company to a point on either a wooden or steel signal pole, a minimum of 40 inches below secondary power lines. Where attachment points are made on steel poles, the City of Phoenix will furnish a point of attachment for telephone wire connection and insure that the resistance from the pole to ground shall not exceed 25 ohms. Any termination equipment other than point of attachment will be furnished and installed by the telephone company.

The City of Phoenix will be permitted a load of 2. 5 mils per signal to a maximum of 60 mils per pair of wires.

Reconstruction

In the event the company modifies its plant from overhead to underground, the City of Phoenix will provide an underground conduit from a manhole to the signal controller or point of attachment location. The company will furnish and install the necessary cable in the conduit run. Any change in repeater station locations by the City of Phoenix may require the City of Phoenix to rent extra cable necessary to reach the new locations.

Service

In the event the company does not have telephone cable available for any signal location, it shall provide service to the City of Phoenix as soon as possible. The company shall provide 24 hours a day, 7 days a week, service to the City of Phoenix to repair and maintain wires leased by the City of Phoenix.

Tariff

The company shall bill the City of Phoenix monthly for rental of leased wire at the rate for intra-exchange channels as filed with the Arizona Corporation Commission. The current rate is:

First $\frac{1}{4}$ mile or fraction thereof $3. 00
Each additional $\frac{1}{4}$ mile or fraction thereof $0. 625

The rates stated in this contract are subject to change upon filing and acceptance by the Arizona Corporation Commission of tariffs providing different rates.

Mileage of lines in use by the City of Phoenix shall be determined as the direct air-line distance between all signal locations connected, starting at the intersection of Central Avenue and McDowell Road and measured so as to produce the lowest total intra-exchange mileage charge. The mileage will be computed separately in $\frac{1}{4}$ mile multiples (fractional $\frac{1}{4}$ miles being considered as full $\frac{1}{4}$ miles) between each pair of signals. The interconnection of the City of Phoenix signals shall be considered as one continuous channel and the charge of $3.00 for the first $\frac{1}{4}$ mile, or fraction thereof, shall apply only once to the channel.

Signal Networks

SAMUEL CASS

Commissioner
Metropolitan Toronto
Traffic Engineering Department

With the conclusion of World War II there came an unprecedented growth in the number of motor vehicles on the streets of our cities. To meet the challenge, traffic engineers looked to various means of improving the tools already at hand. The traffic control signal was already taking its place at the head of the list of devices which could be used to regulate and promote more orderly traffic flow. However, as more and more traffic signals began to appear, it became evident that the disruption to traffic flow caused by frequent stops along any route was undoing the benefits which would otherwise be derived.

From necessity, there soon evolved several examples of linked signals, which were coordinated to provide a greater degree of continuity in traffic flow. These groups of linked signals are called "networks."

The methods of linking varied widely, however, a method which is still used extensively today involves the use of an interconnecting cable joining the several traffic signal control units which are to be linked. One of the units serves as a master, and the balance are slaves. The function of the master is merely to maintain the established synchronization between each of the units.

Later developments involved centralized control. In the earlier examples, the central control provided for greater flexibility by permitting a larger number of timing cycles than was normally accommodated by the intersection control units. Central control also permitted greater flexibility in selecting the time at which changes in signal timing were to go into effect.

The next evolutionary step was almost predictable. The selection of the time at which various signal timing arrangements would go into effect had been predetermined and activated by time clocks; with the advent of devices which could detect traffic flow on the streets it became practicable to permit the selection of various signal timing arrangements to be activated by the changes in actual traffic flow. The development of the electronic arts produced the necessary devices for measuring the traffic flow. The means were now at hand to provide for a direct link between actual traffic flow and the selection of various pre-arranged signal timing patterns. So it was that there appeared a new central traffic signal control, which was generically called an "analog computer." Through this type of control a giant step was taken in harnessing the traffic signals in a manner more sensitive to actual traffic demands than had previously been the case.

In June 1963, the Municipality of Metropolitan Toronto created a central control system for a signal network that was to encompass all of the signals in the metropolitan area. To accomplish this task, a very large "digital" computer was installed, which was connected to every signal control unit through leased telephone line. In addition, a large number of vehicle detectors were installed to provide the computer with actual traffic flow data. This was the first time that a digital computer was used for this type of task.

One of the advantages in using a digital computer was the fact that it has no built-in traffic control functions, but must be specifically programmed for each task. As a result, it was possible to arrange for network operation and single intersection operation in various modes and thus compare the effect on traffic flow of each method. For the first time a realistic comparison and appraisal could be made by actual field trials of various modes of operation rather than relying on theoretical analyses or simulation techniques.

The centrally controlled traffic signal system was not specifically to be a research tool, although the possibilities for this were very great. It was basically to be an

127

EFFECT OF DIFFERENT MODES OF SIGNAL OPERATION ON TRAFFIC CONDITIONS AS SHOWN BY FI

Street Name	Street Type	No. of Signals	Length (mi)	Average Travel Time (min)							Average Speed			Coe T Re
				Random	Coordinated Pre-Timed	Change (%)	Coordinated Traffic Responsive	Change (%)	Improved Traffic Responsive	Change (%)	Random	Coordinated Pre-Timed	Change (%)	
University Avenue	6-Lane arterial	13	1.7	6.15	4.85	-21.2	5.14	-16.8	4.28	-30.4	16.6	21.1	+27.0	
Yonge Street	4-Lane arterial	42	10.8	36.97	39.73	+7.5	37.26	+.8	36.68	-.7	17.6	16.3	-7.4	
Mt. Pleasant Road and Jarvis St.	4-Lane arterial with street cars	25	5.6	20.74	16.93	-18.4	18.55	-10.6	17.27	-16.7	16.2	19.9	+22.8	
Broadview Avenue and O'Connor Dr.	4-Lane arterial	11	4.2	14.95	11.10	-25.8					16.8	22.6	+35.4	
St. Clair Ave. W.	4-Lane arterial with street cars	20	4.5	15.94	13.50	-15.2					16.9	20.0	+18.4	
St. Clair Ave. E.	2-Lane arterial	9	2.9	7.50	7.03	-6.3					23.2	24.8	+6.9	
Dundas Street E.	4-Lane arterial	13	3.0	9.57	8.25	-13.8					18.8	21.9	+16.5	
Davenport Road	4-Lane arterial	9	2.7	9.32	7.35	-21.0					17.4	22.0	+26.4	
Gerrard Street E.	4-Lane arterial with street cars	17	4.6	16.88	15.67	-7.2					16.3	17.6	+8.0	
Average values per mile of roadway		4	4.4	3.5	3.1	-11.4	3.3	-5.7	3.2	-8.6	17.1	19.4	+13.4	

Note: During the period covered by these studies the number of vehicles registered in Metropolitan Toronto increased by 9.6 percent, whereas the number of reported motor vehicle accidents increased by 1(

operational system in which advantage would be taken of the latest techniques in operating a network of signals. To determine the optimum or most desirable methods of controlling traffic flow, the computer was programmed to permit trying several techniques. The base for comparison was a random operation of all the existing signals. The elements recorded were speed and delay, number of stops, and accidents.

TRAVEL TIME WITH NETWORK SIGNAL CONTROL—LINEAR NETWORK

The first program controlled a coordinated signal system on 9 routes. These routes were programmed as linear networks; i. e., each route was optimized for through travel, with no regard for intersecting routes. However, they were all two-way streets which would require bi-directional consideration. The total number of signals involved was 159. There was an average of 4 signals per mile for some 40 miles. The results of these tests are shown in Table 1, and a representative sample of the results is shown in Figure 1. The improvement in travel time varied from 6. 3 to 25. 8 percent on eight of the nine routes. On one route there was an actual loss in travel time of 7. 5 percent. The average improvement on the nine routes was 11. 4 percent.

These tests also showed a reduction in the number of involuntary stops averaging 43. 8 percent. On individual routes the reduction in involuntary stops varied from no change to a reduction of 58 percent.

GRID NETWORK

The next stage of development involved a two-fold change. First, three of the previously mentioned routes were programmed in a grid network; i. e., consideration was also given to through movement on the cross routes. Second, the timing and directional patterns were activated by traffic flow on the vehicle detectors rather than by a pretimed basis. As can be expected, the average travel time on the three routes was not as good as when they were programmed as a linear network.

By this time, however, Toronto had progressed in familiarity with the digital computer to the stage where the machine could be used to formulate the signal timing schemes. The computer was, therefore, used to develop an optimized timing arrangement for the grid network and the results (Table 1) indicate the improvement which followed. On one route the reduction in travel time was 21. 2 percent with a linear network, 16. 8 percent with the grid network, and 30. 4 percent with the improved grid network. In addition, during the interval of time between the tests of the random timing and the improved grid network there had been a vehicle volume growth of approximately 9. 6 percent.

ED AND DELAY STUDIES AND ACCIDENT ANALYSIS ON VARIOUS SUBURBAN ARTERIAL STREETS

			Number of Involuntary Stops						Number of Vehicle Accidents per Year								
									Total Accidents			Accidents at Intersections			Accidents Between Intersections		
Improved Traffic Responsive	Change (%)	Random	Coordinated Pre-Timed	Change (%)	Coordinated Traffic Responsive	Change (%)	Improved Traffic Responsive	Change (%)	Before Control	After Control	Change (%)	Before Control	After Control	Change (%)	Before Control	After Control	Change (%)
23.8	+43.1	4.8	2.0	-58.0	3.2	-33.4	2.1	-56.0	201	185	-8.0	174	157	-9.8	27	28	+4.0
17.7	+.6	19.1	13.2	-30.6	10.9	-42.8	10.8	-43.5	949	1012	+6.7	658	762	+15.8	291	250	-14.1
19.5	+20.4	10.0	4.2	-58.0	6.4	-36.0	5.9	-41.0	410	363	-11.4	316	259	-18.0	94	104	+9.6
		5.4	2.1	-61.0					146	132	-9.6	119	90	-24.4	27	43	+59.2
		6.5	3.5	-46.2					625	590	-5.6	466	417	-10.5	159	173	+8.8
		1.8	1.8	Nil					154	150	-2.6	108	117	+8.3	46	33	-28.3
		3.8	2.1	-44.8					205	201	-1.9	159	148	-6.9	46	53	+15.2
		3.8	3.1	-18.5					213	257	+20.6	182	218	+19.8	31	39	+25.7
		7.7	4.8	-37.7					247	280	+13.3	163	191	+17.2	84	89	+5.9
18.8	+9.9	1.6	.9	-43.8	1.1	-31.2	1.0	-37.5	79	80	+1.2	59	59	Nil	20	20	Nil

TRAFFIC ACCIDENTS

A comparison of accident experience was made on the nine routes in the original study area. The results of the accident comparison are also given in Table 1.

The total number of accidents on the nine routes did not change during the test period. However, accidents generally went up by 10.6 percent during the period. Further analysis is necessary to verify whether system operation has a significant effect on traffic accidents.

COORDINATED NETWORK WITH TRAFFIC-RESPONSIVE SPLIT SELECTION

The next stage in the improvement of the network signal control was the provision of traffic-responsive adjustment of the cycle split at major intersections while maintaining the network cycle and coordination. This would not affect the travel time on the route to any great extent, but could affect the congestion at each intersection.

It had been observed that, even during the period of heaviest traffic flow, there was a cycle-by-cycle variation in the number of vehicles arriving at any intersection. The number of arrivals per cycle was observed to vary by as much as 50 percent. It would seem to be logical, therefore, that the proportion of green time should vary cycle by cycle in order to take advantage of the varying number of arrivals. The computer was, therefore, programmed to provide the network coordinated control, as previously described, with the added capability of permitting the proportion of green to be varied within the system cycle length in accordance with traffic detections at each of the intersections so affected. Testing was performed to validate this arrangement.

CONGESTION AT INTERSECTIONS

For the most part, the vehicle detectors are located approximately 300 ft from the signalized intersection. The number of vehicles that could store in this distance is normally able to clear on the next green light. Congestion is, therefore, indicated when the queue extends beyond the detector and, as a result, movement over the detector is very slow. For comparative and test purposes, congestion has been arbitrarily defined as the condition prevailing when traffic flow across the detector falls below 12 mph. At the same time, to insure that the slow movement is due to congestion and not some other factor, the computer is directed to accept only those indications of slow traffic when the volume rate is in excess of 250 veh/hr per approach. These parameters of speed and volume are derived by the computer from measurements of the pulses generated at the loop detectors.

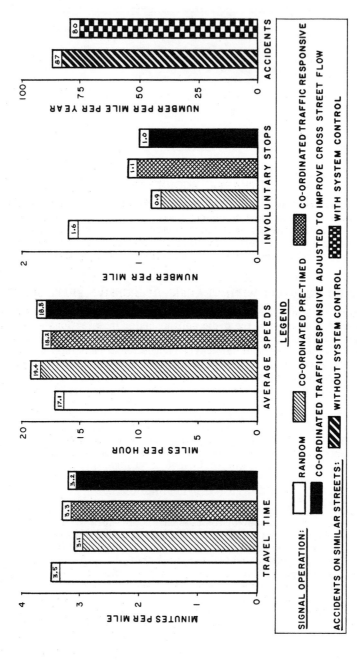

Figure 1. Overall effect of different modes of signal operation on traffic conditions as shown by floating car speed and delay studies and accident analysis.

TABLE 2
COMPARISON BETWEEN THE EFFECT OF PREDETERMINED AND COORDINATED TRAFFIC-
RESPONSIVE SIGNAL OPERATION AT VARIOUS LOCATIONS

Intersection	Time of Day	Coordinated Predetermined			Coordinated Traffic Responsive			Percent Change		
		Congested Cycles (%)	Volume, All Approaches (veh/hr)	Volume, Two Critical Approaches (veh/hr)	Congested Cycles (%)	Volume, All Approaches (veh/hr)	Volume, Two Critical Approaches (veh/hr)	Congested Cycle	Volumes, All Approaches (veh/hr)	Volume, Two Critical Approaches (veh/hr)
Church-Bloor	7:30-9:30	63	2434	1521	36	2614	1693	-43	+7.4	+11.3
Jarvis-Wellesley	7:30-9:30	21	2633	1997	6	2701	2040	-71	+2.6	+ 2.1
Jarvis-Carlton	7:30-9:30	14	2558	1738	11	2409	1718	-21	-5.8	- 1.2
Yonge-College	7:30-9:30	33	2360	1343	29	2390	1360	-12	+1.3	- 1.3
Yonge-Lawrence	7:30-9:30	47	3259	1956	8	3278	1975	-83	+0.6	+ 1.0
Jarvis-Dundas	7:30-8:00	45	2167	1461	33	2193	1483	-27	+1.2	+ 1.5
Jarvis-Dundas	8:00-8:30	60	2552	1659	35	2574	1683	-42	+0.9	+ 1.4
Jarvis-Dundas	8:30-9:00	43	2430	1560	31	2456	1587	-28	+1.1	+ 1.7
Jarvis-Dundas	9:00-9:30	18	2185	1361	17	2245	1402	- 6	+2.7	+ 3.0
Average		38.2	2509	1622	22.9	2540	1660	-40	+1.3	+ 2.3

The percentage of congested cycles at nine major intersections was compared during the morning rush hours. The comparison is between conditions existing when the co-ordinated network operation was using predetermined cycle splits as against conditions when the cycle splits were varied in response to traffic actuation. The results of this test are given in Table 2 and indicate that in every case the number of congested cycles was less when traffic actuations varied the split of green time. The improvement was 40 percent fewer congested cycles. Figure 2 shows the improvement at some selected intersections.

FULLY TRAFFIC-RESPONSIVE SIGNAL OPERATION

Experience to this date has shown that there are usually a few critical intersections in the grid network, at which a queue will develop during the peak traffic flow which nullifies the effect of coordination as far as continuous traffic flow is concerned. When this occurs, the value of retaining such intersections within the coordinated network is very dubious. Experiments have therefore been conducted with dropping such a signal out of coordination and operating it as a fully traffic-responsive isolated intersection. Under this scheme, the signal has freedom to vary its split and cycle almost infinitely. Each green phase is permitted to extend itself until the advantage of further extension is nullified by the increased vehicle delay on the red phase. The cycle is made up of the sum of the green phases. Within the limited experience, it would seem that a series of intersections operating in this manner would tend to coordinate themselves by platoon recognition.

Figure 3 shows the effect on queue length at a test intersection, achieved by fully traffic-responsive operation. The advantage is principally achieved by optimizing capacity and by balancing delay between all approaches. A similar improvement in the average approach density at the test intersection is shown in Figure 4.

THE DIGITAL COMPUTER AS A STUDY TOOL

An important advantage in the use of a digital computer for traffic control is related to its inherent ability to be used for study and analysis purposes. In this way, the traffic engineer can quickly be made aware of the effectiveness or non-effectiveness of any traffic control changes. At this time, a library of thirteen analysis programs and six data preparation programs has been developed. These programs are designed to search the magnetic tapes storing a detailed record of all the events reported to the computer during routine control operation. The tape contains a second-by-second record of the aspect of every signal under control, traffic count, and pulse length at each detector. From this, one can arrange for graphical or tabular summaries of traffic counts, space-time diagrams, volume-lane occupancy graphs, and numerous other presentations of the data.

132

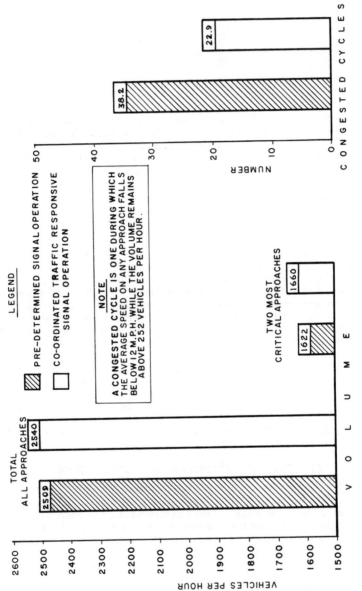

Figure 2. Overall comparison between the effect of predetermined and coordinated traffic-responsive signal operation.

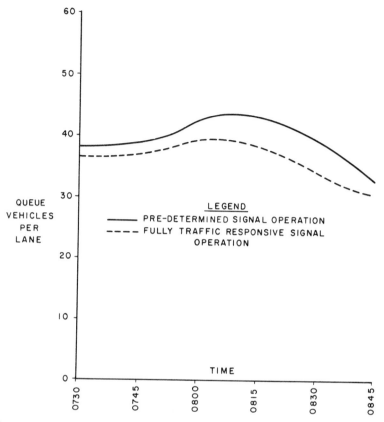

Figure 3. Comparison between the effect of predetermined and fully traffic-responsive signal operation as shown by the measurement of average queue length at a single intersection.

SPACE-TIME DIAGRAM

Figure 5 is a printout taken from the computer of actual signal operation of ten signals in a coordinated linear network. The time of operation is between 7:30 a. m. and 7:45 a. m. The traffic flow is predominantly southbound and the printout shows the progression available to each direction of traffic. Figure 6 shows a printout in which one intersection controller was deliberately dropped from coordination. The effect on the progression through the area is immediately discernible.

TIMING PLAN CHANGES

Figure 7 is a printout of two adjacent signals. The location is in the vicinity of the Maple Leaf Gardens on a night of a National Hockey League game. The printout at the left depicts variations in traffic volumes at a location used to trigger changes in signal timing for the network in the vicinity of the hockey arena. The reaction to the release of the large volume of traffic after the game can be seen by the plan changes, which take place during the evening. The printout at the right illustrates the similarity of traffic flow at an adjacent intersection which forms part of the network affected by the plan changes. Figure 7 is representative of traffic-responsive network operation.

Another example of the value which can accrue to traffic movement at a single intersection resulting from the ability of the system to select various timing plans as traffic demands vary is shown in Figure 8. The printout of derived density, taken from the

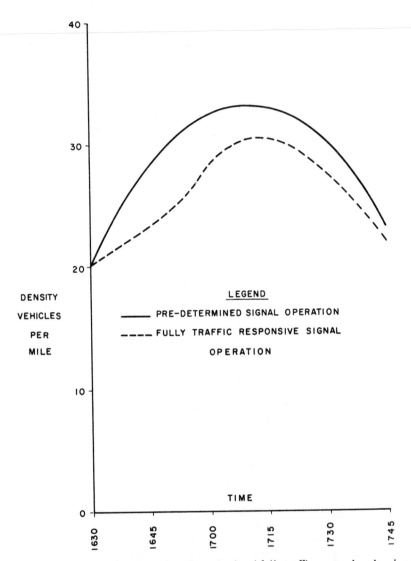

Figure 4. Comparison between the effect of predetermined and fully traffic-responsive signal operation as shown by the measurement of average approach density at a single intersection.

computer record tape, at a single intersection compares conditions when the timing plans are free to select pre-rush-hour and post-rush-hour plans, as well as a peak and rush-hour plan, as against conditions when a restraint is applied to prevent any change except from moderate traffic to peak traffic. The selection of the pre-rush-hour plan prevents a build-up of traffic density. This advantage is maintained throughout the peak period. The post-rush-hour plan assists in shortening the total duration of the heavy traffic period.

VOLUME-LANE OCCUPANCY RELATIONSHIP

At the present time, it is necessary to relate speed and traffic volume in order to avoid misleading interpretation of detector data by the traffic signal control program. For

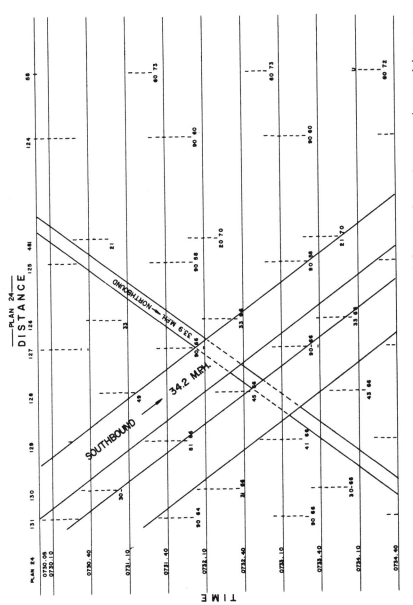

Figure 5 Computer-derived space-time chart showing correct peak-hour signal operation on an urban arterial street.

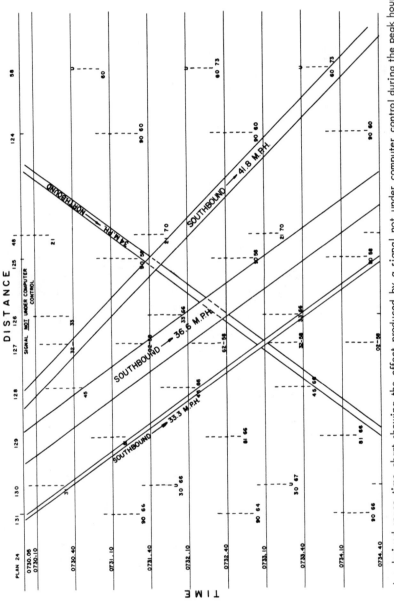

Figure 6. Computer-derived space-time chart showing the effect produced by a signal not under computer control during the peak hour on an urban arterial street.

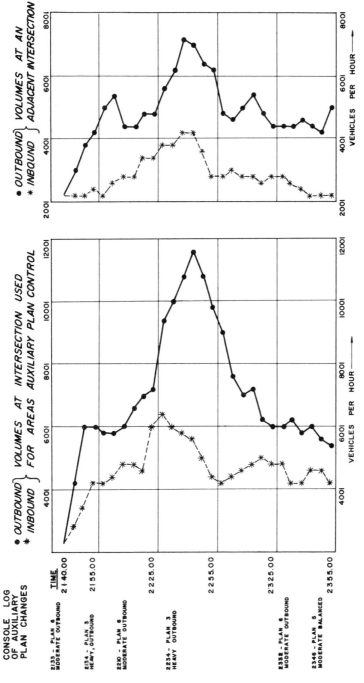

Figure 7. Computer-derived operation plan change points related to traffic demand.

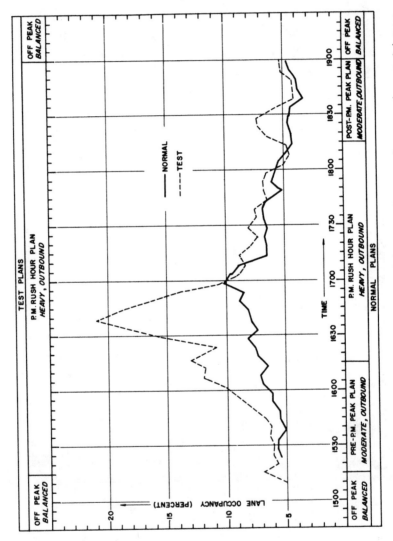

Figure 8. Effect of a plan change malfunction on peak–hour intensity at a point on an urban arterial street.

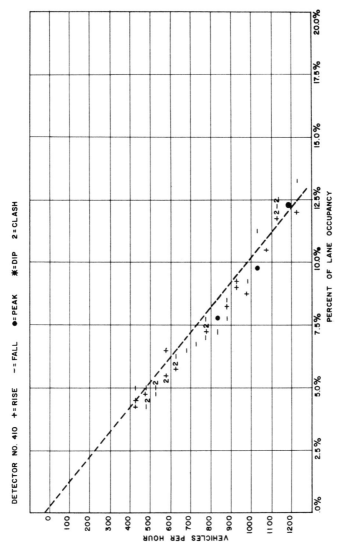

Figure 9. Computer-derived volume–lane occupancy relationship for free flowing traffic.

140

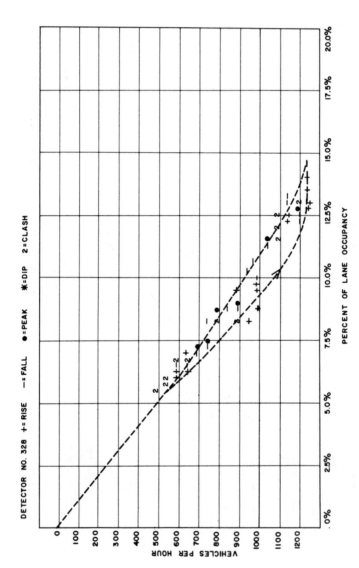

Figure 10. Computer-derived volume–lane occupancy relationship for traffic on a signalized intersection approach.

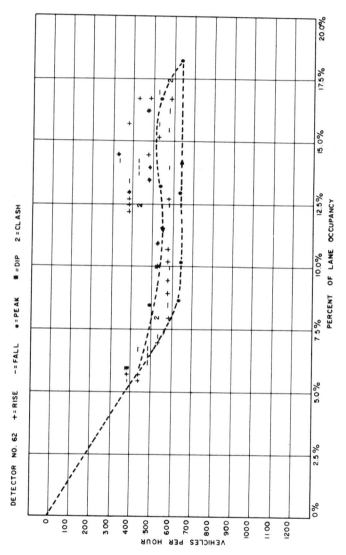

Figure 11. Computer-derived volume-lane occupancy relationship for congested traffic.

Figure 12. Metropolitan Toronto traffic control computer center.

example, a low volume might represent very little traffic, or very congested traffic. To interpret this volume count, the speed (as represented by pulse length) must be ascertained. Thus a low volume at free-flow speeds means there are few vehicles, whereas low volume at very low speed means congested conditions. The possibility has been examined for replacing the two parameters which are presently used, with a single representative parameter. Such a parameter might be lane occupancy as measured by the ratio of pulse length to total time. In an attempt to examine relationships of volume and lane occupancy, computer printouts were obtained for a number of locations having differing degrees of congestion. Figure 9 shows the relationship at an intersection where traffic was relatively uncongested even at high volumes. The relationship appears linear.

Figure 10 shows the relationship when some congestion was noted at high volumes. As the volumes reduced, the lane occupancy curve did not return along the same line, but formed what might be termed a "hysteresis loop." Figure 11 shows conditions at an intersection which was congested throughout the period of study. It would appear that the relationship is similar to the hysteresis loop in Figure 10. Much study is still required before lane occupancy can be reliably used as a single parameter to trigger timing plan changes. Figure 12 shows the computer center.

CONCLUSIONS

There are distinct advantages to be derived from signal network operation, however, the timing plans and coordination plans require careful designing. The extent to which improvements may be obtained is difficult to predetermine. This indicates the need for more research of an empirical nature, using actual systems, to determine simpler and surer methods of designing optimum timing and coordination plans, and methods of evaluation to permit a predetermination of the extent to which improvement is possible.

REFERENCES

1. Gazis, D. C., Bermant, O. Dynamic Traffic Control Systems and the San José Experiment. Proc. International Road Safety Congress, September 5-10, 1966.
2. Cobbe, B. M. Development of Traffic Signals for Area Traffic Control. British Ministry of Transport.
3. Miller, A. J. A Computer Control System for Traffic Networks. Proc. Second International Symposium on Traffic Theory, OECD Publication, Paris, 1965.
4. Hillier, J. A. Glasgow's Experiment in Area Traffic Control. Traffic Engineering and Control, Dec. 1965.
5. Hillier, J. A. Appendix to Glasgow's Experiment in Area Traffic Control. Traffic Engineering and Control, Jan. 1966.
6. French, Rae A. Urban Traffic Signals. Proc. ITE, 35th Annual Meeting, 1965.
7. Casciato, L., and Cass, S. Pilot Study of the Automatic Control of Traffic Signals by a General Purpose Electronic Computer. HRB Bull. 338, pp. 28-39, 1962.
8. Hewton, J. T. The Metropolitan Toronto Signal System. Proc. Symposium on Area Traffic Control, Institution of Civil Engineers, London, 1967.

Simple Types of Intersection Improvements

JAMES E. WILSON

Traffic Engineer

California Division of Highways

Examine any surveillance system, find a concentration of accidents and you will usually find an intersection at the root of the problem. This is not meant to be an earth-shattering statement but a simple truth. And if there were degrees of truth, we would find it near the 100 percent end of the scale in urban areas. For this reason, the simple intersection has not been given the attention it deserves. Just stop and contemplate the number of intersections in this country (it is questionable whether anyone knows how many there are). Visualize how many vehicles might be stopped in the middle of the intersection at any one moment in time waiting for a turn of one kind or another. To put it bluntly, think of the rear-end exposures, unless of course they enjoy the protection afforded by various types of simple traffic engineering improvements.

Of the more than 500 minor improvement evaluation reports being analyzed by the California Division of Highways 380 are considered to be urban in nature. They are classified into 12 types of improvements, 5 of which deal directly with the intersection in one way or another. Table 1 shows a breakdown of the various types and number of locations studied. To further emphasize the problem, of the 1725 locations turned up in the inventory of "hot" spots in complying with Bureau of Public Roads directives, 1275 were found to be in the urban environment and 960 were of the intersection type. Tables 2 and 3 give the information gathered in the inventory and the breakdown by type of project.

To illustrate what simple measures will accomplish, several projects have been chosen, most of which involve some type of left-turn treatment. It is in this area that California can get a high "pay off." Left-turn lanes at intersections without signals reduce accidents on an average of 50 percent. It is this device that will reduce the "rear-end" exposure and provide a comfortable means of making a left turn. There are several ways to accomplish this. To implement many of these, it is necessary on occasion to remove parking on either one or both sides of the street—this is not always easily accomplished. However, it is a price that business people and motorists must pay for safety. Diagrams have been prepared showing experience with several intersections receiving various kinds of median treatment. They are summarized by types and reveal some interesting findings.

Figures 1 and 2 reflect a before and after accident condition at a T-intersection of US 50 and a two-lane street. US 50 is a four-lane highway with average speeds of 45 mph in this area. A left-turn pocket for vehicles entering Wisseman Drive was provided by raised bars and curbing.

In one-year before and after periods, total accidents dropped from 9 to 5

TABLE 1

MINOR IMPROVEMENTS PROJECTS SUMMARY

Type of Improvement	No. of Projects	Change in Accidents (%)
New signals	140	-14
Modified signals	28	-9
New signals with channelization	65	-20
Modified signals with channelization	45	-35
Flashing signals	45	-34
Safety lighting	41	-29
		-60[a]
Delineation	17	-9[b]
Protective guardrail	14	-60
Intersection channelization	53	-34
Reconstruction	30	-30
Signs	22	-53
Miscellaneous	6	+37
Total	506	
Urban	380	
Rural	126	

[a]Night accidents only.
[b]Based on accident rate change.

144

TABLE 2

SUMMARY OF INVENTORY PROJECTS

Types of Projects	No. of Projects	Improvement Costs—$1,000		
		Total	State	Other
01 New signals[a]	215	4,700	2,700	2,000
02 Modified signals[a]	180	2,000	1,240	760
03 New signals with channelization[a]	115	3,800	2,400	1,400
04 Modified signals with channelization[a]	180	4,050	3,150	900
05 Flashing signals[b]	25	150	130	20
06 Safety lighting[c]	80	800	600	200
07 Delineation	50	200	200	0
08 Protective guardrail	60	1,300	1,300	0
09 Intersection channelization[a]	165	2,600	2,500	100
10 Reconstruction[d]	225	14,200	13,200	1,000
11 Signing and marking[e]	375	1,500	1,480	20
12 Other	55	1,200	1,100	100
Totals	1,725	36,500	30,000	6,500

[a]Intersection locations.
[b]About 90 percent of flashing signals & beacons are at intersections.
[c]About 75 percent of lighting projects are at intersections.
[d]About 30 percent of reconstruction projects include intersections.
[e]About 40 percent of signing and marking projects are at intersections.

Total intersection locations = 1,160

TABLE 3

CALIFORNIA'S THREE-YEAR HIGHWAY SAFETY PROGRAM

Item	Rural		Urban		Total	
	Number	Percent	Number	Percent	Number	Percent
Miles of state highway	12,226	(86)	2,034	(14)	14,260	(100)
Total locations investigated	908	(19)	3,920	(81)	4,828	(100)
Total locations to be improved	450	(26)	1,275	(74)	1,725	(100)
Percent of investigated locations to be improved	50		33		36	
Total intersection locations to be improved	200	(18)	960	(82)	1,160	(100)
Percent of all improvements which are at intersections	44		75		67	

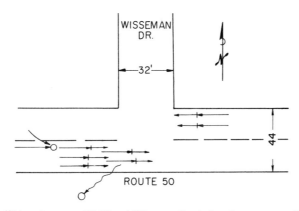

Figure 1. Collision diagram: US 50 and Wisseman Dr. before improvement (1-yr period).

146

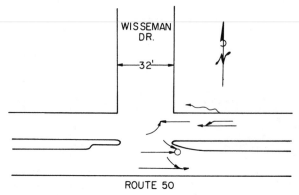

WISSEMAN DR.

32'

ROUTE 50

Figure 2. Collision diagram: US 50 and Wisseman Dr. after improvement (1-yr period).

with the accident rate decreasing 0.91 to 0.43 accidents per million vehicles entering the intersection, a 48 percent reduction. Rear-end and approach left-turn accidents declined from 7 to 1. If these intersecting accidents continue, concerning left-turning vehicles from Wisseman Drive, an escape acceleration lane could be provided in the median for this movement.

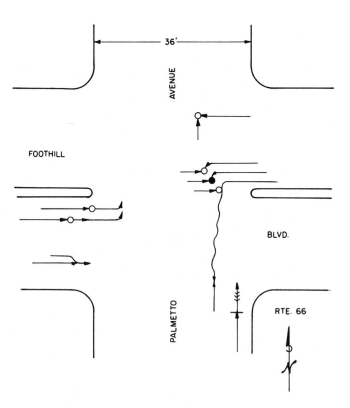

36'

AVENUE

FOOTHILL

BLVD.

PALMETTO

RTE. 66

Figure 3. Collision diagram: Foothill Blvd. (US 66) and Palmetto Ave. before improvement (1-yr period).

Because of a rather large number of accidents occurring at the Palmetto Avenue intersection on Foothill Boulevard, the City of Fontana requested that the State make a study for possible signalization of this intersection.

US 66 on Foothill Boulevard is a four-lane highway divided by a 4-ft painted median. Palmetto Avenue is a two-lane city street. After a traffic count, it was decided that there was not a sufficient volume of traffic to warrant the expense of signalization. However, it was decided to use painted channelization to provide refuge for left-turning vehicles which was accomplished by prohibiting parking on one side of this highway to obtain the necessary width for the left-turn lane.

Traffic volumes increased 5 percent from an entering ADT of 15,400 to 16,200 vehicles. Total accidents were reduced from 8 to 1 in equal 1-yr periods before and after the channelization with the accident rate (accidents per million vehicles) dropping from 1.42 to 0.17, an 88 percent reduction. Rear-end and approach left-turn accidents decreased from 5 to 0, indicating a high degree of success for this painted channelization improvement. Figures 3 and 4 show this improvement.

As mentioned earlier, it is not always possible to experience a significant drop in accidents. Sometimes judgment is inaccurate, and another type of improvement should have been made. For example, US 66, on Fifth Street, in San Bernardino, is a 64-ft wide, four-lane highway. Muscott Street, a 52-ft wide, two-lane city street, is the north leg of a T-intersection with the east-west highway. The ADT remained about the same at 16,000 veh/day for the one-year before and after periods.

In the before period (Fig. 5), seven accidents occurred, two of which involved pedestrians. Three were the rear-end type and involved vehicles turning left into Muscott. It was decided that painted channelization on Fifth Street could reduce this hazard.

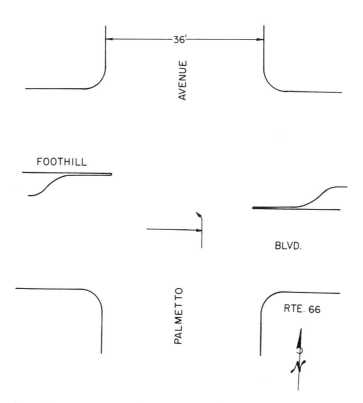

Figure 4. Collision diagram: Foothill Blvd. (US 66) and Palmetto Ave. after improvement (1-yr period).

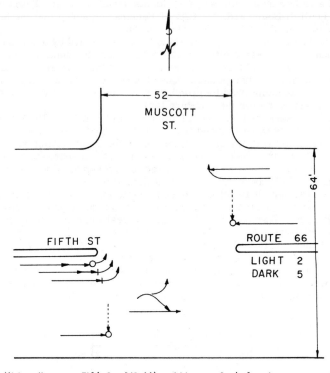

Figure 5. Collision diagram: Fifth St. (US 66) and Muscott St. before improvement (1-yr period).

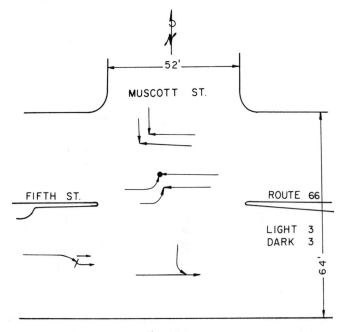

Figure 6. Collision diagram: Fifth St. (US 66) and Muscott St. after improvement (1-yr period).

In the after period (Fig. 6), six accidents occurred, two of which were the approach left-turn type. Both involved vehicles turning left into Muscott.

It appears that 3 rear-end accidents were traded for 2 approach left-turn accidents. However, when a day-night breakdown was made, it was discovered that 5 of the before accidents and 3 of the after accidents occurred at night. Part 2 "Safety Lighting" of the Evaluation of Minor Improvement Study recommends the installation of safety light-ing if 4 night accidents occur in 12 months, or 6 night accidents occur in a 24-month period. Since this criterion is satisfied, safety lighting should be considered at this intersection.

US 50 in Stockton has 2 intersections with a one-way couplet. These intersections have been signalized and lighted for many years with a one-lane left-turn movement provided from the State highway. The inside through lane of this four-lane highway was allowed the option of also turning left or going straight ahead at these intersections (relative to the signal phase). The electrical features were not altered appreciably when the optional lane was established.

Entering ADT at Center Street increased 15 percent from 28,700 to 33,100 vehicles with total accidents increasing from 9 to 16 and approach left-turn and rear-end acci-dents increasing 7 to 9. The accident rate increased from 0.88 to 1.33 accidents per million vehicles.

Entering ADT at El Dorado Street increased 19 percent from 31,200 to 37,100 ve-hicles with total accidents dropping from 19 to 13 and approach left-turn and rear-end accidents from 12 to 6. The accident rate decreased from 1.67 to 0.96 accidents per million vehicles. Neither of these intersections experienced statistically significant

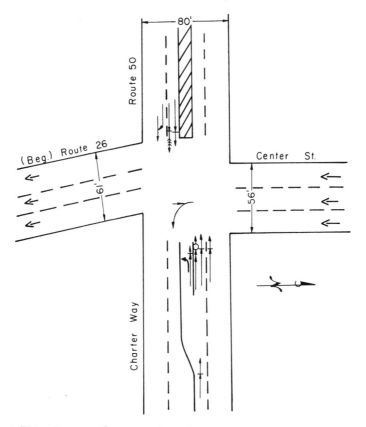

Figure 7. Collision diagram: Charter Way (US 50) and Center St. before improvement (1-yr period).

150

total accident changes thus indicating these changes could have occurred by chance. Figures 7, 8, 9 and 10 are before and after collision diagrams of these intersections.

A portion of the accident problem stems from the fact that when a vehicle in the optional lane wants to turn left and is waiting for the green arrow, it effectively reduces the highway to only one lane in this direction when the through traffic has a green indication. (The city police have been ticketing these drivers waiting for the green arrow for blocking traffic.) A better solution would be to add an additional through lane thus giving two mandatory left-turn lanes and two through lanes.

Something that may be unusual to some but which has been found very successful for years is the two-way left-turn lane through minor intersections. This treatment is reserved for locations where there are numerous private openings of low volume, and long blocks usually having low volumes entering or leaving the side streets. Where volumes are heavy, either at private drives or public streets, normal channelization is used.

To solve some problems at intersections, more drastic action is necessary. On what was formerly US 101 (Figs. 11 and 12) near San Diego, 5 intersections were blocked off by curbing across the median. Engineers are sometimes fearful that closing some openings would aggravate problems at others. In this case, 10th through 14th Streets were closed to left turns, thus forcing all vehicles to turn left at 9th Street and 15th Street which were signalized. The highway had an ADT of approximately 31,000 vehicles during both the before and after periods. Total accidents decreased

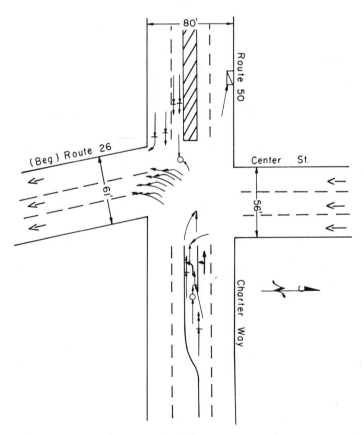

Figure 8. Collision diagram: Charter Way (US 50) and Center St. after improvement (1-yr period).

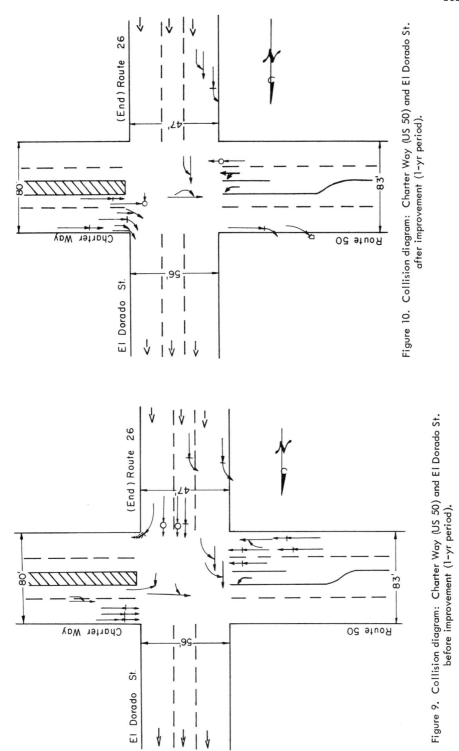

Figure 10. Collision diagram: Charter Way (US 50) and El Dorado St. after improvement (1-yr period).

Figure 9. Collision diagram: Charter Way (US 50) and El Dorado St. before improvement (1-yr period).

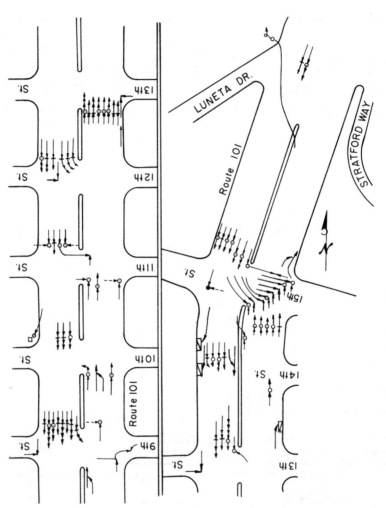

Figure 11. Collision diagram: US 101 in Del Mar before improvement (1-yr period).

153

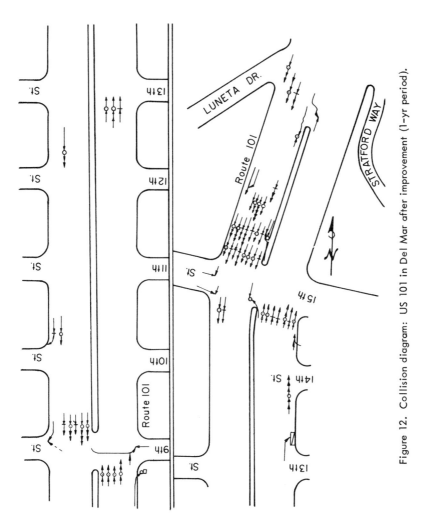

Figure 12. Collision diagram: US 101 in Del Mar after improvement (1-yr period).

154

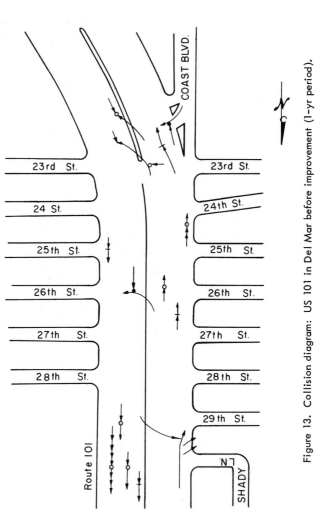

Figure 13. Collision diagram: US 101 in Del Mar before improvement (1-yr period).

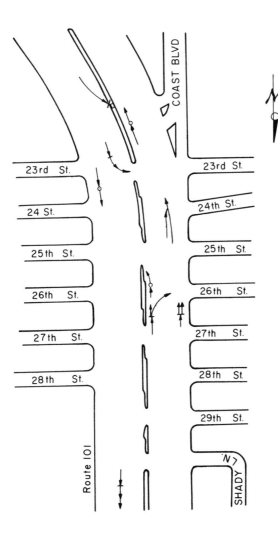

Figure 14. Collision diagram: US 101 in Del Mar after improvement (1-yr period).

from 83 to 60 with rear-end and approach left-turn accidents dropping from 56 to 50 and crossing accidents dropping from 16 to 3. There was one fatal accident and 40 injury accidents (75 injured) in the before period with 35 injury accidents and 47 people injured in the after period.

At another series of intersections (Figs. 13 and 14), every other block was closed in the median. This was also on US 101 in the same area as the previous example. There was a total of 7 intersections with 3 of them closed in the 1-yr after period. The ADT was the same as mentioned before with total accidents decreasing from 14 to 9 on this four-lane highway. Rear-end and approach left-turn accidents dropped from 10 to 7. Fatal accidents dropped from 2 (2 killed) to none while injury accidents dropped from 7 (17 injured) to 3 (4 injured).

Table 4 summarizes data at 40 unsignalized intersections with a breakdown of the types of channelization used to provide the protection for the left-turning vehicles. The methods used are paint, raised bars with paint, and curbs. The number of accidents are shown on the first line, the accident rate on the second line and the percent change in accident rate on the third line of the after period. The "S" indicates the change is significant at the 0.10 level of the χ-square test.

Total accidents and rear-end accidents were reduced significantly in all three types with raised bars and curbs yielding greater reductions than painted channelization. Lesser and insignificant reductions are noted in the left-turning accidents.

Table 5 is a rural-urban breakdown of the 27 painted channelized intersections. As might be suspected, much greater accident reductions are noted at rural intersections. Although rear-end accidents again were reduced significantly in both groups, urban crossing or broadside accidents were significantly increased. Perhaps drivers used the painted areas as a normal path in these heavier traffic conditions. Also, there is a possibility that these urban intersections did at the time meet the capacity requirements for a traffic signal.

TABLE 4

LEFT-TURN CHANNELIZATION

(Unsignalized)

			Total No.	Improved	Worsened	No. Change	Years of Experience	Ran off Road	Other	Sub-Total	Left Turn	Rear End	Crossing	Other	Sub-Total	PDO	Injury	Fatal	Day a/	Night a/	Total Accidents	Million Vehicles	Equivalent PDO (EPDO)	Severity Index (SI)
Painted	Before	No. of Accidents	27				31½	11	4	15	37	68	27	10	142	84	71	2	98	59	157	134.5	522	3.3
		Rate						0.08	0.03	0.11	0.28	0.51	0.20	0.07	1.06	0.62	0.53	0.01	1.09	1.33	1.17		3.88	
	After	No. of Accidents	27	2^s	0	25	31½	16	2	18	24	17^s	37	10	88^s	64	40^s	2	58^s	48	106^s	134.1	316	3.0
		Rate						0.12	0.01	0.13	0.18	0.13	0.28	0.07	0.66	0.48	0.30	0.01	0.65	1.08	0.79		2.36	
		% Rate Change						+50	-67	+18	-36	-75	+40	0	-38	-23	-43	0	-40	-19	-32		-39	
Curbed	Before	No. of Accidents	7				10	1	6	7	4	36	6	8	54	44	15	2	38	23	61	68.8	146	2.4
		Rate						0.01	0.09	0.10	0.06	0.52	0.09	0.12	0.78	0.64	0.22	0.03	0.83	1.00	0.89		2.12	
	After	No. of Accidents	7	3^s	0	4	10	3	1^s	4	4	4^s	10	3	21^s	22^s	3^s	0	18^s	7^s	25^s	77.7	40	1.6
		Rate						0.04	0.01	0.05	0.05	0.05	0.13	0.04	0.27	0.28	0.04	0	0.35	0.27	0.32		0.51	
		% Rate Change						+300	-89	-50	-17	-90	+44	-67	-66	-56	-82	-100	-58	-73	-64		-76	
Raised Bars	Before	No. of Accidents	6				9	5	2	7	11	60	6	11	88	54	40	1	67	28	95	66.4	300	3.2
		Rate						0.08	0.03	0.11	0.17	0.90	0.09	0.17	1.33	0.81	0.60	0.02	1.51	1.27	1.43		4.52	
	After	No. of Accidents	6	4^s	0	2	9	6	0	6	5	3^s	13	4^s	25^s	18^s	12^s	1	18^s	13^s	31^s	69.6	96	3.1
		Rate						0.09	0	0.09	0.07	0.04	0.19	0.06	0.36	0.26	0.17	0.01	0.39	0.56	0.45		1.38	
		% Rate Change						+12	-100	-18	-59	-96	+111	-65	-73	-68	-72	-50	-74	-56	-69		-69	
Total	Before	No. of Accidents	40				50½	17	12	29	52	164	39	29	284	182	126	5	203	110	313	269.7	968	3.1
		Rate						0.06	0.04	0.11	0.19	0.61	0.14	0.11	1.05	0.67	0.47	0.02	1.12	1.24	1.16		3.59	
	After	No. of Accidents	40	9^s	0	31	50½	25	3^s	28	33^s	24^s	60^s	17^s	134^s	104^s	55^s	3	94^s	68^s	162^s	281.5	452	2.8
		Rate						0.09	0.01	0.10	0.12	0.08	0.21	0.06	0.48	0.37	0.20	0.01	0.50	0.73	0.58		1.61	
		% Rate Change						+50	-75	-9	-37	-87	+50	-45	-54	-45	-57	-50	-55	-41	-50		-55	

a/ Assume 2/3 MV for Day and 1/3 MV at night for rate calculations.
"S" Indicates change is significant at the 0.10 level using the Chi-Square Test.

TABLE 5

LEFT-TURN CHANNELIZATION
(Painted)

			PROJECTS					ACCIDENT DESCRIPTION																
								ACCIDENT TYPE								SEVERITY			LT COND.					
								SINGLE VEHICLE			MULTIPLE VEHICLE								[a]	[a]				
			Total No.	Improved	Worsened	No. Change	Years of Experience	Ran off Road	Other	Sub-Total	Left Turn	Rear End	Crossing	Other	Sub-Total	PDO	Injury	Fatal	Day	Night	Total Accidents	Million Vehicles	Equivalent PDO (EPDO)	Severity Index (SI)
Urban	Before	No. of Accidents	12				12 10/12	4	4	8	18	34	14	5	71	43	35	1	45	34	79	67.4	259	3.3
		Rate						0.06	0.06	0.12	0.27	0.50	0.21	0.07	1.05	0.64	0.52	0.01	1.00	1.53	1.17		3.84	
	After	No. of Accidents	12	1^s	0	11	12 10/12	6	2	8	14	11^s	26^s	8	59	43	23	1	33	34	67	66.7	187	2.8
		Rate						0.09	0.03	0.12	0.21	0.16	0.39	0.12	0.88	0.64	0.34	0.01	0.74	1.54	1.00		2.80	
		% Rate Change						+50	-50	0	-22	-68	+86	+71	-16	0	-35	0	-26	+1	-15		-27	
Rural	Before	No. of Accidents	15				18 4/12	7	0	7	19	34	13	5	71	41	36	1	53	25	78	67.1	263	3.4
		Rate						0.10	0	0.10	0.28	0.51	0.19	0.07	1.06	0.61	0.54	0.01	1.18	1.13	1.16		3.92	
	After	No. of Accidents	15	1^s	0	14	18 4/12	10	0	10	10	6^s	11	2	29^s	21^s	17^s	1	25^s	14	39^s	67.4	129	3.3
		Rate						0.15	0	0.15	0.15	0.09	0.16	0.03	0.43	0.31	0.25	0.01	0.55	0.63	0.58		1.91	
		% Rate Change						+50	0	+50	-46	-82	-16	-57	-59	-49	-54	0	-53	-44	-50		-51	
Total	Before	No. of Accidents	27				31 2/12	11	4	15	37	68	27	10	142	84	71	2	98	59	157	134.5	522	3.3
		Rate						0.08	0.03	0.11	0.28	0.51	0.20	0.07	1.06	0.62	0.53	0.01	1.09	1.33	1.17		3.88	
	After	No. of Accidents	27	2^s	0	25	31 2/12	16	2	18	24	17^s	37	10	88^s	64	40^s	2	58^s	48	106^s	134.1	316	3.0
		Rate						0.12	0.01	0.13	0.18	0.13	0.28	0.07	0.66	0.48	0.30	0.01	0.65	1.08	0.79		2.36	
		% Rate Change						+50	-67	+18	-36	-75	+40	0	-38	-23	-43	0	-40	-19	-32		-39	

[a] Assume 2/3 MV for Day and 1/3 MV at night for rate calculations.
"S" Indicates change is significant at the 0.10 level using the Chi-Square Test.

Additional study has revealed that painted left-turn channelization reduces accidents as much if not more than physically protected intersections (raised bars and/or curbs) on highways where the zoned speed is 55 mph or greater.

One more type of improvement involving a signal is the complete removal of the normally used refuge island to protect a left-turn signal head. In one urban area roadway having four lanes with left turns at all signalized intersections, the problem was two-fold. Motorists were running into the islands and the snow plows (it was in a heavy snow area) were hitting the islands. This highway handled peak-day traffic of over 50,000. The removal of the islands necessitated the use of long mast arms for signal support. After data are not yet available, but it appears that accidents will be reduced and snow-plowing operations simplified.

CONCLUSIONS

The intersection should and will come in for more attention particularly where more effort can be devoted to reducing delay at signalized intersections. Pay-off in accident reduction may be great with separate turning lanes but simpler treatment such as relocating bus stops from the near to the far side, liberal restriction of parking near intersections, and proper control of driveways near intersections, may also help. Unfortunately, no before and after information was available at this time.

Addendum

PHOENIX, ARIZ.

A simple intersection improvement example is shown in the before and after collision diagrams (Figs. 15 and 16) for a pavement widening project in Phoenix. A factual study of the accident patterns identified a clear need for left-turn channels on 32nd Street. There was also considerable traffic delay and congestion. It was determined that four lanes of traffic plus a left-turn channel were needed.

158

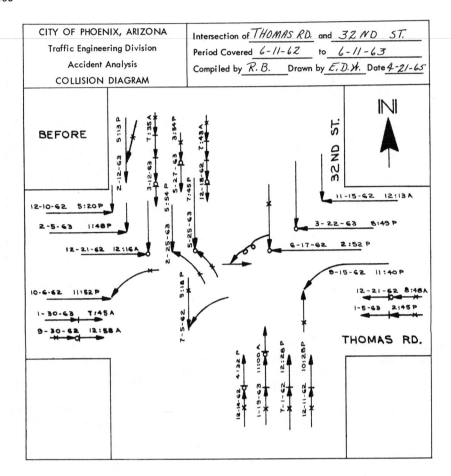

Figure 15.

It is important to understand that the foundation of much of the Phoenix major street system, to this day, is the old 16-ft wide concrete pavements installed in 1919. These have been slightly widened from time to time over the years. However, 32nd Street was essentially a narrow, two-lane road in both directions before this improvement.

The project was combined with several others to be included in a contract for street resurfacing and sealing and other bottleneck projects. Combining these projects re-

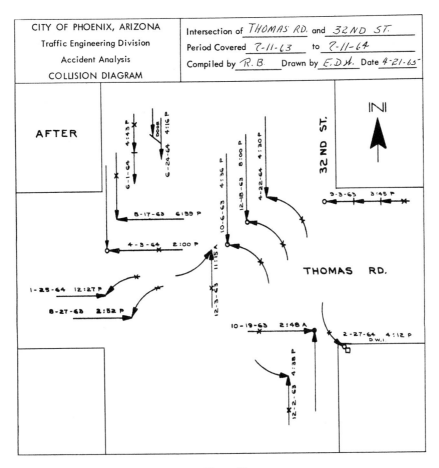

CITY OF PHOENIX, ARIZONA	Intersection of *THOMAS RD.* and *32 ND ST.*
Traffic Engineering Division	Period Covered *7-11-63* to *7-11-64*
Accident Analysis	Compiled by *R. B.* Drawn by *E. D. H.* Date *4-21-65*
COLLISION DIAGRAM	

Figure 16.

sults in construction savings, because the contractor is already doing work in nearby streets or intersections, and in this way, avoids duplicating moving-in and moving-out costs. The total cost of this improvement was $900.

Figures 15 and 16 demonstrate the effectiveness and economy of the bottleneck elimination program in reducing accidents and relieving congestion. This is a program that provides relatively great returns for relatively small investments.

Accident Reduction Through Channelization
Of Complex Intersections

JOHN F. EXNICIOS
City Traffic Engineer
City of New Orleans

The primary purpose of an intersection is to interchange traffic in the various cardinal directions. The amount of interchange movements depends primarily on the land-use activity immediately adjacent to the intersection. As intersectional traffic increases and turning movements are generated in larger numbers, it is often necessary to introduce special channelization to control traffic. This may be in connection with a traffic signal, or with other traffic control devices; such as STOP and YIELD signs. In many instances, the increase in the various turning movements at an intersection is accompanied by a similar increase in accidents. Proper channelization has been found to be an effective means of reducing the accident frequency as well as providing the additional capacity for the required intersectional movements. Three examples show how channelization has accomplished these objectives.

DEMPSTER STREET, SKOKIE, ILL.

Dempster Street (Fig. 1) in Skokie, Illinois, a residential suburb of Chicago, is an arterial connecting with an interchange of the Edens Expressway west of Lockwood Avenue. Before the improvement, parking was permitted on both sides of Dempster Street, which had a width of 56 ft. Gross Point Road measured 42 ft, and crossed Dempster Street diagonally at a point 50 ft east of Laramie Avenue. Gross Point is also a major traffic route, whereas Laramie is a collector. The intersection of Dempster Street and Lockwood Avenue is located approximately halfway between the Edens Expressway Interchange and the Gross Point Road intersection.

A peak-hour volume count from all six approaches at the intersection of Dempster-Gross Point-Laramie amounted to 3300 vehicles. A three-phase, fully actuated signal was used at this intersection.

During the 2-yr period, 1962 and 1963, there was a total of 197 reported accidents along Dempster Street between the Edens Expressway and LeClaire Street which is on the eastern end of the improvement project. Of these accidents, 143 occurred at the intersections, with 107 involving property damage only and 36 involving personal injury. Fifty-four accidents occurred at mid-block with 46 involving property damage only and eight involving personal injury.

Eastbound travel speeds on this section of Dempster Street averaged 16.5 mph during the a.m. peak and 17.3 mph during the p.m. peak. Westbound speeds averaged 23.4 mph during the a.m. and 18.5 mph during the p.m.

In 1964, a geometric redesign project was undertaken in order to increase travel speeds and to reduce accidents along this stretch of arterial road. Dempster Street was widened to four travel lanes divided by a barrier median between LeClaire Avenue and the Edens Expressway. Parking was removed from both sides of Dempster Street between LeClaire Avenue and the Edens Expressway. Additional left-turn lanes were provided on Dempster Street at three locations: Gross Point Road, Lockwood Avenue, and at a mid-block driveway entrance to a major parking facility serving a bowling alley. Gross Point Road was widened to four lanes divided by a median with additional left or right-turn lanes at the intersection of Dempster. A polyphase controller was installed. Additional improvements included the diverting of Laramie Street into Gross Point Road, south of Dempster, with a traffic signal controlling the point of intersection. North of Dempster, Laramie Avenue was posted southbound, was denied the through and left-turn movement, and was forced into a right turn into westbound Dempster. The intersection of Dempster and Lockwood was widened, channelized with medians, and signalized.

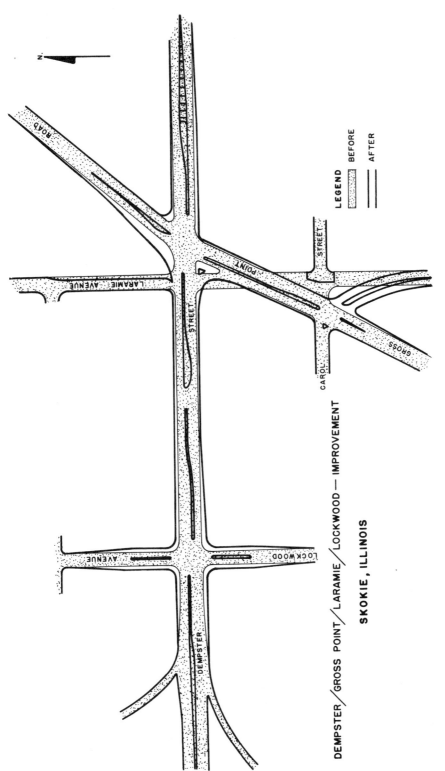

DEMPSTER / GROSS POINT / LARAMIE / LOCKWOOD — IMPROVEMENT

SKOKIE, ILLINOIS

LEGEND

BEFORE

AFTER

Figure 1.

An accident analysis for 1965 and 1966 indicated a 30 percent reduction in accidents as compared to the rate for 1962 and 1963. The 2-yr total of 197 was reduced to 139 after the improvements were made. Mid-block property damage accidents were reduced significantly from 46 to 25, with all accidents of this type being reduced from 54 to 40. All intersectional accidents were reduced from 143 to 99. The number of accidents involving parked cars was reduced from 25 to 3, and the driveway accidents were reduced from 17 to 4. These reductions are especially significant considering the fact that during the same period of time there was a 26 percent increase in accidents throughout the city.

Another significant improvement was travel speeds on Dempster Street were increased 9 percent during the a.m. peak hours and 20 percent during the p.m. peak hours.

AIRLINE HIGHWAY, METROPOLITAN NEW ORLEANS

In Metropolitan New Orleans, La., US 61 (Airline Highway) is the main connector between New Orleans International Airport and the CBD. This four-lane arterial carries approximately 40,000 veh/day, and one of the major cross intersections (Fig. 2) is David Drive (north) and Hickory Street (south). At this intersection the Airline Highway is divided by a 4-ft median; and Hickory and David are undivided, two-lane, two-way roadways with some minor right-turn channelization at the intersection. Approximately 350 ft west of the David-Hickory intersection, the Airline Highway crosses a drainage canal on a four-lane bridge. The intersection was operating beyond its capacity considering the extremely large number of left turns from Airline Highway into Hickory Street. Hickory is a main feeder into Harahan, a residential subdivision of New Orleans. Traffic was controlled by a semi-actuated, two-phase controller and left turns were permitted to move on the green signal.

During 1962, there were 64 accidents involving 39 personal injuries and an estimated property damage cost of $21,600. Of the total accidents, 43 were rear-end collisions, 9 involved left-turning vehicles from Airline, 7 were right angles, and the remaining were of the side-swipe and fixed-object type.

In 1963, a major re-channelization was accomplished in order to reduce the accident frequency. The location of the four-lane bridge immediately adjacent to the intersection created a difficult problem in the redesign of this intersection. The approach roadways of Airline Highway were widened and left-turn lanes were provided for each direction. A fully actuated, three-phase signal controller was placed into operation, and additional signal display was provided at the intersection. The total cost of this improvement was $40,000.

An after study showed that a total of 27 accidents occurred one year after the improvement as compared to 64 during the one-year before period. Personal injury accidents were reduced from 39 to 12, and the cost of property damage accidents from $21,600 to $5,900. Thus, total accidents were reduced 58 percent with personal injuries being reduced 69 percent and property damage 73 percent. The types of accidents which occurred in the year following improvement were 15 rear-end collisions, 4 right angles, and the remaining were of various other types. It was concluded that 39 percent of the improvement cost was off-set in the first year of operation due to the reduction of property damage alone without considering the reduction of personal injury.

BARKSDALE HIGHWAY, SHREVEPORT

In Shreveport, La., Barksdale Highway is a main connector between that city and Bossier City (Fig. 3). A regional shopping center is located on Barksdale Highway at the intersection of Dee Street in the southwest quadrant. This shopping center is a large generator of traffic and accounts for an appreciable amount of the traffic using the intersection of Barksdale Highway and Dee Street. Of the total 20,200 vehicles using this intersection daily, an appreciable amount would turn left from Barksdale into Dee Street. Barksdale Highway is a four-lane divided highway and before 1964, left turns were permitted from both directions into Dee Street. A separate left-turn lane was provided for the eastbound approach only. There are service roads parallel-

163

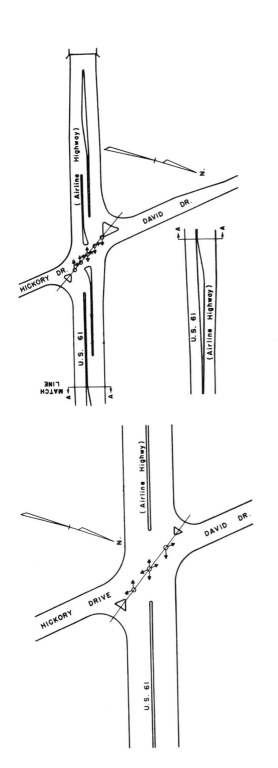

U.S. 61 (Airline Highwy)/DAVID DR./HICKORY DR.   U.S. 61 (Airline Hwy.)/DAVID DR./HICKORY DR.

METAIRIE, LOUISIANA   METAIRIE, LOUISIANA

BEFORE   AFTER

Figure 2.

164

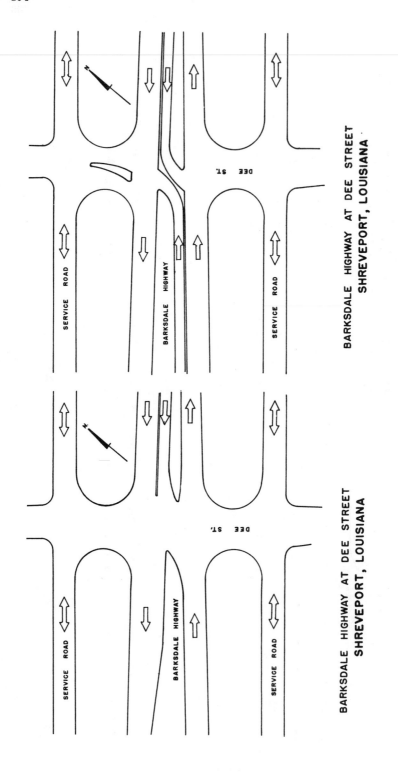

BARKSDALE HIGHWAY AT DEE STREET
SHREVEPORT, LOUISIANA

AFTER

BARKSDALE HIGHWAY AT DEE STREET
SHREVEPORT, LOUISIANA

BEFORE

Figure 3.

ing the main road of Barksdale on each side of the intersection. There is a high-level bridge on Barksdale to the east of this intersection. The north and south service roads connect under this bridge at a point just to the east of the intersection. The closeness of the bridge and the resulting grade on the eastern approach made signalization impracticable at this location. A 26-month analysis showed 18 accidents at the intersection. These involved 16 right angle, one head on, and one side-swipe accident. Of the total accidents, 15 involved personal injury and the cost of property damage for all accidents was $9300.

During 1964, a major redesign was accomplished at the intersection of Barksdale and Dee Street. The main improvement was the closing of the crossover in the center median prohibiting north-south movement on Dee Street across Barksdale. Left-turn lanes were provided for both approaches of Barksdale Highway and islands were provided on Dee Street between the service road and the main roadway of Barksdale. The total cost of the channelization project was $2100. There was not a single reported accident during the 26-month period following the improvement. This 100 percent reduction in accidents resulted in off-setting more than four times the improvement cost considering property damage alone. The reduction in personal injuries further increased this off-set value.

CONCLUSIONS

These three examples indicate the value of simplifying, by means of channelization, traffic movements through an intersection. They are also examples of public funds being expended wisely, with the motoring public reaping the true profit.

Addendum

WASHINGTON, D.C.

Figure 4. Example of a traffic circle underpass, 16th and M Streets, N.W., Washington, D.C.

Major Route Improvements

JAMES L. FOLEY, JR.
Commissioner of Transit and Traffic
City of Baltimore

Major route improvements fall into two general categories. The first is major physical improvements involving the expenditure of relatively large sums of money. The other is the use of traffic control measures either as extensive applications of one measure or a combination of several measures which together form a significant improvement.

Major physical improvements consist of widening, reconstruction, addition of medians, etc. The use of a series of traffic control measures is the second type of major route improvement. One example of this technique is the Wisconsin Avenue Study in Washington, D.C., which was presented in the BPR report "Increasing the Traffic Carrying Capability of Urban Arterial Streets." Another is the Jackson Boulevard study reported in Highway Research Board Proceedings, Volume No. 30.

There may be some feeling that the first category should not be included as a traffic engineering measure; however, many engineers believe that when street improvements are made, the traffic engineer should participate through the application of traffic engineering measures in order to obtain the greatest possible benefit. How he participates will vary depending on the type of organization in which he works. In some cases, he will be part of the highway or street department where he can exert his influence on the designer rather directly. In other cases, the traffic engineering department is completely separated, as it is in Baltimore. In this case, good liaison is required to assure that the best traffic engineering features are included in the design.

The effectiveness of an improvement can be measured by several criteria—the most important of which is probably accident reduction. Operating improvements such as increased capacity, improved operating speeds, and reduced delays are also important. The ideal solution would be one which resulted in improvements in all categories; however, the reduction of accidents without significant volume change or an increase in volume without an increase in accidents could both be considered effective.

In Baltimore, a major physical improvement was made to Druid Park Lake Drive. A 40-ft wide, two-way highway was widened to provide two 32-ft roadways with a 4-ft curbed median separating opposing traffic flows. Volume and accident data are given in Table 1, which is an example where the effectiveness of the improvement showed up as reduced accidents. The improvement may be somewhat more significant than would appear from figures, Table 1, because of a bias in the traffic count. This was due to a temporary closure of one of the major feeders from the north. During approximately one-half of the accident reporting period, this approach from the north was closed to traffic.

TABLE 1

DRUID PARK LAKE DRIVE[a]

Item	Before	After	Change (%)
Width	40 ft	Two 32-ft roadways plus 4-ft median	—
ADT	28,900	28,200	-2
Injury accidents	11	9	-18
Total accidents	39	30	-23

[a]Length of reconstruction, 1/2 mile.

It became apparent in the development of the data for this paper that before-and-after studies often require analysis of a complete system, or at least, an examination of what might be happening on adjacent thoroughfares. In the northwest portion of Baltimore, Jones Falls Valley forms a major traffic barrier. The character of the Valley limits the number of crossings possible. Two of these crossings are Northern

TABLE 2

NORTHERN PARKWAY[a]

Item	Before	After	Change (%)
Width	22 ft	Two 36-ft roadways plus 16-ft median	—
ADT	14,700	26,500	+79
A.M. peak hour	1,135	2,995	+172
P.M. peak hour	1,410	2,385	+69

[a]Length of reconstruction, 1 mile.

TABLE 3

COLD SPRING LANE[a]

Item	Before	After	Change (%)
Width	36 ft	50 ft	—
ADT	28,300	36,200	+28
A.M. peak hour	2,300	2,200	-4
P.M. peak hour	2,670	3,810	+43

[a]Length of major street widening, 3/4 mile.

Parkway and Cold Spring Lane. Both thoroughfares have been improved in recent years.

The Northern Parkway improvement was a major reconstruction of a magnitude which might be called a semi-expressway. It replaced a narrow 22-ft wide highway.

Traffic volume on Northern Parkway increased from an ADT of 14,700 before to 26,500 after. Additional data are given in Table 2.

Cold Spring Lane was widened from a 36-ft two-way road, to 50 ft. No significant alignment changes were made. While the Cold Spring Lane traffic increases were not as large, they were, nevertheless, significant. The daily traffic increased from 28,300 to 36,200, as given in Table 3. These significant volume increases occurred without a measurable change in accidents.

Widening roadways within the available right-of-way is probably the least expensive method of improving the capacity of a major street. Dundalk Avenue in Baltimore is an example of such an improvement. Before its improvement, it consisted of two 24-ft roadways separated by a wide median. The median was not particularly scenic, and in its early days, had been the right-of-way for interurban service to Sparrows Point. The improvement consisted of widening the two roadways to 36 ft and providing separate left-turn lanes in the median. Traffic data are given in Table 4.

Traffic volumes increased from 16,900 without transit vehicles to 20,250 including buses. Unfortunately, records do not show the improvement in operating speed, but a visual analysis indicates that the operating characteristics raised from level of service F to approximately D. The improvement raised the capacity of Dundalk Avenue to a point greater than that of the approach streets which supply traffic to it.

An example of the benefits obtained from limiting the opportunities for making left turns is the reconstruction of Skokie Boulevard in Skokie, Ill. Extensive commercial activity with numerous driveways resulted in a high incidence of mid-block accidents. Before the reconstruction, this type of accident accounted for 60 percent of the total.

The reconstruction consisted of widening a 56-ft two-way facility to two 36-ft roadways separated by a median with left-turn bays. Consolidating all turns at the cross streets required the addition of a multiphase traffic signal. The accident reduction was impressive, especially in the face of a city-wide increase of 26 percent. As would be expected, intersection accidents increased due to revised driving patterns. Data are given in Table 5.

TABLE 4

DUNDALK AVENUE[a]

Item	Before	After	Change (%)
Width	Two 24-ft roadways plus median	Two 36-ft roadways plus median	—
ADT	16,940	20,250	+20
A.M. peak	1,170	1,770	+51
P.M. peak	1,650	2,130	+29

[a]Length of reconstruction within right-of-way, 1 1/4 miles.

TABLE 5

SKOKIE BOULEVARD[a]

Item	Before	After	Change (%)
Width	56 ft	Two 36-ft roadways plus median	—
Total accidents	151	98	-35
Injury accidents	62	38	-39
Intersection accidents	59	75	+27
Mid-block accidents	92	23	-75

[a]Length of widening, $\frac{1}{2}$ mile.

In 1963 the remaining streetcars were removed from Baltimore. This permitted application of specialized traffic engineering techniques such as left-turn lanes and improved traffic signal timing. In a 4-mile portion of the York Road-Greenmount Avenue System, it was possible to use both techniques. At two locations where the street is over 50 ft wide, by the use of pavement markings the center 10 ft was allocated as left-turn lanes. In addition, a PR traffic control system was installed on the northern portion of the system. Data are given in Table 6.

In the morning peak, the trip time decreased from 18 to 16 min. In the afternoon peak, the improvement in travel time was slightly better, from 19 min before to 15 min after.

These changes occurred in the travel time while traffic volumes increased 29 percent, from 16,900 to 21,600 ADT. Peak-hour experience was even more startling in that the morning peak direction traffic volume increased 55 percent, and the afternoon outbound increase was a surprising 170 percent. Undoubtedly, the large increase in volume partially accounted for the small change in running time and delays.

An additional benefit, for which no numerical value can be given, is the elimination of left-turn traffic from several residential streets. In one of the cases where the left-turn lane was provided, the turns could be allowed during the peak hour. These had been prohibited before due to delays which they caused to the fixed-wheel transit vehicles. Based on after traffic counts, some 200 to 250 left-turns "loopers" were removed from the residential side streets, which are heavily used pedestrian routes for school children.

To show that all improvements are not necessarily going to be successful, there is the case of a street widened from a winding, two-lane highway to a less winding, four-lane highway which resulted in traffic reducing from 15,200 veh/day to 6900 veh/day. This reduction is not due to any inherent failure of the improvement, but

TABLE 6

GREENMOUNT AVENUE-YORK ROAD[a]

Item	Before	After	Change (%)
Inbound:			
Peak travel time	18 min	16 min	-11
Number of delays	8	9	+12
Total delay	5 min 12 sec	3 min 39 sec	-30
Peak-hour volume	730	1130	+55
Outbound:			
Peak travel time	19 min	15 min	-21
Number of delays	10	10	0
Total delay	5 min 23 sec	4 min 46 sec	-11
Peak-hour volume	570	1550	+170
ADT	16,900	21,600	+28

[a]Length of improvement, $4\frac{1}{4}$ miles.

rather to the concurrent opening of a parallel freeway. It is likely, however, that the money has not been wasted because the street serves an area which has a very high growth potential. Several large apartment buildings are now under construction.

CONCLUSIONS

In view of the increasing volumes all over the nation, it is apparent that we must continue to provide for this growth. The cited examples show that both techniques, reconstruction and extensive applications of traffic control measures, are required to accomplish this goal.

Addenda

PHOENIX, ARIZ.

Major Street Improvement Examples

24th Street—McDowell to Thomas. This street was reconstructed in 1962. Prior to this, it was a two-lane street which flared to four lanes at major intersections. The pavement width varied from 28 ft in mid-block sections to approximately 44 ft at major intersections. The street was improved to a 64-ft pavement width with curbs and gutters, and was marked for four lanes throughout. Left-turn channels were provided at all important intersections.

Accident Data:

Before (6/1/61 to 6/1/62):
   Total accidents = 29
   Accident rate = 5.86 Acc./MVM
After (6/1/63 to 6/1/64):
   Total accidents = 32
   Accident rate = 4.43 Acc./MVM (26% reduction)

Traffic Volumes:

ADT:
   Before (1962) = 13,600
   After (1966) = 23,100 (70% increase)
Peak hour:
   Before (1962) = 603
   After (1966) = 1383 (130% increase)

Travel Time (Average Speed):

Before (1962) = 23.3 mph
After (1966) = 26.8 mph (16% increase)

Cost:

Engineering   = $ 42,400
Right-of-way =   140,000
Construction =   293,100

   Total $475,500   Plus storm drain = $179,000

7th Street—Camelback to Bethany Home. This street was reconstructed in 1965. Prior to this, it was a two-lane street which varied from 25 to 35 ft in width along mid-block sections, and flared out to a four-lane street of 40 to 45 ft in width at major intersections. The street was reconstructed to a 64-ft pavement width with curbs and gutters. All curb parking was prohibited, and the street was marked for four lanes with a painted median which is converted to left-turn channels at street intersections.

Accident Data:

Before (9/27/64 to 3/27/65):
Total accidents = 28
Accident rate = 8.64 Acc./MVM
After (9/27/66 to 3/27/67):
Total accidents = 23
Accident rate = 6.46 Acc./MVM (25% reduction)

Traffic Volumes:

ADT:
Before (1964) = 17,900 to 17,600
After (1966) = 21,000 to 18,100 (10% increase)

Travel Time and Delay Rate:

Average speed:
Before (1962) = 25.2 mph
After (1966) = 30.2 mph (25% increase)

Delay rate:
Before (1962) = 296
After (1966) = none

Cost:

Engineering   = $ 31,100
Right-of-way =   157,000
Construction =   311,200

       Total $499,300

7th Avenue Railroad Overcrossing. This overcrossing was completed in March 1967. Prior to construction, this section of 7th Avenue was a two-lane street, approximately 30 ft wide along mid-block sections, and flared to four lanes at major intersections. Traffic was required to cross 17 sets of railroad tracks at grade along this half-mile section. The overcrossing was constructed to provide four lanes of traffic, separated by an 8-ft raised concrete median divider. A right-turn lane was added at the termination of the structure at its intersection with a major one-way street at the north end and a left-turn lane was provided south of the structure at its intersection with a two-way major street.

Accident Data:

Before (2/18/65 to 2/18/66):
Total accidents = 26
Accident rate = 15.6 Acc.

Traffic Volumes:

ADT:
Before (1965) = 10,900

Travel Time and Delay Rate—Before:

Average speed = 16.7 mph
Delay rate = 835 min/mph

Cost:

Engineering = $ 67,900
Right-of-way =   300,000
Construction =   1,295,000

       Total $1,662,900

TABLE 7

SKOKIE BOULEVARD—CHURCH TO SIMPSON

Location and Accident Type	Number of Accidents		Change (%)
	Before[a]	After[b]	
Stage 1[c]			
Intersections			
Property damage	13	37	+185
Injury type	20	22	+ 10
Subtotal	33	59	+ 78
Midblock			
Property damage	52	13	- 75
Injury type	31	8	- 74
Subtotal	83	21	- 75
Total Stage 1	116	80	- 31
Stage 2[d]			
Intersection			
Property damage	18	9	- 50
Injury type	8	7	- 13
Subtotal	26	16	- 38
Midblock			
Property damage	6	1	- 83
Injury type	3	1	- 66
Subtotal	9	2	- 78
Total Stage 2	35	18	- 49
Total All	151	98	- 35

[a]1962 and 1963 for Stage 1, 1962 only for Stage 2.
[b]1965 and 1966 for Stage 1, 1966 only for Stage 2. (Average annual number of city-wide accidents increased 26 percent from 1962/63 to 1965/66.)
[c]1800-ft length, including two major intersections.
[d]800-ft length, including one major intersection.

The before data show a serious accident problem combined with low average speed and relatively high congestion (delay rate). The after studies will be completed after a comparable time period has elapsed.

SKOKIE, ILL.

Major Route Improvement

Skokie Boulevard was a 56-ft wide north-south major arterial, without parking. Abutting land use includes a community discount center, a neighborhood shopping center, two restaurants, a motel, a large bowling alley, and a large indoor theater. Total parking of these uses is 2300 spaces.

It was widened to six-lane divided, with a barrier median and recessed left-turn bays. Access to abutting land uses was reoriented to a new cross street. This intersection was signalized.

Stage 2 extended the same design one block north to Simpson. The Simpson intersection had 3 three-lane approaches and 1 two-lane approach. Each approach was widened to four lanes, including recessed left-turn bays for all legs, and recessed right-turn bays on two legs. Peak-hour entering traffic at the heaviest intersection is 3400.

Relationship of Roadway Lighting and Traffic Accidents

MATTHEW C. SIELSKI

Director, Driving Environment

National Highway Safety Bureau

Sufficient reliable documentation is available to support the assumption that nighttime traffic accident rates are considerably higher than daytime. The National Safety Council has determined that on a mileage basis the accident frequency at night in urban areas is 3 times that during the day, and in rural areas it is $2\frac{1}{2}$ times higher. A study in Great Britain revealed that the ratio of accidents in darkness to those in daylight is about 3 to 4. Countless other studies made in cities throughout the country illustrate the disproportionate number of accidents at night.

There are many reasons for this unbalanced night accident rate. The following are but a few of the factors which cause driving at night to be hazardous.

1. The average person is poorly equipped to see adequately at night. This problem becomes more serious as one grows older. For example, the glare resistance of the over 65 years of age driver is one-third that of the 25-year-old motorist [1]. Persons at 60 years of age require eight times as much light as those at 20. Therefore, many of the driving assignments involving such factors as speed and roadway conditions become more difficult and hazardous to most drivers when confronted with darkness [2].

2. The physical condition of the average motorist must be recognized. Fatigue, drowsiness, influence of alcohol, and psychological aspects all have a definite influence on one's driving.

3. There is a lack of understanding by many motorists and pedestrians regarding the hazards of night driving. One study revealed that motorists drive faster in the dark than under roadway lighting or in the daytime [3].

The contribution of artificial illumination has been measured in many ways. Substantial reductions have been found in accidents and more significantly, in the serious or fatal rates. However, the degree of illumination necessary to bring about a satisfactory reduction in night accidents has not been scientifically derived. Nor is there an acceptable level of night-to-day accident ratio which would give assurance that proper steps have been taken to provide a safe night-driving environment.

Nevertheless, the provision for improved roadway lighting can bring about accident reduction by reducing some of the problems affecting the night driver. A study by the Texas Transportation Institute revealed that illumination reduces driver tension [4]. Another interesting effect on roadway lighting concerns alcohol and the driver. Since an increase of alcohol level decreases the visual field, an increase in illumination through street lighting may be effective in reducing night traffic accidents caused by those under the influence of alcohol [5].

The Road Research Laboratory has established that the improvement of poor lighting can be expected to reduce all such accidents during hours of darkness by 30 percent. The results also have indicated that fatal accidents may be reduced by 50 percent, and those in which pedestrians are involved by 45 percent [6].

Thus, in summary, it is acknowledged that night driving is hazardous due to many variables. Although we cannot accurately predict the degree of accident reduction through varied levels of roadway illumination, evidence is available to substantiate night accident reduction due to various before-and-after studies.

TABLE 1

EFFECTS OF RELIGHTING ON NIGHT FATAL ACCIDENTS

Street	Miles Relighted Since 1952	Night Fatal Accidents	
		3 Year Average, Before	8 Year Average, After
Western Ave.	23.5	10.33	4.37
Halsted St.	14.3	7.33	6.12
State St.	9.6	9.67	2.75
Diversey Ave.	6.3	3.67	0.63
Roosevelt Rd.	5.8	5.00	2.12
Michigan Ave.	7.2	6.00	1.38
63rd St.	11.0	3.00	1.12

RESUME OF BEFORE-AND-AFTER STUDIES

The following studies contain valuable information illustrating to some degree the success several cities achieved by installing new or improved roadway lighting.

Chicago, Ill.

Street Lighting Modernization Program. Since 1952, the City of Chicago has embarked on a street lighting modernization program on 77.7 miles of arterial streets which comprise about 10 percent of the total Chicago arterial street system mileage. The lighting units were designed for an intensity of 2.0 ft-c. Table 1 gives the before and after results in traffic accidents. The average per year of night fatal accidents fell from 6.43 to 2.64; this represents a 59 percent reduction.

Michigan Boulevard. A study of the effect of illumination on the nighttime accident rate of Michigan Boulevard revealed a substantial accident reduction, and was directly related to the degree of illumination (7). Table 2 summarizes the results of this study.

Chicago Expressway Study. A two-year study was made of 50 miles of freeways in the Chicago Metropolitan Area (8). The night-to-day rates for all accidents ranged between 1.3 and 2.0 for the lighted freeways while the unlighted had a ratio of 3.1. The night fatal accident rate for the lighted freeways had an average of 3.6 as contrasted to 12.5 for the unlighted. At least 100 lives have apparently been saved as a result of the lighted freeways.

Detroit, Mich.

This study was made on Evergreen Road which is a major street in a residential area. It is 40 ft wide with parking on each side. Street lighting was improved in 1964. The section was 1 mile long with a 35-mph speed limit. The ADT before was 9046; after, 9744. Illumination before was 0.6 ft-c; after, 1.0 ft-c. Table 3 gives non-pedestrian accident experience for one year before and after the lighting improvement.

The reduction in nighttime accidents from the number of accidents that would be expected without the lighting improvement is 14 percent. The total number of night accidents was reduced from 33 to 18 for a one-year period.

TABLE 2

EFFECT OF ILLUMINATION ON NIGHTTIME ACCIDENT RATE

Section	Illumination (ft-c)	Night Accident Rate (per MVM)	Reduction[a] (%)
River to 12th St.	0.14	17.9	—
12th to 16th St.	0.35	11.9	71.5
16th to 22nd St.	0.88	9.5	71.7

[a]The actual reduction in nighttime accidents from the number that would be expected without lighting improvement.

TABLE 3
NON-PEDESTRIAN ACCIDENTS BEFORE
AND AFTER IMPROVED LIGHTING

Accident	Before			After		
	Day	Night	All	Day	Night	All
Fatal	0	0	0	0	0	0
Injury	9	6	15	6	3	9
Property damage	30	27	57	19	15	34
Total	39	33	72	25	18	43

TABLE 4
ACCIDENTS BEFORE AND AFTER
IMPROVED LIGHTING

Type	Before		After	
	Day	Night	Day	Night
Non-Pedestrian:				
Fatal	0	0	0	0
Injury	38	34	24	40
Property damage	100	94	124	60
Pedestrian:				
Fatal	0	0	1	0
Injury	6	6	5	6
Total	144	134	154	106

The 14 percent reduction is derived as follows:

B = Day accidents before improvement   = 39
A = Day accidents after improvement   = 25
b = Night accidents before improvement   = 33
a = Night accidents after improvement   = 18

In estimating the effect of lighting, R is designated as the ratio of the <u>actual</u> number of accidents in darkness after the lighting improvement to the number of night accidents <u>expected</u> if the improvement were not made. Thus,

$$R = \frac{\text{Number of night accidents after improvement}}{\text{Expected number of night accidents}}$$

The expected number of night accidents without improvement is calculated as $b\frac{(A)}{(B)}$.

Thus,

$$R = a \div b\frac{(A)}{(B)} = \frac{a}{b} \div \frac{A}{B}$$

$$R = \frac{18}{33} \div \frac{25}{39} = 0.86$$

Therefore, the reduction in night accidents attributed to the improvement is 14 percent.

Washington, D. C.

Benning Road, a major arterial street located in the eastern section of the city, had its street lights improved from 0.24 to 0.83 ft-c. There were no installation charges for this improvement in 1964 since it consisted only of relamping. However, street light energy costs for the 2-mile section increased $4074 per year. Before 1964, the lamps were 6000 lumen incandescent. They were replaced with 10,000 lumen mercury vapor lamps in new luminaires.

The safety results of this improvement indicated a 26 percent reduction in nighttime accidents from the number of accidents that would be expected without the lighting improvement.

Table 4 gives the actual number of before and after accidents.

Cincinnati, Ohio, Study

In an effort to get a more significant understanding of the value of improved roadway lighting to accident reduction, a comprehensive study was undertaken in Cincinnati by the National Highway Safety Bureau in conjunction with the Traffic Engineering Division of Cincinnati. This study was under the direction of Joseph Lema, Traffic Safety Specialist of the Bureau.

TABLE 5
ACCIDENTS BEFORE AND AFTER IMPROVED LIGHTING

Accident	Before			After		
	Day	Night	All	Day	Night	All
Non-Pedestrian:						
Fatal	0	0	0	0	0	0
Injury	2	0	2	2	1	3
Property damage	34	13	47	36	8	44
Pedestrian:						
Fatal	0	0	0	0	0	0
Injury	1	0	1	0	0	0
Total	37	13	50	38	9	47

TABLE 6
ACCIDENTS BEFORE AND AFTER IMPROVED LIGHTING

Accident	Before			After		
	Day	Night	All	Day	Night	All
Non-Pedestrian:						
Fatal	0	0	0	0	0	0
Injury	0	1	1	4	1	5
Property damage	50	16	66	47	11	58
Pedestrian:						
Fatal	0	0	0	0	0	0
Injury	0	0	0	0	0	0
Total	50	17	67	51	12	63

TABLE 7
ACCIDENTS BEFORE AND AFTER IMPROVED LIGHTING

Accident	Before			After		
	Day	Night	All	Day	Night	All
Non-Pedestrian:						
Fatal	0	1	1	0	1	1
Injury	4	5	9	11	4	15
Property damage	63	19	82	80	17	97
Pedestrian:						
Fatal	0	1	1	0	0	0
Injury	0	0	0	0	0	0
Total	67	26	93	91	22	113

TABLE 8
ACCIDENTS BEFORE AND AFTER IMPROVED LIGHTING

Accident	Before			After		
	Day	Night	All	Day	Night	All
Non-Pedestrian:						
Fatal	0	0	0	0	0	0
Injury	3	2	5	2	2	4
Property damage	18	7	25	23	2	25
Pedestrian:						
Fatal	0	0	0	0	0	0
Injury	0	0	0	0	0	0
Total	21	9	30	25	4	29

Paddock Road

A study of the relationship of safety and lighting was made along three sections of this roadway: Reading to Tennessee, Tennessee to Laidlaw, and Laidlaw to Seymour.

Reading to Tennessee. The section is 0.9 mile long and 44 ft wide with a 40-mph speed limit. The ADT before was 12,000; after, 10,000. Illumination before was 0.1 ft-c, after, 0.9 ft-c. Table 5 gives accident experience for one year before and after the lighting improvement. Reduction in nighttime accidents from the number of accidents that would be expected without the lighting improvement is 33 percent.

Tennessee to Laidlaw. The section is 0.7 mile long and 44 ft wide with 30 and 35-mph speed limits. The ADT before and after was 17,000. Illumination before was 0.15 ft-c; after 0.90 ft-c.

Accident experience is given in Table 6. The reduction in nighttime accidents from the number of accidents that would be expected without the lighting improvement is 31 percent.

Laidlaw to Seymour. The section is 1.0 mile long and 44 ft wide with a 40-mph speed limit. The ADT was 13,000 before; 12,500, after. Illumination was 0.1 ft-c before; 0.9 ft-c after. The accident experience for this section is given in Table 7. The reduction in nighttime accidents from the number of accidents that would be expected without lighting improvement is 38 percent.

Thus, as a result of increased illumination in foot-candles from 0.1 or 0.15, to 0.9, the night accidents have decreased 33 to 38 percent.

Combining these three sections, the resultant statistics are for daytime: 154 before and 180 after, a change of +17 percent; for nighttime: 56 before and 43 after, a change of -23 percent. The reduction in nighttime accidents from the number of accidents that would be expected without the lighting improvement is 34 percent.

Plainville Road. This study was made along a 0.7-mile stretch between Madison and Bramble. The width was 40 ft and the speed limit was 35 mph.

The ADT was 10,600 before and 10,400 after. Illumination was 0.15 ft-c before and 0.90 ft-c after. Table 8 gives the accident experience. The reduction in nighttime accidents from the number of accidents that would be expected without the lighting improvement is 63 percent.

COST-BENEFIT

Regardless of the cost of lighting, a careful study in accident experience before and after lighting improvement supports economic justifications beyond the initial cost of the project.

A recent study of nine highway locations in Virginia revealed the following:

Three year cost of night accidents before	$584,000
Three year cost of night accidents after	143,000
Annual savings in accident cost	134,000
Annual cost of illumination	14,000

A similar comparison can be made of the improved cost-benefit of street lighting on the several miles studied in Cincinnati. It was previously stated that a street lighting improvement was made on Paddock Road. On this 2.6-mile section, existing light posts were used, and an extension arm and light unit were installed at a cost of $100 per unit. The results of the cost-benefit analysis for one year before and one year after is as follows:

Total night accidents before improvement	56
Total night accidents after improvement	43
Annual savings in accident cost	$33,900
Cost of initial illumination installation	7,300

In a motor vehicle accident cost study in Washington, D.C., it was found that the average cost of involvements occurring during darkness ($760) was much higher than the average for those occurring during daylight conditions ($430). Where street lighting was provided, the average cost of involvements at night was only $550 compared with $1340 at locations without street lighting. This is another factor to be considered in the cost-benefit comparison (9).

ACCIDENT REDUCTION VALUE OF LIGHTING

The value of street lighting can be measured in many ways. In addition to providing peace of mind to the traveling public, it affords protection to pedestrians, reduces crime, enhances street appearance, and most importantly, reduces traffic accidents. While no exact prediction can be made in night accident reduction in terms of illumination provided, it becomes prudent for any city to consider a program of improved street lighting where a high night-to-day accident ratio exists.

The Highway Safety Act of 1966 concerns itself with the high number of traffic accidents at night. As a result, a standard has been established for roadway lighting. It provides for the following:

1. A planned program to provide or upgrade roadway lighting at the following locations:

    A. Expressways and other major arteries in urbanized areas.

    B. Junctions of major highways in rural areas.

    C. Locations or sections of streets and highways where the ratio of night-to-day motor vehicle accidents is more than 1.5 times the average ratio for similar locations or sections on the same system of roads and streets.

    D. Locations or sections of streets and highways with high night-to-day ratios of pedestrian accidents.

    E. Tunnels and long underpasses.

2. The American Standard Practice for Roadway Lighting shall be used as a guide for roadway lighting design.

CONCLUSIONS

Any city that wishes to reduce its traffic accident experience will find a practical solution in a program of well-planned roadway lighting. Ample evidence is available to illustrate a reduction in nighttime accident rates on major arterial streets. The standards published by the National Highway Safety Bureau offer a guide for a proper installation.

REFERENCES

1. Marsh, Burton W. Aging and Driving. Traffic Engineering, Nov. 1960.
2. Sielski, Matthew C. Night Visibility and Traffic Improvement. American Automobile Association, 1965.
3. Oppenlander, J. C. Variables Influencing Spot-Speed Characteristics. HRB Special Report 89, 1966.
4. Keese, C. J., and Cleveland, D. E. Intersection and Sign Illumination For Highway Safety and Efficiency. Texas Transportation Institute, Aug. 1966.
5. Arthur D. Little, Inc. The State of the Art of Traffic Safety. Automobile Manufacturers Association, Inc., 1966.
6. Research on Road Safety. Road Research Laboratory, H. M. Stationery Office, London, 1963.
7. Wyatt, F. D., and Lozano, E. Effect of Street Lighting on Night Traffic Accident Rate. HRB Bull. 146, pp. 51-55, 1957.
8. Box, Paul. Public Lighting Needs. A Special Report for the United States Senate, 1966.
9. Wilbur Smith and Associates. Motor Vehicle Accident Costs of Washington Metropolitan Area, 1966.
10. Rex, Charles H. Roadway Lighting for the Motorist. Illuminating Engineering Society, Technical Conference, Minneapolis, Aug. 1966.
11. Christie, M. A. Street Lighting and Road Safety. Road Research Laboratory, H. M. Stationery Office, 1963.

Accident Trends in Cities
and
City Traffic Engineering Staff, Budgets and Responsibilities

DAVID M. BALDWIN
Supervisory Highway Engineer
Bureau of Public Roads

In 1966, urban traffic deaths accounted for 15,900 of the national total of 52,500 killed. The urban toll was only 30 percent of the total, and on a vehicle-mile basis, the urban rate of 3.6 deaths per 100 million vehicle-miles was far below the rural rate of 7.5.

The significant fact, however, is in the trend of urban deaths over the past few years as compared with the situation in rural areas. Table 1 illustrates these trends and clearly points out the emerging importance of the urban accident problem.

The trends in total urban deaths and in the urban death rate are significantly different from those for rural areas. Presumably they are a reflection of the increasing urbanization of the country. This has been adequately reported elsewhere, and it is sufficient to record here that during the decade from 1950 to 1960, the increase of our urban population accounted for more than 100 percent of the total growth of the country. (This was brought about, of course, by a decrease in the rural population.)

The types of accidents resulting in death changed markedly during the last decade. A comparison between 1955 and 1965 shows interesting and significant changes.

The significant points in Table 2 are the major differences in the changes, urban and rural, in two-vehicle and non-collision accidents. The increases in urban accidents of these two types far exceed the changes in rural areas, and are responsible for the fact that the urban mileage death rate remained nearly constant during a period when the rural rate dropped more than 12 percent. Table 3, a comparison by size of city, indicates that the problem is not uniformly distributed.

The comparison of death rates by size groups suggests that the largest cities (over 750,000 population) have experienced the smallest increase in accident rates; in fact their registration rate has actually decreased in the ten years from 1955 to 1965, although it still is higher than for smaller urban places. The largest increases in rates, on the other hand, have taken place in the cities from 100,000 to 750,000 population. Cities below 100,000 population have experienced increases, but not as great.

Non-fatal injuries in urban accidents are greater in total number than those in rural accidents. Three types of accidents account for a large part of the total: pedestrian, two-vehicle and non-collision. The differences between urban and rural experience are given in Table 4. The large number of injuries in urban two-vehicle accidents is immediately apparent. Similarly, although the totals are much smaller, injuries in urban non-collision accidents exceed those in rural non-collision accidents, though the reverse is true for deaths.

Data are not available to permit examination of the type of accident causing deaths and non-fatal injuries by size of city. It may be that the differences in

TABLE 1

MOTOR VEHICLE DEATHS AND MILEAGE DEATH RATES
(1955-1965)

Location of Accident	Deaths			Mileage Death Rate		
	1955	1965	Change (%)	1955	1965	Change (%)
Urban	9,390	15,000	+60	3.5	3.6	+3
Rural	29,030	34,000	+17	8.6	7.4	-14
Total	38,420	49,000	+28	6.4	5.6	-12

Source: National Safety Council. Rate is deaths per 100 million veh/mi.

TABLE 2

TYPES OF FATAL MOTOR VEHICLE ACCIDENTS
(1955-1965)

Type of Accidents	Urban Deaths			Rural Deaths		
	1955	1965	Change (%)	1955	1965	Change (%)
Pedestrian	5,200	5,700	+10	3,000	3,100	+3
Two-vehicle collision	1,900	4,700	+148	12,600	16,000	+27
Other collision	1,290	1,800	+40	2,330	2,800	+20
Non-collision	1,000	2,800	+180	11,100	12,100	+9
Total	9,390	15,000	+60	29,030	34,000	+17

Source: National Safety Council.

TABLE 3

MOTOR VEHICLE DEATH RATES, POPULATION
AND REGISTRATION
(1955-1965)

Urban Population	Deaths per 100,000 Pop.			Deaths per 10,000 Veh. Reg.		
	1955	1965	Change (%)	1955	1965	Change (%)
Over 1,000,000	10.3	10.7	+4	3.9	3.4	-13
750,000-1,000,000	10.3	12.0	+16	3.3	3.0	-9
500,000-750,000	9.8	12.8	+30	2.6	3.0	+15
350,000-500,000	11.1	16.3	+47	2.7	3.1	+15
200,000-350,000	10.1	13.9	+38	2.2	2.5	+14
100,000-200,000	9.5	13.9	+46	2.1	2.5	+19
50,000-100,000	9.0	9.8	+9	2.0	1.9	-5
25,000-50,000	8.9	10.8	+22	1.9	2.0	+5
10,000-25,000	9.0	11.2	+24	1.6	1.9	+19
All cities	9.8	11.7	+19	2.4	2.5	+4

Source: National Safety Council, based on reports by states and local authorities.

Note: Not all cities in the United States are included, but the samples are believed representative. Data for 1955 and 1965 are not necessarily based on identical cities, partly because some cities have moved from one population group to another during the 10 years.

trends in deaths and death rates are related to changes in patterns of accidents.

It is also possible that accident prevention efforts have not been undertaken in all sizes of cities on an equally energetic or effective basis. It must be emphasized here that there have not been any successful attempts to correlate accident experience with the commonly available measures of accident prevention. Thus, there is no opportunity to test an assumption that the largest cities may have carried on better safety programs. Least of all can we say they have had better traffic engineering work, valuable as such a conclusion would be to those devoted to the discussion and encouragement of traffic engineering techniques.

Recht, in his valuable multiple regression study, has demonstrated a correlation between death rates and certain isolated measures of safety work, but the one inescapable conclusion arising from a study of his work is that many of the most logical measures do not show any correlation. Two possibilities exist—we are doing the wrong things, or we have not developed good measuring devices for what we are doing.

To look more closely at the actual situation in cities, ten municipalities were queried on a number of pertinent points. Three cities were selected in the 50,000 to 100,000 population range, three in the 100,000 to 200,000 range, two in the 500,000 to 700,000 range, and two in the 700,000 to 1,000,000 range. In each case, cities were selected which reported a traffic engineer, and also some cities with high activity scores in the National Safety Council's annual inventory program and some with low scores. Responses are given in Table 5.

If any single point stands out, it is that urban accident experience has increased substantially in the past five years. This would of course have been expected on the basis of the earlier report of national trends during the past decade. In only one city— the smallest one examined—did the registration rate fail to rise 25 percent, and several of the increases were 75 percent or more.

TABLE 4

MOTOR VEHICLES DEATHS AND NON-FATAL INJURIES
BY TYPE OF ACCIDENT
(1965)

Type of Accident	Deaths			Non-Fatal Injuries		
	Total	Urban	Rural	Total	Urban	Rural
Pedestrian	8,800	5,700	3,100	140,000	128,000	12,000
Two-vehicle	20,700	4,700	16,000	1,230,000	760,000	470,000
Non-collision	14,900	2,800	12,100	330,000	95,000	235,000
All others	4,600	1,800	2,800	100,000	67,000	33,000
Total	49,000	15,000	34,000	1,800,000	1,050,000	750,000

Source: National Safety Council.

TABLE 5
SAMPLE CITY TRAFFIC DATA

Item	City A		City B		City C		City D		City E	
Population, 1966	53,000		72,000		72,500		172,000		142,130	
MV registration, 1966	17,858		39,754		28,891		72,335		80,000	
Street mileage:										
Freeways	—		7.7 (3%)		—		21.1 (5%)		28^a (7%)	
Arterials	?		73.4 (25%)		29.2 (16%)		103.2 (23%)		55.3 (15%)	
Others	?		213.4 (72%)		157.3 (84%)		330.7 (78%)		294.7 (78%)	
Total miles	140		294.5		186.5		455.0		378	
	1962	1966	1961	1966	1961	1966	1961	1966	1960	1966
Accident experience:										
Fatal	2	2	4	9	1	4	6	14	10	21
Non-fatal injury	376^b	696^b	260	395	?	?	825	1,207	771	715
Property damage	?	?	1,371	1,779	?	?	3,212	4,382	?	?
Total	1,263	1,365	1,635	2,183	2,135	2,540	4,043	5,603	4,362	5,031
Population death rate	4.0	3.7	9.7	17.9	1.5	5.9	4.7	8.9	6.7	14.8^c
Registration death rate	0.9	0.8	2.0	3.1	0.3	1.0	1.0	1.8	1.7	2.6^c
Traffic engineer reports to	City Manager		City Manager		City Engineer		Director of Public Works		Director of Public Services	
Professional TE staff	1		2		1		6		2	
TE operating budget	$41,258		$233,870		$30,600		$885,351		$259,152	
Capital improvement budget	$850		$1,140,000		$30,000		$119,000		$49,865	

^{a}Under construction.
^{b}Non-fatal injuries.
^{c}Estimated.

Greatest needs in the field of traffic engineering:

City A - Getting parking off main streets to improve flow. Wider streets (arterial and main) and traffic signals at several locations to permit arterial street vehicles to cross main streets. Adequate street lighting system on main and arterial streets.

City B - Construction of additional major street systems together with traffic control to improve the flow of traffic. Also, several street intersections need improving by channelizing for more capacity.

City C - Creation of a separate traffic engineering department with a staff; separate budget; full responsibility and authority to initiate and put into effect regulations improving traffic safety. Funds be made available for inter-connection and coordination of traffic signals, all of which are isolated at present. That the City Council and Mayor be made aware of the importance of applying traffic engineering techniques, and give the traffic engineer their support.

City D - More rigid enforcement of traffic regulations. Functioning safety council. Street lighting on arterial streets in outlying and intermediate areas.

City E - One of the problems encountered is the availability of qualified personnel (especially on the sub-professional level). Feel that more under-graduate courses should be offered in the field of traffic engineering.

Item	City F		City G		City H		City I		City J	
Population, 1966	131,000		500,000		670,000		713,214		940,000	
MV registration, 1966	.37,000		230,000		207,000		377,498		238,000	
Street mileage:										
Freeways	15.2 (2%)		15 (1%)		9 (1%)		98.5 (4%)		17 (1%)	
Arterials	109.3 (16%)		200 (20%)		265 (19%)		223 (10%)		450 (32%)	
Others	566.6 (82%)		800 (79%)		1,126 (80%)		1,963 (86%)		933 (67%)	
Total miles	691.1		1,015		1,400		2,285		1,400	
	1961	1966	1961	1966	1961	1966	1961	1966	1961	1966
Accident experience:										
Fatal	15	31	42	73	58	89	50	89	84	118
Non-fatal injury	653	1,233	2,114	2,634	4,458	8,121	2,910	4,537	5,952	8,708
Property damage	2,475	3,140	19,796	23,029	15,174	23,215	11,602	16,422	11,504	15,357
Total	3,143	4,404	21,952	25,736	19,690	31,425	14,562	21,048	17,540	24,183
Population death rate	11.5	25.4	8.8	15.7	9.6	13.3^a	9.5	14.1	9.7	13.3
Registration death rate	2.5	5.3	2.0	3.4	3.2	4.3^a	2.4	3.4	2.7	3.4
Traffic engineer reports to	Mayor		Director of Public Utilities		Director of Streets		City Manager		Mayor and City Council	
Professional TE staff	4		12		4		6		17	
TE operating budget	$275,000		$320,000		$436,284		$478,890		$3,000,000	
Capital improvement budget	$30,000		$300,000		$110,000		$51,105		$160,000	

^{a}Estimated.

Greatest needs in the field of traffic engineering:

City F - The greatest need in the field of traffic engineering is the acquisition and the retention of professional traffic engineers.

City G - More adequate financial and personnel resources for expanded program of upgrading, standardization, and improved maintenance of traffic control devices.

City H - To expand the scope and depth of present operations which would require an increase of staff and additional funding. Although the division is engaged in all aspects of traffic engineering, much more could be accomplished if more time and talent were available.

City I - Probably the greatest weakness is the inadequacy of the arterial street signal system. Much work needs to be done in providing progressive signal systems along the major arteries. We have surpassed or are rapidly approaching the absolute capacity of most major arteries. Widening and dividing these arteries is necessary to add more capacity and widening cannot be accomplished without acquiring more right-of-way. The Urban Transportation Study recommends a construction program of $145 million for freeways and $205 million for major arteries to provide a system that would be adequate until 1985. All we really need is money.

City J - Our greatest need would be the improvement of inter-departmental relationships. At times, it seems like we go around and around the same circle and never arrive at a decision. Another very important need would be a streamlined method of communicating with the Federal agencies, particularly in those areas which result in financial support. Lastly, we need some more vocal citizens speaking for the motorists. The anti-highway people manage to assemble very vocal groups, whereas with the exception of the motor club, there are very few groups who will stand up to be counted when highway plans are being fought over.

TABLE 6

ACCIDENT RATES, STAFF, AND OPERATING BUDGETS IN SELECTED CITIES

Item	City									
	A	B	C	D	E	F	G	H	I	J
Population death rate										
1961	4.0[a]	9.7	1.5	4.7	6.7[b]	11.5	8.8	9.6	9.5	9.7
1966	3.7	17.9	5.9	8.9	14.8[c]	25.4	15.7	13.3[c]	14.1	13.3
Change, %	-8	+85	+294	+89	+121	+121	+78	+39	+49	+37
Registration death rate										
1961	0.9[a]	2.0	0.3	1.0	1.7[b]	2.5	2.0	3.2	2.4	2.7
1966	0.8	3.1	1.0	1.8	2.6[c]	5.3	3.4	4.3[c]	3.4	3.4
Change, %	-11	+55	+233	+80	+53	+112	+70	+34	+42	+26
Traffic engineering professional staff,										
1966, No.	1	2	1	6	2	4	12	4	6	17
Per 100,000 population	1.9	2.8	1.4	3.5	1.4	3.1	2.4	0.6	0.8	1.8
TE operating budget, 1966 ($1,000's)	41	234	31	885	259	275	320	436	479	3,000
Per capita, $	0.77	3.25	0.43	5.15	1.83	2.10	0.64	0.65	0.67	3.19

[a]1962.
[b]1960.
[c]Estimated.

Increases generally occurred in fatals, non-fatal injury accidents, and in property damage cases, suggesting that the changes were actually in accident frequency rather than in accident severity. The data reenforce the conclusion that the urban accident problem is becoming more serious, and rapidly so.

Professional staff to cope with these problems is distressingly meager. On the average, these ten cities report 1.6 professional traffic engineers per 100,000 population, with the highest rate being 3.5 per 100,000. Two are below 1.0 per 100,000.

Traffic engineering budgets are similarly weak. On a per capita basis, the average for operating funds is $1.72. Table 6 indicates these relationships for each of the ten cities.

CONCLUSIONS

The significance would appear to be in the rather low levels of staff and budget. This conclusion is strengthened by the comments of the responsible traffic engineering people in each city in answer to the question: "What do you consider the greatest needs in your city in the field of traffic engineering?" The answers could probably be summarized as: money, men, and authority to use them.

Addendum

TORONTO, ONT.

Correlation of Pedestrian Fatalities and Vehicle Registration

In regard to the request concerning correlation, it was found that vehicle registration is so recorded that it would be an impractical task to separate those for the City of Toronto from those in the rest of "Metro." Accordingly, statistical analysis was applied to a correlation in all of Metro.

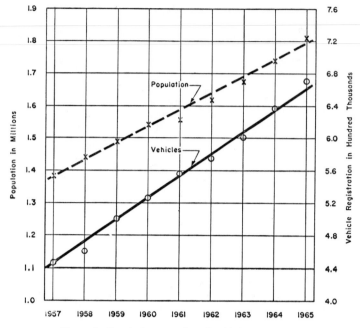

Figure 1. Population growth and vehicle registration.

The first test was to determine whether the change in pedestrian fatalities following the introduction of crossovers was a product of pure change or if the change was significant. In the city, the average number of fatalities in the 20 years prior to the introduction of crossovers was 51.2 per year. Following the introduction of crossovers, the average has dropped to 35.9 per year, a decrease of 15.3 per year or a decrease

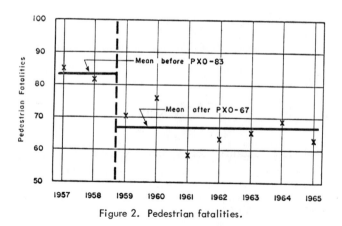

Figure 2. Pedestrian fatalities.

TABLE 7

COMPARISON OF FATALITIES, MOTOR VEHICLE
REGISTRATION AND POPULATION IN
METROPOLITAN TORONTO

Year	Fatalities	Motor Vehicle Registration	Population
1957	85	453,000	1,380,775
1958	81	463,000	1,429,031
1959	71	499,583	1,487,348
1960	77	524,562	1,527,105
1961	58	558,618	1,566,231
1962	63	575,376	1,618,787
1963	65	600,000	1,677,708
1964	69	639,187	1,741,411
1965	63	671,146[a]	1,802,006

[a] Estimate.

of approximately 30 percent. Applying the t-test indicates that this change is highly significant with a probability of only 1 chance in 2,000 that it had occurred by chance.

A similar test of fatalities for all of Metro similarly disclosed that the change was significant at the 5 percent level.

Demonstrating the relative change in population and vehicle registration as compared to pedestrian fatalities, Figure 1 shows the growth of population and vehicle registration. Between 1957 and 1964, motor vehicle registration increased by approximately 40 percent, while population increased about 26 percent. Indications are that this linear increase will continue for some years to come.

However, an analysis of pedestrian fatalities indicates (Fig. 2) that the number of pedestrian fatalities is neither increasing nor decreasing but varying about the average. To test this, a regression analysis was applied which indicated that, unless some innovation occurs, such as happened in 1959 when pedestrian crossovers were introduced, we can reasonably expect the number of pedestrian fatalities to vary only within the standard deviation about the present mean.

Since the number of automobiles is increasing linearly and the number of pedestrian fatalities remains constant, the rate of pedestrian fatalities as related to the automobile registration has been declining at the same proportion that registration is increasing, or about 40 percent between 1957 and 1964 (see Tables 7 and 8).

TABLE 8

PEDESTRIAN TRAFFIC FATALITIES
(Total)

Area	Year Before Crossovers																					After Crossovers						
	1938	1939	1940	1941	1942	1943	1944	1945	1946	1947	1948	1949	1950	1951	1952	1953	1954	1955	1956	1957	1958	1959	1960	1961	1962	1963	1964	1965
City of Toronto	50	44	60	70	48	81	63	73	53	49	50	42	44	43	55	47	52	48	46	46	52	39	46	27	37	32	35	35
Metro Toronto																				85	81	71	77	58	63	65	69	63

Delay and Travel Time Improvements as Related to Traffic Engineering Activities, Staff, and Budget

PETER G. KOLTNOW

Victor Gruen Associates
Los Angeles, California

There is a large and growing concern with cost effectiveness—with the payoff to be expected from alternative investments. The taxpaying public has recently shown a reluctance to support many local capital improvement programs. Public agencies are under substantial pressure to justify requests for increases in budgets and manpower by showing what benefits can be expected to derive from them.

Measurements of costs versus benefits have usually been made in relation to specific improvements. A good example is the cost-benefit ratio analysis which accompanies recommendations for freeway alignments. Much less work has been done in the area of assessing relative return on investment from different transportation schemes. Almost nothing concrete has been done at the local level to relate budget expenditures to the quality of services received.

This condition holds true in the traffic engineering field as in all others. Specific traffic improvement proposals typically include an estimate of the cost of improvement together with an analysis of expected benefits, usually in terms of increased capacity and safety and reduced travel time and user costs. While few cities routinely conduct travel time studies on a continuing basis, there are many before-and-after studies showing changes in traffic service brought about by some specific traffic improvement.

Little has been done to relate changes in traffic service to such things as increasing the traffic engineering budget and manpower of a community, or rearranging the traffic engineering effort to make it more effective. It has been generally assumed that a community with a traffic engineering organization can probably make more effective use of its streets than one without.

In the last few years, however, the question has been raised: "How much more effective?" Generally, the question is brought up by a city which has never had a formal traffic engineering effort but which may soon have one. These communities really want to know what the optimum traffic engineering activity is for a city of their size and nature. Requests are regularly received by the Institute of Traffic Engineers for information of this sort. There are three approaches that can be taken to give the answer.

One approach is to relate the quality of traffic service in comparable communities to the size of their traffic effort. A second is to survey present practice and assume the upper levels of staffing and budgeting to be adequate. A third approach is to compare changes in traffic engineering staffing and budgeting to changes in travel time within one or two cities over a period of time.

The first stumbling block to relating travel time and traffic engineering effort rests with the way in which travel time is measured in different communities. Some attempts have been made to compare travel time in different communities, but such comparisons offer more questions than conclusions. A recent NCHRP project by Alan Voorhees (1) listed work trip times and distances in 17 North American communities ranging in population from 40,000 to almost 7 million. Average travel speeds varied from 18 to 31 mph.

There was no clear relation between city size and average speed, nor did geographic location seem to make much difference. No information was given on traffic engineering effort in each community, of course. It is interesting to note, however, that the

TABLE 1

TRAFFIC ENGINEERING EFFORT VS TRAVEL SPEED

Metropolitan Area	Population	Travel Speed (mph)	Manpower		Budget ($)
			Total	Prof.	
Washington, D. C.	1, 568, 000	25	315	30	6, 500, 000
Baltimore	1, 600, 000	25			
Minneapolis-St. Paul	1, 377, 000	24	160	10	3, 800, 000
Seattle-Tacoma	1, 360, 000	25	174	13	2, 000, 000

"slowest" community was Pittsburgh, a city generally conceded to be the first ever to acknowledge traffic engineering as a distinct profession. The "fastest" city was Los Angeles, where traffic engineering was not a recognized function until the late thirties, about fifteen years after Pittsburgh had established the title of traffic engineer.

The Voorhees report is one of the very few which presents travel times in different communities. The report provides little substantial basis for a comparison of traffic engineering effort versus quality of traffic flow. Reason alone would suggest that comparing traffic flow in different communities is something like comparing oranges and apples. City age and evolutionary stage, topography, natural physical restraints, rate of population growth, and political climate each probably contribute more to helping or hindering traffic flow than do the size and quality of local traffic engineering effort.

There were five cities listed in the Voorhees report which had comparable populations. Four of them had almost identical average peak-hour speeds, with the fifth quite different. An examination of the staffing and budgeting of the four similar communities fails to show any appreciable consistency, supporting the theory that other forces affect the picture. Data are given in Table 1.

Another complicating feature lies in the fact that "traffic engineering" in one community may be quite different from "traffic engineering" in another. Some city traffic engineers have maintenance responsibilities and others do not. Some control street lighting budgets; others do not. In some, signal control improvements made as part of a large construction project are considered as traffic engineering expenditures. In other cities these expenses are buried in construction budgets.

Information from the Voorhees report has been combined with reports made to the National Safety Council in Table 2, which illustrates the relationship between commuting speed, traffic engineering expenditures on a population basis, and traffic engineering

TABLE 2

COMPARISON OF SPEED, BUDGET, AND POPULATION

City	Speed (mph)	T. E. Budget per Capita ($)[a]	Residents per T. E. Employee[b]
Los Angeles	31	2. 28	5, 460
Fort Worth	31	3. 24	3, 550
Tallahassee	30	1. 87	5, 800
Greensboro	30	2. 37	2, 350
Pensacola	30	1. 61	5, 060
Sioux Falls	25	2. 57	10, 900
Seattle-Tacoma	25	2. 53	4, 850
Baltimore	25	2. 46	4, 050
Washington	25	5. 82	2, 840
Minneapolis-St. Paul	24	1. 41	23, 400
Philadelphia	21	0. 82	11, 050
New Orleans	20	0. 64	13, 600
Chicago	20	1. 39	9, 520
Pittsburgh	18	1. 52	6, 560

[a] Budget for traffic engineering department includes materials, labor and administration.
[b] Includes all men regularly assigned to traffic engineering department, including registered professional, non-registered professional, engineer in training, subprofessional, and others.

TABLE 3

LOS ANGELES TRAFFIC DEPARTMENT

Year	Total Manpower	Budget ($)	Travel Speed[a] (mph)
1957	406	3,600,000	24
1960	421	4,200,000	26
1962	421	5,100,000	30
1965	481	5,800,000	32

[a]Average peak hour.

manpower on a population basis. There is substantial variation in traffic engineering budget per resident in communities with comparable commuting speeds. However, as a group, cities with commuting speeds under 25 mph have a per capita traffic budget of less than half of that found in cities with commuting speeds over 25 mph.

It is also possible to compare staffing in cities of the same size, and make subjective judgments about their travel times. The unpublished report (2) of ITE Technical Committee 2D(63) compared allocation of manpower in eleven cities in three population categories. There was a tremendous range in the traffic engineering effort expended in cities of comparable size. For instance, among three cities in the 125,000 population group, the city with the upper level of total manpower devoted to traffic engineering functions showed 17 times the effort of the lower level city. Even when considering professional manpower alone, the upper level city used over five times the manpower of the lower level one. It is most unlikely that travel times in these communities varied to the same degree.

The third approach to assessing the traffic flow benefits to accrue from increased traffic engineering work is to compare changes in travel time to changes in manpower or budgeting in a single community. There are problems here, as well. There are very few cities in which travel time has been measured over a substantial number of years. Even in those where such information has been collected, it is difficult to come to grips with whose traffic engineering effort is being measured, or to judge the effect of other activities taking place over the same period of time.

For instance, reasonably good travel time data are available for the Los Angeles area from 1957 to 1965. Los Angeles City traffic engineering expenditures are also available for the same period. Trend information is given in Table 3.

Obviously, travel times have improved at the same time that the Traffic Department has expanded. There is nothing to show any direct relation between the two, although we would like to think so, of course. During these same years other important changes were taking place. The freeway system grew from 122 miles to 372 miles. Many smaller cities in the area added to their traffic engineering staffs, and substantial sums of money were spent for local street improvements. Surely all these things also had a substantial effect on movement in the community. It is impossible to single out any one of them and ascribe a quantitative value to its impact.

The City of San Diego has also made travel time studies over a period of time. The average peak-hour speed there improved from 18 mph in 1955 to 39 mph in 1964 (3). The change included an 11-mph improvement from 1961 to 1964 alone. The report on the latest study there ascribed the sudden recent improvement largely or entirely to the completion of 25 miles of freeway. It has not been possible to gage the changes in travel time on local streets, where traffic engineering operational changes generally have the greatest impact.

This last point leads into another area entirely—the definition of traffic engineering. In many minds, traffic engineering is still largely an operational activity in which certain principles of traffic control and regulation are brought to bear on existing streets. If this is a valid point of view, then the measurable effect of traffic engineering on a community will be most pronounced shortly after the traffic organization first comes into existence. Traffic engineering is flashiest when it is new, when the operational skills of the profession can be quickly, cheaply and more or less painlessly applied to an overcrowded street system. In such cases, a single traffic engineer can have a substantial effect with a few simple tools and some political backing. As traffic flow improves, however, it becomes harder to improve upon without making more expensive changes or additions to the road system.

Most traffic engineers would be reluctant to limit their professional work to operations. In analyzing traffic engineering functions in cities of 80,000 to 200,000 population, ITE Technical Committee 2H(60) defined eight major areas of interest (4).

1. Surveys and studies related to transportation planning,
2. Transportation planning and programming,
3. Surveys and studies related to traffic operations,
4. Traffic controls and driver aids,
5. Parking and standing,
6. Street use,
7, Design, and
8. Miscellaneous functions.

In cities of this size category, traffic engineers were actually responsible for only slightly more than 50 percent of these essential activities. Traffic engineers were indeed most strongly oriented toward operations, having about 80 percent of the responsibility in this category of work. They had fewest responsibilities in design and planning.

All this suggests that the contributions of traffic engineers, while undoubtedly related to size of organization and budget, are also related to positioning in a municipal agency. This has been particularly well pointed out in another unpublished report (5), that of ITE Committee 2A(62), on the rule-making authority of city traffic engineers. This committee investigated traffic engineering authority in the narrow field of traffic regulation—at the heart of traffic operational activity. In this one area, where traffic engineers might be expected to have established themselves, they had regulatory authority over traffic only 40 percent of the time. In none of the 21 sub-categories in the field of traffic regulation did traffic engineers have authority as much as two-thirds of the time.

The report went on further to point out that the traffic engineering function could be found in any one of at least five positions within city hall, and the traffic engineer himself might report to any one of five different people, ranging from the mayor to the chief of police.

A broader view of traffic engineering holds that there is a wide variety of skills and experiences that a traffic engineer can bring to bear on existing and potential traffic problems. Operational contributions are important, but by no means predominant. Traffic engineering viewpoints brought to bear at the planning stage of road work or land-use change obviously offer many advantages in the interests of efficient traffic flow, although the payoff may lie years ahead and be difficult to relate to manpower at the time of improvement. Another difficulty with measuring the traffic effect of traffic planning activities lies in the fact that many, if not most of these effects, result in problems not arising, rather than in the correction of those that do. In times of great urban growth, unchanging travel times in the face of population increase may signify a substantial traffic improvement.

While traffic engineers still have largely a peripheral impact on highway design, usually in advice relating to channelization and intersection control, the traffic engineering attitude may be seen at work even when a traffic engineer is absent. This attitude reflects a substantial history of feedback from observations of traffic behavior under a variety of conditions. The feedback may be formal, in the form of reports, or informal, in the form of casual observations shared by inquisitive people.

While the traffic engineer should be so positioned in city government that he has an opportunity to comment on highway design work, he seldom if ever has the final decision to make. His success will depend on the traffic orientation of the designer. To this extent, traffic flow is a function of nontraffic engineers, whose attitudes are harder to measure than their budgets.

Once the first flush of traffic engineering success is achieved in a community where traffic engineering is a new experience, the traffic engineer's positioning becomes as important as the size of his staff. The next stage of traffic improvement involves the spending of highway funds where they will have the greatest traffic impact. To be effective in this area, the traffic engineer needs to have a prominent place in establishing capital improvement priorities. Ideally he will help to construct the basic priority system, if any, and will thereafter be responsible for measuring relative traffic needs. This requires staff for measuring purposes, obviously. More importantly, it requires that there be substantial political and technical support for the concept that traffic improvements are among the most important justifications for highway construction.

CONCLUSIONS

The importance of positioning and municipal interrelationships as they affect traffic engineering and its measurable products suggests that hard and fast rules of staffing, budgeting and activities may be a secondary concern. It is conceivable, for instance, that traffic can flow smoothly even in the absence of any formal traffic engineering unit, if traffic engineering skills are basic in other engineering, planning and enforcement groups.

What is important is that those responsible for reviewing and approving land-use changes understand the traffic impact of their decisions, that estimated traffic benefits be a significant factor in decisions on where to spend highway funds, that highway designs reflect a clear understanding of the known interrelationships among road, car, driver and pedestrian, and that traffic regulations and controls should reflect observed and measured conditions.

REFERENCES

1. Voorhees, Alan M. Factors and Trends in Trip Lengths. NCHRP Project 7-4, Highway Research Board (in press).
2. ITE. Allocation of Manpower. Unpublished report of Committee 2D(63), 1966.
3. San Diego Transportation and Traffic Engineering Division. Results of Travel Time Study—1964. Report to the San Diego Metropolitan Area Transportation Study, 1965.
4. ITE. Traffic Engineering Functions. Report of Committee 2H(60), Traffic Engineering, Vol. 33, No. 10, pp. 54-57, July 1963.
5. ITE. Rule Making Authority of City Traffic Engineers. Unpublished report of Committee 2A(62), 1965.
6. Homburger, Wolfgang S. Traffic Engineering Organization and Staffing in California Cities and Counties—1963. ITTE, University of California, Berkeley, May 1963.
7. How To Implement a Program of Traffic Engineering and Roadway Improvements in Your Community. A Public Support Guide, National Safety Council, 1965.
8. ITE. The Present and Future Need for Professional Traffic Engineers. Report of Committee 2F(61), Traffic Engineering, Vol. 34, No. 6, pp. 42-44, March 1964.
9. President's Committee for Traffic Safety. Engineering—A Section of the Action Program for Highway Safety. U. S. Government Printing Office, 1963.
10. Traffic Engineering Functions and Administration. Public Administration Service, Chicago, 1953. (Out of print.)

Land-Use Controls

WILLIAM MARSTON
Deputy Commissioner
Department of Development and Planning
City of Chicago

Today's urban problems are so grave that there can be no let up in cooperation of the traffic engineer and the land-use planner. There is a great force that is pushing new development into the suburbs. This force is powered by the effort of home and factory owners to get away from spreading slums. Countering this outward thrust is the desire of urban-oriented influences to rebuild and renew the city center. It is considered imperative that past mistakes be corrected and the city be renewed. Every effort must also be made to insure that the costly mistakes made in the older areas are not repeated in the new territories.

The city planner and the traffic engineer have great responsibility. They must develop programs for established cities that will reclaim the older areas and yet they must not make mistakes in the newer areas. In correcting past mistakes, the cure must not drive out established residents and businesses or discourage new ones from coming in.

There can be no doubt that poorly planned land areas create chaotic traffic conditions. Homogeneous commercial centers, residential areas, or industrial areas, if properly located and planned, will produce traffic patterns that are better and safer.

Fortunately there is a new awareness of the need for coordinating traffic engineering and land planning. There is less difficulty now in controlling locations of traffic generators. Traffic serving them can now be more adequately controlled. There is another very important positive trend and that is the willingness of designers of facilities such as schools, parks, parking garages, and housing to better relate them to traffic safety and efficiency.

The progress to date in this regard has been dimmed by the tremendous amount of bad planning and bad traffic engineering that exists. The process of correcting these errors will be slow and costly.

The basic objective for an urban area should be to "improve the quality of life," or to "make the city a better place to live, work, and pursue happiness." This objective implies a safer and better environment. These implications require that traffic engineering and land planning be carried out as a team effort.

Having agreed to the basic objective of improving the quality of life in a community, there are specific policies that are needed. Rules that promote these policies should be developed. These rules concern driveway design, curb controls, and so on.

Two equally important major policies that should be recognized are: land uses should be so oriented as to reduce traffic conflict and streets should be planned to improve their environmental influences. With these policies in mind it is possible to prepare a series of statements that can aid materially in achieving the major goal of improved quality of life. Such goals are a usual part of a good comprehensive plan.

A sample set of policies follows this paper. Each policy statement sets forth one or more goals that relate directly to a particular kind of traffic generator or to a particular thing that will affect traffic. For example, there are two goals contained in the statement for "Off-street Parking and Driveways in the Central Area" that reflect overall city policy. These goals are: (a) minimize vehicular and pedestrian movement conflicts within the core by decreasing unnecessary street traffic volumes, and (b) retain the compact functional development of the core area by minimizing the use of land devoted to storage space for motor vehicles.

TABLE 1

COMMERCIAL DRIVEWAY ACCIDENTS RELATED TO TURNING MOVEMENTS

Item	Left		Right		Total		All
	In	Out	In	Out	In	Out	
Number of accidents	378	271	149	137	527	408	935
Percent of total	40	29	16	15	56	44	100
Summary percent	69		31				

Source: Unpublished study, 5-year record, 31.5 miles of major traffic routes, 315 establishments, 567 driveways.

A policy statement on school access establishes school location to achieve the least traffic congestion and the greatest safety. Covered also are pedestrian access and vehicular access.

A general city-wide policy statement on parking and loading reflects goals for reducing congestion, improving environment and increasing safety. Other facilities are also covered by similar statements. These include: "Location of and Access to Police, Fire and Emergency Service Buildings, " "Recreational Parking Facility Design, " "Entrances to Recreational Facilities, " "Periphery Treatment of Parking Facilities, " "Walkways in the Public Way, " and "Fire Lanes. "

In addition to these policy statements some of the city codes reflect basic city policies. For example, the zoning law controls parking facilities and loading areas in connection with new construction. The traffic code includes driveway standards.

In the larger cities it would not be possible for the traffic engineer to be personally involved with every site planning activity. It would be desirable, therefore, to issue policy statements. Statements such as these will make developers, architects, and others aware of the proper design and forewarn them of delays in securing approvals. On the other hand, the traffic engineer should involve himself early in development plans. He should evaluate the site and guide the selection. Internal circulation has an effect on the entrances and exits and needs to be given close attention. He must do all possible to insure conformance with regulations and standards.

There can be no argument that driveways entering major streets create points of accident and congestion. These are actually intersections and as such are potentially dangerous. In crossing a sidewalk an automobile may interfere with pedestrians and create a hazardous condition. Much of the objection to driveways along major streets, particularly in dense urban areas, is the interference to the movement of pedestrians. The inconvenience to pedestrians who are forced to walk around autos standing across a sidewalk is an important consideration in large cities.

Adequate national studies of driveway design (width and radii related to location, major street volume and driveway volume) have not been located. Several studies in the Chicago suburb of Skokie have developed information such as given in Table 1. This study found that inbound movements caused somewhat more accidents than outbound movements. More importantly, the high significance of the left-turn accident hazard is illustrated.

One of the best methods of controlling the left-turn movement along major traffic routes is by a barrier median. To illustrate the accident difference, 5. 7 miles of these

TABLE 2

MAJOR ROUTE DRIVEWAY ACCIDENT ANALYSIS

Item	Service Stations	Commercial and Industrial	Residential	Alleys
Number of openings	175	452	569	42
Annual accident frequency per opening	0. 15	0. 27	0. 02	0. 05
Percent of injury accidents involving left turns	75	81	17	0

Source: Unpublished study, 2-year record, 39.7 miles of major traffic routes, 1238 driveways.

routes having barrier median were separately analyzed. The annual accident frequency was 0. 13 per commercial driveway, compared with 0. 36 per driveway for the routes without such a median.

The ADT of the routes with barrier median ranged from 12, 000 to 15, 000, while the remaining street ADT range was 5, 000 to 25, 000. The street volumes were typical, but the driveway activities were not necessarily comparable, and thus a direct 3 to 1 accident relation is not fully established. To test the actual effect of blocking left turns a before-and-after study was made on one major route improvement project. The driveway accident frequency was 132 per mile per year in the before period, versus 12 per mile per year in the after period.

In Skokie, studies were also conducted of accident frequencies by type of establishment, and accident severity. A summary of these data is given in Table 2, which indicates the great differences between accident frequencies at residential and commercial driveways, as well as the high injury producing significance of left turns.

Data from the study are also available to compare property damage and injury annual accident per driveway frequencies along routes with and without barrier medians:

With Barrier Median		Uncontrolled	
P. D.	Inj.	P. D.	Inj.
0. 013	0. 005	0. 116	0. 05

This study showed 11 times as many property damage accidents and 9 times as many injury accidents along streets without a barrier median. As the low annual accident frequency per driveway (about 1 per $7\frac{1}{2}$ years on the overall average) may be misleading, it should be pointed out that driveway accidents account for 11 percent of all major street accidents in the subject city, and 9 percent of the minor (local) street accidents.

The significance of pedestrian accidents, as related to driveways, warrants detailed study. In Skokie, only 1. 4 percent of driveway accidents involved vehicles striking pedestrians or bicycle riders. A higher rate would be certainly expected in a larger city with far greater pedestrian activity. The question of whether to design driveways about automobile needs (greater width and radii), or pedestrian needs (narrow width at the sidewalk) remains unanswered for the larger city. It may well be that different standards are needed for various areas of any city.

A reasonable standard for driveways to important generators where pedestrian travel is heavy is as follows: The width for passenger cars should be 24 ft and for commercial vehicles 35 ft measured at the property line. The minimum distance between driveways must be 10 ft and the minimum angle of entrance into the roadway should be 45 degrees. There should be ample sight distance; 20 ft between emerging point and the roadway curb and 10 ft from emerging point to the inner edge of the sidewalk being recommended as a minimum.

Driveways that exit or enter a street parallel and adjacent to the roadway are practical and can offer some advantages in certain cases. This system can be used when buildings are set well back so that there is enough space for pedestrians to walk between the driveway and the building. In this case, no pedestrian conflict is experienced and vehicles merge with the traffic stream normally.

The minimum amount of access to major streets from subdivisions is desired. Where possible, connections should exist at signal points—those which permit progressive signal timing along the major street. Where this cannot be accomplished, the entrance should be designed to restrict vehicles to right turns in and right turns out. Signal spacing of about one-fourth mile can provide reasonably good signal timing. No traffic crossing points should be permitted elsewhere either from driveways or access streets. Access points along major streets whether for driveways or minor streets create somewhat similar problems. Turn restrictions and barrier medians should improve safety in both cases. A median which would provide shadowed left-turn protection would be effective at such locations.

TABLE 3

DRIVE-IN BANK OPERATIONS

Item	Example				Average Value
	A	B	C	D	
Number of windows	3	4	2	3	—
Window arrangement	in-line[a]	in-line	in-line	side[b]	—
Average transaction time	80 sec	101 sec	82 sec	60 sec	80 sec
Hourly operating capacity per window	45	36	44	60	46
Maximum observed backup[c]	7	12	8	16	11
Hours open	5½	7½			
Percent of daily activity:					
Peak 30 min	16%	14%	—	—	15%
Peak hour	29%	22%	—	—	25%

[a]Windows end-to-end.
[b]Windows side-by-side (toll booth type arrangement).
[c]During study periods.

Source: Unpublished studies, Paul C. Box and Associates.

Reservoir space for parking areas is extremely important to the proper functioning of major streets. The line of cars waiting on the main roadway to enter a facility creates serious problems. Reservoir space capacity need will depend on whether the parking area is self or attendant parking and on internal design. It is a question of how rapidly a facility can absorb the incoming cars. Experience in Chicago has indicated that for self parking, 5 percent of capacity is a minimum standard for reservoir area. Where attendant parking is used, as much as 20 percent is needed (as a practical matter, 10 percent is generally specified). In this case the design of the reservoir space is an especially important consideration.

Other examples of business activity requiring special reservoir space includes drive-in banks and theaters and car washes. Off-street storage needs (inbound) for car washes have been typically found to reach 20 to 30 spaces, while drive-in theaters need spaces equal to 10 percent or more of total operating capacity. The growth of drive-in bank facilities is continuing, and data from several studies are given in Table 3. These studies indicate a typical reservoir need of 10 to 20 spaces for drive-in banks.

CONCLUSIONS

The best results are obtained when land development and transportation improvements are planned and carried out as a unified process. The best physical planning and improvement programs are those that are carried out with control over both land and transportation. While this is not generally the case in the United States, much can be accomplished through voluntary coordination. A renewal or development plan must consider off-street parking, control of street frontage, and control of street access. The major or arterial street, because of its character, cannot be a segregated artery that will handle only through traffic. It must be, in part, a collector-type street and it is likely that it will always have to perform as an access street to some degree. Land-use control should be exercised to allow the major streets to better perform their proper function. Land planning could reduce unwanted uses.

REFERENCES

1. McGrath, William R. The Urban Thoroughfare System. Eno Traffic Quarterly, Oct. 1966.
2. Osborne, Henry. The Buffalo Truck Route System. Eno Traffic Quarterly, July 1953.
3. Wilbur Smith and Associates, Highway Classification in Illionos. Oct. 1965.
4. Public Administration Service. Procedure Manual—Standards for Street Facilities and Services.
5. Barton-Aschman Associates, Inc. Needs and Opportunities for Coordinating Renewal and Transportation Improvement.

6. Comprehensive Plan of Chicago—1966. Department of Development and Planning, City of Chicago.

7. Loutzenheiser, D. W. Coordination of Highway and General Urban Planning. Proc. ITE, 1961.

8. Hammer, Philip. Proc. ITE, 1961.

9. Engelen, Rodney B. The Opportunity Is Here. Traffic Engineering, April 1962.

10. Fagin, Henry. Transportation Systems Planning as an Influence on Urban Land Uses. Traffic Engineering, June 1963.

11. Excerpts from a Panel Discussion. Harold F. Hammond, Moderator, Traffic Engineering, June 1963.

12. Recommended Practices for Subdivision Streets. Project Committee 6E(62), Traffic Engineering. [Extensive bibliography contained] Jan. 1967.

13. Hurd, Fred W. Land Use Planning and Highway Engineering. Public Works, June 1964.

14. Carroll, J. Douglas, Jr. New Ways To See Land Use and Transportation. Civil Engineering, Aug. 1964.

15. Pollard, William S., Jr. Operations Research Approach to the Reciprocal Impact of Transportation and Land Use. Journal of the Urban Planning and Development Division, ASCE, May 1966.

16. Eberhard, John R. Technology for the City. International Science and Technology, Sept. 1966.

17. Arterial Planning Standards. Chicago Area Transportation Study, March 1967.

18. Urbanized Area Transportation Study. Manual of Street and Highway Improvement Standards and Typical Cross-Sections. Illinois Division of Highways, Bureau of Planning.

19. Paul C. Box and Associates. Selected Parking and Traffic Generation Data. Feb. 1967.

20. Marconi, William. Driveway Accidents in San Francisco. Traffic Engineering, Jan. 1967.

Appendix

PROPOSED POLICIES

POLICY ON OFF-STREET PARKING AND DRIVEWAYS IN THE CENTRAL AREA

In planning for a city it is recognized that the valuable lands at the core of the Central Business District should be devoted to the primary function of the CBD rather than to storage space for motor vehicles. The development of off-street parking facilities is and will continue to be of importance for accessibility to the CBD. Poorly planned parking development will prevent proper arrangement of land uses, impede the movement of mass transit, cause serious traffic congestion, and impair the safety and convenience of pedestrians. It is apparent, therefore, that proper location and operation of parking facilities are essential considerations if planning goals for the CBD are to be achieved.

Two goals which directly affect parking policy for the CBD are:

1. Minimize vehicular and pedestrian movement conflicts within the core area by decreasing unnecessary vehicular street traffic volumes; and

2. Retain the compact functional development of the core area by minimizing the use of land devoted to storage space for motor vehicles.

To attain these goals certain actions must be taken, among which is the limiting of nearly all types of off-street parking facilities to the periphery of the CBD.

For the purpose of planning and regulating parking facilities, the central area as herein referred to shall be divided into three areas:

    1. Core area
    2. Periphery area
    3. Intermediate area—the area between the periphery area and those areas bordering the near-in expressways.

Core Area

Area within the CBD which comprises the highest commercial and shopping density.
    Parking Facilities. It is in the public interest that the provision of additional off-street parking in the core area be minimized. Therefore it shall be the practice to:

    1. Discourage the voluntary provision of off-street parking in connection with new structures; and
    2. Discourage the construction of any additional commercial (fee) off-street parking facilities.

    Driveways. To attain the goal of minimizing pedestrian and vehicular movement conflicts in the core area, driveway permits will be issued only where the use of the driveways would not create unreasonable and unjustified interference with pedestrians and with vehicular movement. Unreasonable interference with pedestrians will be considered to result when more than 14,000 pedestrians use the sidewalk, on a typical weekday between the hours of 8 a.m. to 6 p.m., that must be crossed by a driveway. Unreasonable and unjustified vehicular interference will be considered to result when the adverse effects of such interference are not offset by advantage gained by elimination of curb use through use of the driveway. When such a driveway will affect more than 9,000 but less than 14,000 pedestrians on a typical weekday between the hours of 8 a.m. to 6 p.m., driveways may be considered acceptable, but special pedestrian protection, such as warning devices, may be a requirement of the driveway permit when issued. In this latter case and in all other instances there may be other requirements, such as restrictions on turning movements in and out of a driveway and restrictions as to hours of use.

Periphery Area

The area adjacent to and beyond the core area, but still a part of the central area.

    1. Encourage the provision of parking facilities connected to the core area by convenient means of pedestrian movement.
    2. Encourage the vehicular access and egress to lower level streets.

Intermediate Area

In all other portions of the central area and for the area one block on either side of expressways.

    1. Encourage the construction of large capacity parking facilities for long-term parking with convenient access and egress to expressways.
    2. Provide mass transit connections from these parking facilities directly to the CBD core area.

POLICY ON SCHOOL ACCESS

All schools and related educational facilities such as playgrounds and libraries should be carefully located and designed to provide convenient access and maximum traffic safety for pupils and visitors.

Location of School Sites

Elementary schools should be located so that the pupils are required to cross as few major thoroughfares as possible. These schools should be located on local streets and have connections with a system of park malls whenever possible. High schools should be located on major thoroughfares to provide access to public transportation and to avoid generating heavy traffic on local streets.

Location of Playgrounds

Whenever possible, a school building and local playground and park area should be combined on one site which is not divided by streets. If a street does divide an otherwise desirable site, the possibility of closing this street should be carefully studied. When such a combination is not feasible, the divided site should be linked by a pedestrian grade separation of adequate and attractive design.

Pedestrian Access to Schools and Playgrounds

1. School and playground entrances and exits should be located and designed so that pupils are encouraged to cross streets at controlled intersections or at points where a planned system of park-malls connect with the school site. Both students and non-students should be encouraged to use cross-walks which are protected by traffic signals, crossing guards, or pedestrian grade separations. Sidewalks should be designed to standards adequate to handle the heavy volumes of school traffic.

2. Playgrounds fronting on major streets should be designed with barriers such as fencing or plant material walls to deter those at play from running into the street. These barriers should be designed so that they protect those at play but do not unduly restrict the visibility of motorists or interfere with police surveillance. The playgrounds should contain space and facilities adequate to meet recreational requirements.

Vehicular Access to Schools

1. Vehicular access to parking facilities and service drives should be designed to maximize pupil safety and to minimize the impact on the amount of space devoted to play areas.

2. Provision should be made for safe emergency access. Fire lanes at school sites should provide both ingress and egress from two or more boundaries of the site. Parking restrictions and site planning should allow an unobstructed clearance of 35 feet from the buildings so that fire fighting and rescue equipment can operate effectively.

3. School bus loading and unloading areas should be located so that passengers may be facilitated with safety.

POLICY ON PARKING AND LOADING

Terminal facilities must be considered an integral part of the transportation system of any urban area. Inadequate parking and loading facilities can produce traffic congestion on streets and highways, economic losses to commerce and industry, hazards for pedestrians, and undesirable conditions on residential streets.

Parking spaces and loading berths should be located completely off the public way wherever possible. All parking and loading facilities must be designed and operated so that they do not result in interference with the proper movement of vehicular and pedestrian traffic on public streets, alleys or sidewalks.

Parking

On-Street Parking. The magnitude of the parking problem and the lack of off-street parking in older areas of the city is such that on-street parking must be allowed. However, on-street parking should be allowed only on those roadways which can accommodate their required traffic demand in addition to the parking. The allowed parking should be designed for maximum safety to moving vehicles, parkers, and pedestrians.

1. In accordance with the city code, "The parking of vehicles diagonal to the roadway may be permitted only on the streets at their termini beyond the last cross-street intersection and on streets which serve only as service drives...." On those streets which serve only as service drives, and where high parking demand cannot be met

through off-street parking, angle parking should be allowed if constructed and operated in accordance with Department of Traffic designs and standards. In these cases the street must be designated a service drive by City Council ordinance after a traffic study indicates that it is not required for through traffic. The angle parking design must include adequate provision for pedestrians and two moving traffic lanes in addition to the parking lanes. Proper signing and paint markings must accompany the parking lay-out. (This type of parking is particularly well suited for high-density industrial areas.)

2. Parking and standing shall be prohibited at all designated bus stops for a distance of sufficient length to properly curb a bus. The bus stop shall be used for unloading and loading of passengers only.

3. Parking restrictions shall be installed on all routes where traffic engineering studies indicate a periodic or full-time necessity.

4. All preferential streets must be kept clear of stalled and parked vehicles during periods of heavy snowfall.

5. In redevelopment areas and in areas of new development, off-street parking should be provided and curb parking prohibited whenever possible.

Off-Street Parking. The provision of off-street parking should be encouraged. Zoning ordinances, building codes, etc., should be revised to include adequate require-ments for the quantity of off-street parking and these requirements should be strin-gently enforced. Property owners have the responsibility for providing vehicular stor-age space off the public way.

Off-street parking for residential use should be located within 500 feet of the dwelling unit and connected to the dwelling unit by a safe and lighted walkway.

POLICY ON LOCAL STREET DESIGN AND LOCAL STREET SYSTEMS

Local streets should serve as direct access to properties abutting them. They should be devoid of through traffic, but the system must be convenient, efficient, understand-able and safe.

Local Street Design

Right-of-Way. The desirable local street right-of-way is 66 ft; minimum right-of-way for a conventional local street is 50 ft. Whenever the full right-of-way is available, the full street shall be considered. In areas where one-half or 33 ft of right-of-way is dedicated, every effort must be made to secure the remaining 33 ft of right-of-way. In the event it becomes impossible to secure the full right-of-way before a street pavement is needed, the street shall be constructed to one-half its ultimate width. However, in cases where anticipated traffic demands or safety considerations dictate, pavement widths in excess of one-half the ultimate width shall be required.

Pavement. The minimum desirable local street pavement width is 34 ft in residen-tial areas and 38 ft in industrial and commercial areas. Lesser widths may be accept-able in special cases if parking can be restricted, but two moving lanes of adequate width must be available at all times.

Sidewalks. Sidewalks must be at least 6 ft wide if separated from the roadway by a parkway, and at least 8 ft if located immediately adjacent to the curb. In residential areas parkways should be provided wherever possible.

Through Traffic. Through traffic may be discouraged from using local streets by any of the generalized methods, subsequently described, providing location and design are approved by the Commissioner of Traffic.

Dead-Ending. Dead-ending local streets without adequate terminal provision will not be allowed. Absolute minimum radius dimension for a cul-de-sac pavement is 31 ft with a minimum right-of-way width of 78 ft.

Easements. A right-of-way for utilities, emergency lanes and/or sidewalks should be provided to connect culs-de-sac to other streets or other culs-de-sac. The emer-gency lane and/or sidewalk should be constructed in conjunction with the cul-de-sac construction.

Culs-de-sac. Culs-de-sac should not be allowed where the length of street, density of frontage development, design of frontage, and/or traffic generation of frontage is such that provision of a cul-de-sac will result in traffic volumes on the local street in excess of 2, 500 vehicles per day.

Lighting. Lighting of all local streets and sidewalks should be in accord with standards established by the Illuminating Engineering Society.

Curbs, Gutters and Sidewalks. All local streets, including culs-de-sac, must have curbs, gutters and sidewalks.

Sidewalk and parkway design should incorporate landscaping wherever possible. Landscaping should be designed so that it does not restrict the visibility of motorists or pedestrians. Public services (hydrants, post office boxes, light standards, etc.) should be located so that they do not reduce the effective sidewalk widths to less than 5 ft. Traffic signing, street lighting, etc., should be coordinated so that a minimum of utility poles is required.

Off-Sets. Right-of-way jogs and intersectional off-sets will not be allowed.

Local Street Systems

Continuity. Both ends of all local streets should connect with other streets by a continuous pavement or by a utility-emergency easement.

Fire Hydrants. The street system should be such that fire hydrants can be located at a maximum spacing of 300 ft, and so that water lines can be interconnected.

Access for Fire Protection. Access roadways or fire lanes must be provided to anything that will burn and to any location where people may have to be rescued.

Bus Stops. The design of street systems should allow for the maintenance of bus stops so that the maximum distance to a bus stop over a reasonably direct course will be no more than $\frac{3}{8}$ mile.

Rapid Transit Access—Pedestrian. Pedestrian access to and from present and proposed rapid transit stations via walkways or streets should be convenient and direct.

Rapid Transit Access—Vehicular. Present and proposed rapid transit stations must be provided with vehicular access.

Neighborhood Access. Major access points to neighborhoods should be at quarter-mile traffic signal points on preferential streets.

Alley Connections. Combining the local street system with an alley system is not acceptable. Streets must not terminate at alleys unless a turnaround facility is provided.

Through Traffic. Discouraging through traffic from local streets should not take precedence over convenience, safety and efficiency considerations.

Approval. Location and design of all streets and alleys must be approved by the Commissioner of Traffic.

Special Considerations

The previously mentioned standards apply to conventional subdivisions and neighborhoods. In special instances, such as planned developments, housing projects and areas where local service is provided by private streets, some of the restrictions may be modified. In these cases, plans will be reviewed and approved by the city departments concerned to insure compliance with reasonable standards of safety, traffic capacity and aesthetics.

POLICY ON LOCATION OF AND ACCESS TO POLICE, FIRE AND EMERGENCY SERVICE BUILDINGS

The location of and access to police, fire, and emergency service facilities is dictated by the nature of the service they provide. They are treated separately according to the way in which the community is served.

Emergency Service Buildings

This classification is primarily emergency medical facilities. Those who are served by this type of facility are served at the location. It must therefore be readily accessible.

1. Emergency service facilities should be located on or near a main street which carries the greatest volume of traffic to the facility.

2. Emergency entrances should be accessible from a street, rather than an alley, by means of a driveway with separate entrance and exit. If the driveway terminates at the emergency entrance, a turnaround facility should be provide.

3. Emergency entrances should be located so that there is no conflict with vehicles using other facilities of the hospital or building (delivery, visitors, etc.).

4. Emergency entrances must be kept clear at all times. Off-street parking should be provided for emergency vehicles whose operators must remain at the facility following use of the emergency entrance.

5. Parking should be restricted in the area of the emergency entrance when it is necessary to maintain clear access.

6. The emergency entrance should be clearly lighted and marked with identifying signs.

Fire Department Facilities

Fire stations and other fire department facilities are used primarily for the storage of emergency equipment and housing and training of personnel. The facilities also have limited use as emergency first aid stations. The general locations are determined by the fire department's administrative policy regarding distribution of forces. The specific location and its arrangement should be guided by the following:

1. Fire stations should be located on a preferential street or a street which will provide access to a preferential street.

2. There should be traffic control signals when necessary to permit rapid egress from the station.

3. On-street parking should be restricted adjacent to and opposite the entrance to the station.

4. The station should be clearly lighted at all times.

5. There should be distinctive marking and signs to properly identify the station.

Police Department Facilities

Police stations and other police facilities contain administrative and service units of the police department, prisoner detention facilities, and court units. The general location would be determined by the department policy regarding location of facilities. The specific location should be guided by the following:

1. Police stations should be located on main streets to provide convenient access.

2. There should be off-street parking which would conform to the pertinent provisions of parking policies.

3. The station should be clearly lighted at all times.

4. There should be distinctive markings and signs to properly identify the station.

POLICY ON PERIPHERY TREATMENT OF PARKING FACILITIES

All parking facilities should be carefully planned and designed to provide for the convenience and maximum safety of the patrons and public with a minimum of interference to adjacent uses, both public and private.

Acceptable safety and aesthetic treatment of the periphery should include the following design concepts:

1. The periphery of the facility shall have barriers. These barriers may be in the form of guardrails, retaining walls, or other protective obstructions structurally sufficient to stop and contain any vehicle within the facility.

2. Adjacent to public ways, some type of open fencing in addition to the barrier described above should be provided where pedestrian control is necessary.

3. Adjacent to private property, and type of fencing or screening conforming to the Municipal Code and good design practice shall be used.

4. Screening with plant material should be encouraged, particularly when the parking facility is located in a residential area. Planted border strips are desirable and should be provided wherever possible. All landscaping shall be of a type that does not interfere with the safe operation of the facility.

5. The peripheral treatment adjacent to public ways of all unattended parking facilities shall be of a type that will tend to discourage criminal activity and not interfere with police surveillance.

POLICY ON WALKWAYS IN THE PUBLIC WAY

Walkways are an integral part of the street system of an urban community. They should provide the pedestrian with a safe and efficient means of movement and may also be used to guide pedestrian traffic. Their construction should be required whenever and wherever a new street or thoroughfare is built. Guide lines, which should be followed in determining their location and construction, are as follows:

1. There should be continuous public walkways in all new developments, subdivisions, and renewal projects.

2. Elevated walkways should be encouraged where separation of pedestrian and vehicular traffic is desirable or where special amenities or design considerations are desirable. Pedestrian tunnels should be utilized as a device for separating pedestrians and vehicles only when other means are not applicable or where the tunnels are part of a specially designed system. Appropriate barriers should be erected to preclude at-grade crossings where grade separated facilities are available.

3. Space for walkways shall be reserved on both sides of the public way, according to the schedule set forth in the Municipal Code.

4. Walkways must be a minimum of 6 ft in width, if separated from the roadway by a parkway, and at least 8 ft wide if located immediately adjacent to the curb.

5. Where pedestrian volumes are exceedingly large, such as at transit stops and in shopping areas, walkways should be of sufficient width to accommodate pedestrian traffic.

6. Walkways shall be kept free and clear of all unnecessary obstructions. Public services (hydrants, post office boxes, light standards, etc.) should be located so that they do not reduce the effective sidewalk width to less than 5 ft.

7. All walkways shall be adequately lighted.

8. Where culs-de-sac are constructed, a right-of-way should be provided for the construction of a walkway lane to connect it to another street or cul-de-sac.

9. Walkways not to exceed 2 ft in width may be constructed parallel to and adjoining the curb, where necessary for access to and from vehicles.

10. Construction of carriage walks leading from the curb to the sidewalk should be encouraged.

11. All sidewalk construction shall conform to the standards as provided in the Municipal Code.

12. Bus loading areas shall be provided with paved surfaces.

POLICY ON FIRE LANES

In view of the hazards to life and property due to fires it is mandatory that adequate access to building structures be provided where public rights-of-way do not readily afford such. Ideal exterior accessibility is where a building or structure can be approached on all sides by fire and/or rescue apparatus. Use of properly located fire lanes will accomplish this accessibility. The following standards are required for the fire lanes:

1. Fire lanes shall be so located as to accommodate ladder and rescue work, as determined by the fire department. Fire hydrants shall be readily accessible from the fire lanes.

2. The fire lanes shall be of sufficient width and strength to accommodate and support fire and emergency vehicles, and shall be designed with adequate turnaround facilities.

3. The fire lanes shall be kept clear at all times from vehicles other than those of emergency nature. Approved barriers shall be provided at entrances to fire lanes and posted to discourage use by non-emergency vehicles.

4. No parking shall be allowed in front of fire lane entrances. Appropriate signs shall be erected in accordance with city traffic ordinance.

5. Site plans for proposed developments requiring fire lanes shall be submitted to the municipal agencies concerned for approval.

POLICY ON RECREATIONAL PARKING FACILITY DESIGN

While design requirements for recreational parking coincide generally with requirements for any other type of parking, there are some aspects to recreational parking which merit special consideration. One such aspect is involved with the extremely large fluctuation in parking demand due to the seasonal or periodic qualities inherent in attendance at many recreational activities. Another aspect is the frequent association of recreational parking with non-commercial land developed to high landscape standards.

Since attendance reaches large volumes on occasion, recreational areas should be serviced by mass transit facilities wherever possible. Accommodating peak attendance demands solely by automobile transportation results in the creation of abnormally large paved areas which are only sporadically used.

The following special considerations should be applied in the design of recreational parking facilities:

1. The design of large recreational parking facilities should minimize potential conflict with mass transit operations. Ingress and egress features, as well as reservoir space, should be planned to maintain reasonable access for mass transit service to the recreational facility involved, even when congestion exists at the associated parking facility, and on the roadways servicing it. Terminal facilities for mass transit vehicles should be included in recreational parking design if the storage of such vehicles is involved with the operation of the recreational facility.

2. In order to induce economy in land usage, dual use of recreational parking areas—such as shopper parking combined with stadium parking or employee parking combined with some other type of recreational parking—should be considered wherever possible.

3. Recreational parking facilities which are located in a park-like setting should be aesthetically compatible with their surroundings.

4. The location of recreational parking facilities should take into consideration the capability of the adjacent roadway system to absorb the traffic generated by the recreational activities.

5. The layout of any large parking facility should allow for flexible use so that the area of the parking lot to be used for any event which induces less than total capacity parking demand can be restricted to the area needed for that event.

6. To avoid the unnecessary paving of land, consideration should be given to the use of lawn or other unpaved areas for the storage of vehicles at recreational activities occurring infrequently. The potential difficulities occasioned by inclement weather do not justify the existence of large expanses of paved areas which rarely would be utilized for parking.

7. If suitable unpaved acres exist adjacent to recreational parking areas constructed to accommodate normal parking demands, the design of the parking facility should allow for their utilization in handling overflow parking occasioned by abnormal demands.

POLICY ON ENTRANCES TO RECREATIONAL FACILITIES

All recreational facilities, such as parks, playgrounds, zoos, conservatories, and similar areas, should be carefully planned to provide maximum safety for patrons. Pedestrians, especially children, should be encouraged to use protected crosswalks, and wherever possible, those protected by traffic signals. Vehicular and pedestrian access to recreational areas should be separated and designed for safe operation and for minimal interference with through traffic movement on adjacent streets. The following standards should be applied to recreational facilities:

1. Pedestrian entrances and exits should be located and designed to encourage use of protected locations such as crosswalks, passerelles and pedestrian tunnels.

2. Active play areas fronting on streets should be designed with barriers such as fencing, walls, or plant materials to deter those at play from running into the street. These barriers should be designed so that the visibility of motorists and pedestrians is not restricted.

3. Pedestrian entrances at grade should be located at signalized intersections where feasible. The use of pedestrian crossing signals should be considered when pedestrian volumes warrant.

4. Automobile access points to large city-wide recreational facilities should be located on major streets wherever possible. Automobile access to small neighborhood recreational facilities should be on local streets.

5. Off-street parking and off-street passenger loading and unloading zones should be considered where recreational uses generate a need for these facilities.

6. All entrance drives and parking areas should be visible and lighted to facilitate police surveillance.

7. Bus stops which serve these facilities should be located so that unprotected street crossings by pedestrians are minimized.

8. Entrances for pedestrian and vehicular traffic should be well defined for the purpose of alerting pedestrians and motorists to the use of the area.

9. Fire lane policy provisions will apply to recreational facilities.

Addendum

PHOENIX, ARIZ.

The following is a comparison of mid-block accident experience on two portions of Central Avenue, Phoenix, Ariz., for a two-year period ending January 1, 1966. One section, from McDowell to Thomas, does not have median islands, while the second section, from Thomas to Indian School, does have median islands.

Comparative Measures	No Median	Median
Total Mid-Block Accidents	279	238 (14% lower)
Accident Rate	11.2 Acc./MVM	8.9 Acc./MVM (20% lower)
Personal Injuries	94	63
Estimated Economic Loss	$340,000	$240,000 (30% lower)
Volume—ADT	36,000	38,500

These median islands cost about $48,800, including landscaping and decorative lighting. This comparison demonstrates the fact that median islands substantially reduce the accident rates of high-volume streets by eliminating random mid-block conflicts.

Local Streets

JOHN P. CAVALLERO, JR.
Deputy Commissioner
Department of Transit and Traffic
City of Baltimore

The urban "local street" generally accounts for a substantial portion of all urban street mileage. Because streets are ranked and classified from a traffic-carrying viewpoint, there is a tendency to undervalue local streets (they are often referred to as "minor streets") and short shrift is frequently given to maintenance attention, traffic control and long-range planning. The primary function of local streets is that of providing access to abutting properties. Supplying curb parking may be a secondary function of local streets, but parking should only be allowed under proper circumstances in order to minimize accident potential. Local streets may also absorb varying quantities of through traffic and truck traffic, which will tend to increase hazard, cause pavement breakdown, and adversely affect living amenities.

The critical need to understand and accommodate rising traffic loads in our intense urban centers has required that a great deal of attention properly be devoted to the major city streets—such as arterials and downtown streets. However, a fresh concern with the amenities of city living has given rise to a new examination of the role of local streets, especially an interest in their potential to exert a better environmental influence on the city dweller. This paper attempts to provide a brief insight into these streets, revealing some of their problems, and describing traffic engineering treatments which have been used for improvements.

COMPOSITION AND MAGNITUDE

Figure 1 shows a typical local street cross section. A paved roadway width of 34 ft is adequate for local street vehicular needs, while provision of sidewalks and curbs presents a full measure of pedestrian safety (1). In addition to increasing pedestrian safety, provision of sidewalks and curbs lessens fixed-object (trees, signs, etc.) accident potential to vehicular traffic by virtue of the barrier effect presented by vertical curbing and sidewalk width. Street drainage, cleaning and maintenance, and snow-plowing efforts are also improved with constructed sidewalks and curbs.

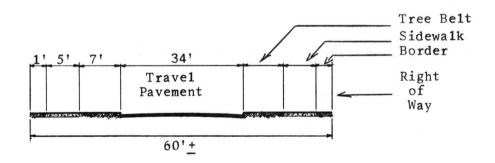

Source: Institute of Traffic Engineers

Figure 1. Local street cross section.

TABLE 1

PEDESTRIAN DEATHS, ANNUAL AVERAGE

Position	Urban	Rural	Total
Walking in roadway	132	415	547
Playing in roadway	148	198	346
Standing in roadway	154	133	287
Total	434	746	1,180

Source: Accident Facts, National Safety Council.

Though some sub-division developers and individual lot owners may be reluctant to supply walks and curbs due to costs, high pedestrian generations of urban residential areas, especially children walking to and from school, fully justify sidewalk and curb provisions. In 1965, 1450 children in the 5 to 14-year age group died in pedestrian accidents (2). The incidence of pedestrian-in-roadway deaths for both urban and rural areas is given in Table 1.

One study indicated that of all pedestrian fatalities in urban areas, "some 11 percent of these involve pedestrians in, but not crossing roadways" (1).

Traffic carrying ability is by no means the only available criterion for determining the value of streets. An understanding of the importance of local streets can be gained from an idea of their extent within the total street system. Table 2 gives a breakdown of the total street mileage of three typical cities. Inclusion of alleys as local streets in City C would result in a proportion of local streets, to all street mileage, of approximately 72 percent, which is similar to the smaller size City A.

CHARACTERISTICS AND FUNCTIONS

The limited service requirement of access and egress imposes only low traffic demands on local streets—generally under 3000 vehicles ADT. Normally, it can be expected that only a relatively small percentage of all traffic will be "through traffic"; that is, not having an origin or destination within the immediate locale.

Local streets will typically be developed with residential land use, and indeed, most neighborhood streets will be of the local street variety. However, local streets with mixed land uses are not uncommon, as well as local streets having exclusively commercial, institutional, or industrial land uses. In City A for example, 92 percent of the mileage is abutted by residential, park or school uses, while the remaining 8 percent is business and industrial use. Exclusive residential use by no means requires that a street section be classed local street; one may find numerous examples of exclusive residential use abutting major arterial facilities.

Other valuable functions which can be provided by local streets include parking, and the potential to enrich environmental influence (social amenity). These specific functions tend to be inferiorly supplied by higher type streets. These functions are not necessarily always well supplied by locals, but obviously, there is much less likelihood of major streets, because of their traffic role, accommodating curb parking, or exerting a beneficial environmental influence on people.

TYPICAL PROBLEMS

Like water, urban traffic continually seeks lines of least resistance. This dynamic quality of urban traffic can force serious traffic pressures on sections of local streets.

TABLE 2

TYPICAL LOCAL STREET MILEAGE

	Pop.	Land Area (sq mi)	Local Streets (mi)	Percent of Total	Alleys[a] (mi)
City A	65,000	10	115	71	—
City B	153,000	23	158	61	—
City C	950,000	79	874	63	500

[a]If public rights-of-way, should be considered as local streets. They are shown here under City C for comparative purposes and are not public rights-of-way in this case.

204

Such overflows can be minimized by developing and maintaining a high quality of flow on major traffic routes. However, even under ideal conditions, local streets occasionally experience problems similar in nature to those experienced by higher grade streets. Basically, these are traffic problems related to intersections (crossing flows), and problems which occur between intersections (often related to parking). There is one problem, however, unique to local streets—the problem of preserving local streets as such.

Obviously, the best way to limit unwanted traffic intrusions is to design out this potential in the original system plan. The Institute of Traffic Engineers has developed design policies for sub-divisions which seek to provide not only for the proper functioning of local streets in a traffic sense, but also strive for "maximum livability"(3). Figure 2 shows a neighborhood cluster-type street plan that assures a minimum level of through traffic flow. In intersection design considerations, for example, several studies have conclusively shown T-type intersections to be safer than "cross" types. In City A for example, the injury accident rate was found to be $5\frac{1}{2}$ times greater at cross type local street intersections (Table 3).

Many American cities gradually developed their street systems in grid patterns, allowing local streets to be sandwiched between major streets with frequent connections between the two, thus making the locals vulnerable to traffic diversions. When faced with an accomplished fact in street arrangement, it is possible to create by traffic engineering techniques, an artificial arrangement of neighborhood street flow which discourages through traffic movements. Figure 3 shows such a treatment in schematic fashion, using one-way sections and intersection controls to break continuity of flow— an operating feature anathema to through traffic.

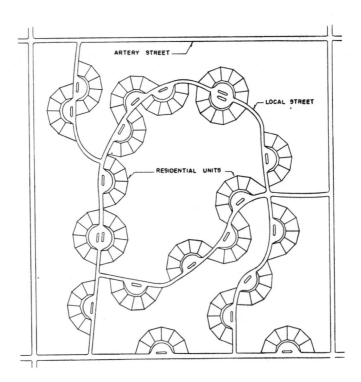

Source: Institute of Traffic Engineers

Figure 2. Neighborhood street plan.

TABLE 3

MINOR STREET ACCIDENTS BY TYPE

Intersection Type	Number of Intersections	No. Accidents			Two-Year Accident Rate[a]		
		Inj.	P.O.	Total	Inj.	P.O.	Overall
90° T	168	7	42	49	0.04	0.25	0.29
90° cross	309	67	125	192	0.22	0.40	0.62
Skewed T	39	0	1	1	0.00	0.03	0.03
Skewed cross	13	1	6	7	0.08	0.46	0.54
90° L	37	1	7	8	0.03	0.53	0.22
Total	566	76	181	257	0.13	0.32	0.45

[a]Per intersection.   Source: Reference (4).

One special word of caution with regard to this treatment. One-way streets and intersection control devices require the studied judgments of a competent traffic engineer; it is extremely risky business when indulged in by anyone other than specially trained people. The proliferate use of traffic control devices, such as STOP and YIELD signs, tends to breed contempt to all traffic control devices and encourages violations. The habit of violation proneness can lead to serious consequence. One study of unwarranted local street intersection stop signs found violation rates of 74 to 90 percent (5). For a number of reasons there is also no guarantee that such treatments will be successful. One study carefully developed a system of locals and majors within a large sub-division, only to encounter substantial objections from the residents it was designed to benefit (6).

Another study resulted in conversion of a local two-way street to one-way operation in order to discourage through movements. A poll of residential opinion before and after indicated that 37 residents were for and 4 were opposed to one-way streets in the before study; 68 were for and 6 opposed in the after study.

The after study also indicated an accident reduction at one intersection from 11 accidents in a 3-yr period before one-way control, to 2 accidents in the 3-yr period after one-way control (7).

INTERSECTION PROBLEMS

There are basically two types of local street intersections: a local street intersecting another local street, and a local street intersecting a major street (the threshold from

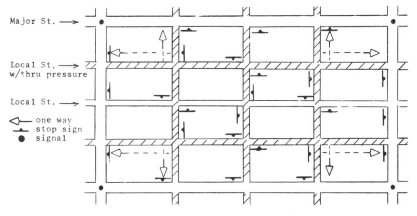

Figure 3. Schematic traffic control plan for local streets.

TABLE 4

ACCIDENTS BY TYPE INTERSECTION AND CONTROL

Type Intersection	Type Control	Number of Intersections	Number of Accidents	Annual Number Per Intersection
Major-minor	2-way stop	282	494	2.0
Minor-minor	4-way stop	3	0	0.0
Minor-minor	2-way stop	106	32	0.3
Minor-minor	Yield	111	66	0.6
Minor-minor	None	430	102	0.2

Source: Reference (5).

local system to major street system). Intersections of the latter type are understandably more susceptible to accidents because vehicles enter or cross heavier traffic levels, and traffic control measures will be correspondingly more stringent. Table 4 gives results of one study of accidents by type of control and intersection.

Minor intersections (local street vs local street) should operate relatively free of serious accident frequency because of the low volume characteristic. Most intersections will be suitable, therefore, for operation under prevailing right-of-way laws, without posted control. Typical minor street volume levels are revealed by results of the study given in Tables 5 and 6. Accidents that do occur at minor intersections generally cannot be blamed on traffic pressure or insufficient crossing opportunities. Most often, they are the result of driver error or restricted visibility—the latter a typical city condition caused by the close building lines, hedge and tree growths, etc.

Improvements to sight distance, and hence a greater degree of safety, can be obtained by adoption of laws limiting the height of greenery at intersections such that the normal driving line of sight (approximately 4-ft driver eye height) is not impaired. On level streets, this sets a maximum height above sidewalk level of 24 to 30 in. for shrubbery. A similar requirement coupled with appropriate building setback regulations can be added to the local zoning code to insure proper intersection clearance. Figure 4 shows a recommended "sight triangle" provision for a zoning code.

When accidents occur at minor intersections in residential areas, residents will often seek traffic controls far more stringent than are required by traffic conditions. Traffic engineering study may raise the level of control if such need is indicated, but more often low-keyed improvements such as corner parking clearances, various signs, and paint lines are instituted.

MID-BLOCK PROBLEMS

Urban residential density most often increases as one draws closer to the central city, generally reaching a peak level in the so-called "inner city" areas which surround the urban core. Although vehicle ownership on a family or person basis will tend to decline with closeness to the core, this advantage is quickly lost to the sheer numbers of people and the fact that resident off-street parking provisions also lessen with closeness to the core. A study in City A showed mid-block accident frequency in multiple family areas with dense curb parking to be nearly four times the frequency in single-family areas (4). The study also found 71 percent of mid-block accidents to be caused by parked cars.

From these circumstances emerges the urban dilemma over street parking. On

TABLE 5

MINOR STREET VOLUMES

Item	Block Sections	
	Single-Family Areas	Multiple-Family Areas
No. locations	283	94
Avg. peak hr[a], vph	40	80
Lowest peak hr[a], vph	2	18
Highest peak hr[a], vph	117	205

[a]Two-way volume.   Source: Reference (5).

TABLE 6

INTERSECTIONS

Control	Single-Family Area		Multiple-Family Area	
	Sample Size	Total Entering Vol. (vph)	Sample Size	Total Entering Vol. (vph)
Four-way stop	10	110	0	—
Four-way stop	9	90	3	370
Yield	13	180	2	230
None	39	90	18	150
Total	$\overline{71}$	110	$\overline{23}$	190

Source: Reference (5).

one hand, curb parking is nearly a necessity to residents. On the other hand (with the often limited width of urban local streets), the presence of heavy curb parking obstructs passage, raises car vs car accident potentials, presents extremely difficult street maintenance problems (cleaning and plowing), is unsightly and cluttering, and increases the potential for pedestrian accidents, especially in the highest density neighborhoods where sidewalks and streets often become play areas.

Table 7 gives data from a study which also suggests a relationship between residential density, street width, parking and mid-block accident experience. Figure 5 shows one guide (8) for the regulation of parking and traffic, with reference to a range of local street widths.

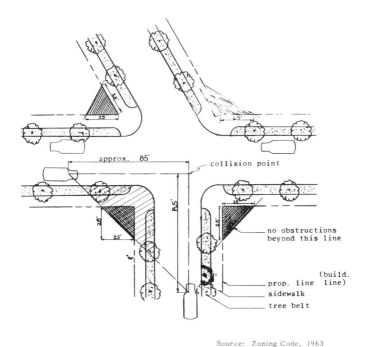

Source: Zoning Code, 1963
New Haven, Conn

Figure 4. Sight distance regulation, typical zoning code.

TABLE 7

RESIDENTIAL DENSITY AND
MID-BLOCK ACCIDENT INFLUENCE

Study Block	Length (ft)	Width (ft)	Rate Per 100 Ft		Mid-Block[a] Accidents
			Residents	Cars	
1	400	60	32.5	10.0	1
2	300	60	33.0	7.5	-
3	350	36	40.6	12.2	3
4	300	36	43.0	13.0	2
5	600	35	9.8	3.0	-
6	900	30	6.6	2.8	-
7	800	23	40.5	12.0	2
8	400	29	14.0	4.2	-
9	400	36	8.2	2.5	-
10	300	30	5.6	1.6	-

[a]24 months.

Source: Unpublished study, Department of Traffic and Parking, City of New Haven.

When serious off-street parking deficiencies exist, it is worth considering adoption of neighborhood one-way patterns which can provide more street area for curb parking while requiring less street area for the passing of traffic. As a rule of thumb, with a rate of 12 or more family units per 200 ft of residential street, full use of both curbs for parking still will not satisfy demands, and some off-street parking must be provided. Also, these areas will tend to experience higher mid-block accident rates. Creating residential off-street parking lots in high density areas, via spot clearance of depreciated structures, can be one solution to this problem.

CONCLUSIONS

Much can be said about the impact of the automobile on urban living. In the residential areas of urban society the auto touches closest to our lives, this particular reason, more so than essentially superficial problems relative to accidents or parking needs, suggests that more deliberate and objective attention be focused on the management of local streets. This increasing need to guide and shape our urban environment should

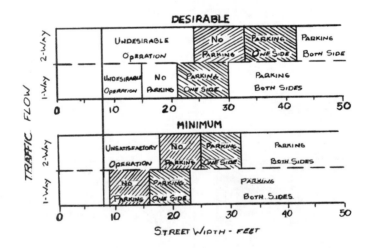

Source: Traffic Engineering Magazine
March, 1967

Figure 5. Local street traffic regulation.

Figure 6. Court Street rehabilitation, Wooster Square Renewal Project, New Haven, Connecticut.

be recognized as sufficient justification to view the function of local urban roadways from the perspective of effect on urban living, rather than solely from the viewpoint of traffic function. This is illustrated in Figure 6.

REFERENCES

1. Box, Paul C. Sidewalk Needs. Publication pending, 1967.
2. Accident Facts. National Safety Council, 1965.
3. Recommended Practice for Sub-Division Streets. Traffic Engineering Magazine, p. 15, Jan. 1967.
4. Box, Paul C. Accident Characteristics of Non-Arterial Streets. Highway Research News, Feb. 1965.
5. Box, Paul C. Traffic Control at Minor Intersections. Municipal Signal Engineer, p. 21, Jan.-Feb. 1966.
6. Alta Vista Terrace and Wyngate Study. Montgomery County, Maryland, Unpublished study, Jan. 1960.
7. Plymouth Street One-Way Study. Dept. of Traffic and Parking, New Haven, Conn., Unpublished study.
8. Local Street Parking Criteria. Traffic Engineering Magazine, p. 32, Mar. 1967.
9. Sutermeister, Oscar. Neighborhoods and Traffic. Traffic Quarterly, Oct. 1960.
10. Bagby, Scott. Protecting Good Neighborhoods From Through-Traffic Decline. Traffic Quarterly, Oct. 1954.
11. Marks, Harold. Subdividing for Traffic Safety. Traffic Quarterly, July 1957.

Addendum

CHICAGO, ILL.

A consultant working for the North Beverly Improvement Association, a community organization within the City of Chicago, found that the community was experiencing an excessive amount of through traffic, and they recommended a number of street closings and culs-de-sac to divert this traffic. This plan ran into considerable opposition from both the residents and the city. The reasons for this opposition were as follows:

1. The construction costs for these changes would be excessive for the results attained, and no doubt this work would have to be financed through special assessment.
2. The changes would result in a street pattern which would be very confusing and inconvenient to both visitors and area residents. A large number of residents were strongly opposed to the plan for this reason.
3. There would be inadequate access to many parts of the North Beverly area by fire department vehicles.
4. The positive approach of encouraging the use of preferential streets by improving them should be used instead of trying to discourage through traffic from using minor streets without alleviating the traffic problems that put them there in the first place.

The solution finally recommended was a system of one-way streets which could be put into effect almost immediately. It was expected that such a system would eliminate almost all of the rush-period through movements being made. Further studies were made and showed that no modifications in the one-way system or more radical solutions were necessary.

Traffic Engineering and Community Support
(Cities Under 100,000)

DANIEL J. HANSON
Deputy Director for Traffic Engineering
Department of Highways and Traffic
District of Columbia

Data in this paper are related to obtaining community-wide support for traffic engineering programs in smaller cities, including Champaign and Peoria, Ill. (population 50,000 and 125,000, respectively) and also St. Louis County, Mo. In St. Louis County, with a population of 850,000, there were some 96 cities, towns and villages ranging in size from under 100 to the largest community of University City with a population of over 50,000.

An important element very often overlooked in the traffic engineering program is direct contact with community leaders. It is one thing to prepare a commissioner's order or traffic regulation for the mayor, city council or board of aldermen. However, it is an entirely different matter to communicate to community leaders the real intent and goals of a sound traffic engineering approach, particularly in connection with improving existing street utilization.

Basically, city officials and legislators support street improvements, worthwhile traffic engineering projects and other desirable governmental changes. However, the most prominent of our constituents will often react in violent opposition to these changes if they are not well informed in advance. In this regard, it should not be intimated that we need to conduct popularity polls on contemplated traffic improvements. On the other hand, it is highly essential that a large part of the community be well advised in advance as to the program, goals, implementation plan and anticipated results.

This job is particularly difficult to accomplish in the smaller communities. Initially, it might seem that the larger the city the farther removed from the public the traffic official becomes, and he thereby has a certain layer of insulation from the public and public opinion. On the other hand, when one is involved in a smaller city situation, he must face the day-to-day direct contact with many constituents. The smaller community probably has more traffic experts per capita than the larger metropolitan areas where the majority of people have long ago given up in disgust regarding current traffic inadequacies.

Establishing a working liaison with citizen groups, service clubs, Parent-Teachers Associations and other professional organizations in the small community is initially a rather simple task. Admittedly it is time consuming, but the ratio of benefits received increases rapidly when the average citizen is well informed about the latest parking restriction proposals, one-way street plan, new traffic signal installation, change in speed limits or other similar street utilization improvement which is being contemplated.

Nobody can become more irate than a former friendly merchant when unknown to him a sign crew installs a parking restriction directly in front of his store. Likewise, the three-hour laundry, doughnut shop or gasoline station proprietor can become hostile when one-way street signs are suddenly installed on his corner without his prior knowledge.

The installation of parking meters is probably a good example in this regard. Many merchants tolerate one and two-hour parking restrictions as long as they and their sales personnel can violate these regulations "just a little bit." However, when a plan is proposed to install meters at these same locations, many merchants are opposed on the basis of anticipated lost business. A big selling job often has to be done, well in advance, in order to make the merchants fully realize the many advantages of increased turnover, case of enforcement and the end result of making more parking spaces available than under a non-metered arrangement.

Personal experience indicates that this selling job is almost impossible to accomplish, after the fact. Therefore, we should take the time, in advance, to advise abutting property owners and retailers what we have in mind before we start breaking up the concrete for new parking meter posts. Sometimes a sympathetic Chamber of Commerce representative, or other similar community leader, can be found to help champion the cause for better street utilization.

The traffic engineer in the small community should be, and in fact must be, a very public-spirited citizen if he is to be truly effective. This does not mean that the traffic engineer must be a politician. However, he certainly should be well informed on all of the basic community needs, well beyond the limited scope of his responsibility in improving street utilization.

The traffic engineer does not have to be a joiner, but certainly should make himself available as a member of any official governmental speakers bureau roster. If no such roster is available the traffic engineer should seek other means of letting community groups know that he is a willing participant in their gatherings. In this regard, the traffic engineer should have available at least two or three "canned" presentations which he can deliver on short notice. The monthly speeches prepared by the American Road Builders Association are good examples of this type of "ready made" material.

Often such last minute invitations are the most productive because, first of all, you usually get a program chairman or club president off the hot seat for not having another speaker available. Second, such presentations are usually well received because you can talk about your program for better street utilization and you are not on the defensive or committed to discuss some after the fact, hot issue.

The Lions Club can be used as one example. In Peoria, the Downtown International Lions Club met every Tuesday noon at a hotel one short block from the City Hall. Over 70 percent of the 100 members attended the meeting each week. In fact, if one did not show up by 12:15 p. m. the Secretary usually called your office to see if you were sick. Serving as a last minute substitute speaker on several occasions gave the author an excellent chance to "test the wind," "float a few bombs" and otherwise obtain a rather broad indication from community leaders as to their thoughts regarding the newest traffic propositions.

This case is equally true for any service club, fraternal organization or business group. In fact, a personal service club experience has been found to lead to many direct contacts with Rotarians, Optimists, Kiwanians, Sertomans and other service groups. Belonging to one such organization can open up many other doors to community leaders which otherwise would not have been available.

A brief presentation should be emphasized. It is far better to come back three times for 20-minute presentations than to give an audience a single one-hour dose once a year. Visual aids, including charts and color slides, are most helpful in presenting your traffic engineering story to community leaders.

Visual aids probably offer the best approach toward providing ready made programs before groups, especially on short notice. A collection of 2 by 2-in. colored slides can make possible a ready reference for a number of different type talks on a varied range of subjects. These slides can even be grouped according to categories such as school programs, safety organizations, and women's groups in order to provide a program of special interest to the group involved. The collection of slides in St. Louis County numbered several hundred and even made it possible to send out more than one traffic disciple, simultaneously.

Copies of annual reports of the department's activities are an excellent door opener as far as establishing community support is concerned. In this respect, a recent newspaper supplement insert by West Palm Beach, Fla., is a good example of this type of approach. This tabloid not only told what the city had done in the last year but also indicated many of the proposed accomplishments for the future. Peoria prepares a similar newspaper supplement once a year.

Another example is the Annual Report from the St. Louis County Division of Traffic. There are many more similar annual reports which are equally well received by community leaders. Many traffic officials think such a report is totally unnecessary and exclaim "I just don't have the time to prepare it," however, in this case the time is well spent.

Brief documentary evidence of a before and after one-way street operation, parking prohibition, street improvement or traffic signal project are helpful tools in keeping the citizen leaders well informed. While this takes time and effort, many engineers have encountered the situation where numerous public hearings, delays, referral back to committees and other obstacles in their paths held up a most worthwhile street utilization project for months or even years. A little better line of communication with community leaders might help turn plans into progress.

As a rule of thumb, the traffic engineer should spend somewhere between 10 and 25 percent of his time in the small city dealing with community leaders and other official groups. These contacts could take many forms, but should be of such a substantial nature that the community is well informed at all times of the latest street utilization improvement projects.

Another excellent method of telling the traffic engineering story is publication of special reports dealing with bond issue proposals, projects listed in long-range public works programs and other major arterial street utilization projects. One lesson to be learned in this respect is not to attempt to include too much or too many items in any single package.

As an example, in March 1964 a 12 proposition $104,000,000 bond issue program was proposed in St. Louis County. Although the majority of propositions received well over a 50 percent favorable vote, a two-thirds majority was required for passage of each item.

Shortly thereafter, a special citizens emergency bond issue committee was appointed to review all of these issues before resubmittal to the voters. In their wisdom, it was agreed that only three proposals should be included at a special bond issue election which was held in June 1965. These three items totaled slightly in excess of $40,000,000 and subsequently were all approved by well over the required two-thirds majority.

The success of this approach was obviously due to a good working relationship between community leaders and county officials. It should be pointed out that two of the three successful proposals related to improving the most heavily traveled arterial roads, bridges and intersections in St. Louis County, including some 20 separate projects and completion of an inner-belt expressway.

The citizens emergency bond issue committee, consisting of prominent community officials, was a real working group and was certainly instrumental in the successfulness of this effort. Flyers, maps, tax explanation sheets, postcards, business letter postscripts, suggested personal letter and telephone call plans, a well-prepared question and answer sheet, and other literature were most useful in this campaign.

Some of the soundest traffic engineering proposals very often gather dust on a shelf. This is many times due to a lack of understanding and appreciation of the merits of the proposal on the part of the general public. It is, therefore, essential that motorists and citizens alike be kept well informed regarding proposed traffic changes.

Any suggested improvement and alterations in street utilization, traffic regulations and control devices should be well publicized in all forms of public media. Newspaper items, radio coverage, and television appearances all form essential elements in a broad public information and education program. The traffic official needs not only financial support, but also public support in order to transform ideas into reality.

Many of the traffic proposals will be involved enough to dictate the preparation of sketches, other documents and visual aids. A short summary of pertinent statistical data is very helpful and when presented graphically can be very convincing. On the other hand, a long recitation of numbers and more numbers can turn an otherwise good story into a deadly tale. Citizens should certainly not be bored with massive presentations of statistics. However, use of a few well chosen facts and figures will always make for an improved and more interesting presentation.

The following summary is a typical list of public appearances which might be required on the part of a traffic engineer in a small community in a single year.

Meetings with municipal officials	25
Safety organizations and traffic committees	16
Improvement associations and civic groups	12
Radio and television programs	10
Religious, business and women's groups	9
School programs	8
Total	80

This schedule is merely an example; certainly different circumstances in any given community might dictate a variation in this list. However, if the traffic engineer in the small city is making less than one public appearance per week, he should be strongly urged to take another look at his public relations program.

CONCLUSION

A willingness to appear before citizen groups and community leaders can, per man-hour spent, be the best investment in time a traffic engineer can make. Annual reports, extensive use of all forms of public media, visual aids, presentations before groups and other means of contact with the community are truly essential ingredients in improving street utilization through traffic engineering techniques.

Community Support for Traffic Engineering
(Cities Over 100,000)

WILLIAM MCGRATH

Transportation Coordinator

Boston Redevelopment Authority

Every treatise or textbook on traffic engineering stresses the importance of obtaining public understanding and support for traffic engineering activities. It seems to go without saying that this is necessary, but there appears to be a dearth of literature specifically on how this is to be accomplished.

Part of the problem seems to be that obtaining community support is more an art than a science. There are no yardsticks for measuring the success that can be made. One can only recall whether a particular project or total program has been a success or a failure and evaluate whether community support or the lack of it was a contributing factor. One may also consider what specific steps were taken to obtain support and evaluate this relative success.

Of necessity, therefore, this will be a rather personal report based on what was done and, human memory being what it is, mostly describing only the successes.

All the actions described were undertaken from 1955 to 1963 in New Haven, Conn. New Haven is a city of 150,000 population, the center of the metropolitan area of about 350,000. Subsequently, the author moved to Boston, an area more than 5 times as large. My present position offers little opportunity to become involved with direct operational traffic engineering activities, but the general observation can be made that the larger the city, the more formalized the relationships with community support groups and the more difficult they are to establish.

In New Haven, the institution of widespread traffic engineering techniques began with the creation of a Department of Traffic and Parking in 1955. This event occurred during the tenure of Mayor Richard C. Lee, who came from a public relations background and understood the need for community support of all successful public actions. With this kind of leadership, it was possible to learn the techniques of deriving support for traffic engineering endeavors.

Before describing some of the activities undertaken, it might be well to state the basic conclusions as to what are the ingredients of achieving community support. Four areas of activity can be identified, any one of which may be essential and certainly helpful. All of them together can help guarantee success.

1. Provide specific groups and the general public with sufficient information in advance of major traffic activities so that they will understand what is happening and what is expected of them in the operation of the system.

2. Provide sufficient information to specific groups and the general public as to why certain traffic changes are being made so that they will understand and support the changes.

3. Consult in advance with specific groups on specific improvements to seek their views and knowledge and to gain their support by virtue of their participation.

4. Use the services available from specific groups in collecting and analyzing data and results and in otherwise participating in such direct fashion that they are part of the program from inception to execution.

As one looks about a city to find specific groups which can lend community support one finds they exist in a great variety of size, strength, objective, interest and formality of organization. No one group is the same as another and each must be approached in terms of its individuality. The discussion which follows identifies the kinds of groups and the kinds of interplay undertaken with them in New Haven.

CITIZEN'S ACTION COMMISSION

Early in his administration, Mr. Lee saw the need for a specific organization of community leaders who could be rallied to support his programs. He sought to find the leaders who could organize a large group of 300 persons involved in banking, retailing, industry, law, education and civic organizations. This group was organized in a highly formalized structure with an executive director and with various committees, one of which was to deal with traffic and transportation. The Commission was given no legal powers or authority as such, but through its executive committee and its several working committees it was to give the Mayor and administrative staff its guidance, views, and public support where justified. For several years, it was frequently consulted in respect to the overall plans for improvement of the city. Major plans for freeway location, revisions to the city street system, traffic directional and operational control changes, and solutions to the off-street parking problem were reviewed in detail. The net result was their overall support of the program and the good will engendered with them personally and with other organizations with which they were associated.

CHAMBER OF COMMERCE

New Haven had an active Chamber of Commerce which was interested in all things affecting business activity and the development of the city. Its members had their own major points of desired improvements, of which traffic and parking were far from the least. A continuing series of meetings was conducted to review in detail the street changes to be made in the central business area and the off-street parking program. Wherever possible, their ideas and plans were integrated into the plans of the city. Their own media of expression through their house organ and formal meetings were used to disseminate information on plans and projects. Certain very specific activities were undertaken.

1. Before 1955, the Chamber had instituted a stamp validation plan for retail subsidization of off-street parking. The city participated in this activity. The Chamber was the clearinghouse for validated stamps and provided its own staff services in clearing payments and in checking trends and use of the program. Cooperation with the Chamber virtually guaranteed support of the off-street parking program and, due to the members' knowledge of this program, engendered their support of necessary curb parking restrictions which they might otherwise have found objectionable.

2. A major effort conducted with the Chamber was a complete revision of the one-way traffic operations of the central area streets in conjunction with the opening of the new central freeway distributor. This plan was worked out carefully block by block. There was one meeting at which one retail merchant insisted that a certain street scheduled to be operated one-way must be kept two-way for convenience of access and must have curb parking on both sides for the convenience of customers. The width of the street and the traffic volumes made these requirements practically impossible. When he was asked directly how he proposed the traffic engineer make the system work under those conditions, he threw up his hands and said, "How should I know, that's your problem. You're the traffic engineer around here." It almost goes without saying that this disclosure of his attitude and the members' knowledge of the problem prevented this specific objector from having an adverse influence on the plan. As a further illustration of how far detailed work of this nature can go, at the last minute it was agreed that a street which the traffic engineer had scheduled for reconversion from one-way to two-way movement would be left one-way because it was the opinion of the Chamber officials that it could not operate as a two-way street.

3. As a followup to the Chamber's participation in planning the major one-way street change, the traffic engineer carried out a difficult promise and assignment which further showed the cooperative nature of the enterprise. He undertook to obtain access to state sales tax data of the merchants throughout the central area affected by the one-way plan. A before-and-after study of sales tax receipts related to general business activity was prepared and presented to the Chamber. Its findings were sufficient proof to justify continued support of the plan as it had been installed.

PARENT TEACHERS ASSOCIATION

The Parent Teachers Associations of any city can be a help or a hindrance to good traffic engineering in the residential areas. They vary in scope and ability from school district to school district, but there is no question of their deep concern for traffic safety activities in the vicinity of the schools. To establish proper contact with each group, the traffic engineer undertook a series of appearances at PTA meetings as a scheduled speaker. These appearances provided the opportunity to describe the objectives of the traffic engineer's program. They also resulted in receipt of any number of complaints and suggestions on the spot during question and answer periods. After a clear picture of the interests of these groups was achieved, a project was conceived in which they could participate. It had become evident to the traffic engineer that he had inadequate knowledge of the placement of signs and markings which already existed throughout the residential areas. It was equally obvious that it would take quite some time to gather this information with a limited staff. Accordingly, it was proposed that the entire PTA structure organize itself into a data collection force for the inventory of signs and markings throughout the residential areas of the city. The traffic engineer's office prepared all necessary documents, maps and forms, conducted several instructional and organizational meetings, and then turned it over to the PTA groups which employed well over 200 members on the project. Within one week, the entire endeavor was completed and returned to the traffic engineer's office for analysis and recording. It was found that due to the inexperience of the recorders, many data were inaccurate and unusable, although major parts of it could be and were salvaged. It was admitted in the traffic engineer's office and among the PTA leadership it had not been as successful as hoped as a data gathering procedure, but nevertheless, it had succeeded in demonstrating to the membership the areas in which they could participate and demonstrated their willingness to do so.

A search was made for further participation, frankly aimed at the purpose of minimizing unwarranted complaints and requests for increasing numbers of protective devices in the form of crosswalks, school-crossing guards and school signs. The traffic engineer's office established a more formal process with the aid of the Education Department. Under the new process, the traffic engineer prepared specific maps and a write-up of the safety devices and provisions to be maintained and in full operation prior to the beginning of every school year. These were distributed to special PTA meetings held a month before school opening. With these in hand, parents had the opportunity to understand the overall school safety program and to respond wherever they felt it could be bettered, but in any event, they were assured their problems were not being overlooked.

BOY SCOUTS OF AMERICA

The Boy Scouts had established in New Haven a participation in government activity. This took the form of troopers occupying various public seats for a full day, one day each year, in a quasi-execution of the governmental functions. This program was entered into enthusiastically by the traffic engineer's department and led to discussions of possible further participation. There came a time when it had been decided to install a major program of towing illegally parked vehicles in the peak traffic hours. While a number of devices to inform the public of the program and its purposes were employed, one of the most significant and useful was a courtesy tag operation conducted under the auspices of the Boy Scouts. For a full week, prior to the commencement of enforcement, Boy Scouts from all troops of the city, totaling over 100, patrolled peak-hour restricted areas and tagged all vehicles with a special courtesy ticket prepared for the purpose. The ticket resembled a parking ticket in all respects, except it bore no fine and no towing liability but instead, courteously explained its purpose and the purpose of the regulation. It is felt that this undertaking was a major factor in general public acceptance of what can often be one of the most difficult traffic improvements to institute in a city. It went further in that it won the interest of a sizable number of boys for the traffic improvement program, which interest and enthusiasm they could communicate to their fellows and their parents.

YALE UNIVERSITY

Yale University is a very large and very critically located institution. Its proximity to the central business area makes all of its traffic and all of the general city traffic intermingle in such a way that they are a problem to each other. Relationships in regard to traffic were not the only problems, however, therefore, the Mayor established a strong and continuing relationship with the University. In the traffic field, this in turn took the form of continuous conferences on the plans and programs of the city. It was a formal relationship which enabled both parties to find mutual solutions to their problems. A specific matter of great importance was University agreement to refuse release from University obligations of any students with outstanding unpaid parking violation tickets. This one action alone helped keep parking spaces cleared as required by regulation and helped minimize animosity between residents of the city and students of the University.

TRANSIT COMPANY

Mass transit is provided by a private company. Under these circumstances, they are somewhat at the mercy of public actions by the public agencies. However, in 1951, they had shown their strength by joining forces with the Chamber of Commerce and the local newspaper to completely destroy a one-way traffic operation system which had been installed and which, in their opinion, was detrimental to their transit operations. To avoid any recurrence of this, all plans for street changes which would affect the transit company were reviewed thoroughly with company personnel. Changes in plans were made when it was clear that they would in fact be detrimental to transit operations. Their desires for the location of bus stops, based on their own knowledge of their own operation, were accepted wherever possible. They were treated, rightfully, as an integral portion of the city's traffic and transportation system.

TAXI CAB ASSOCIATION

It has been said that taxi cab drivers are the best ambassadors of good or ill will that a city may have. Certainly, they have attitudes toward all things happening in the city and very often express them quite freely to passengers. In acknowledgment of this, a series of meetings was set up with the Taxi Cab Association for full disclosure to the drivers of the plans of the city in general and specifically in traffic improvements. Drivers were invited to express views on the adequacy of traffic routings and specifically, on the location of taxi loading zones in relation to the city's activities. In return, although not all agreed in some of the actions of the city, they were well informed both for the benefit of their own operation and in answering the queries of passengers.

FILLING STATION OPERATORS

No organization of filling station operators was found or created. It was noted, however, that they are considered major information sources by drivers. Accordingly, a program was instituted of making available, on request, a large-scale map of the basic one-way street patterns which could be used for easy reference in answering questions of drivers. This was found to eliminate caustic or derogatory remarks concerning the system by persons whose only real problem was a lack of understanding.

THE PARKING PUBLIC

An important segment of the traveling public which needs to know and understand the parking program is the driver when he is about to park his vehicle. Drivers are a very difficult public to reach in respect to curb parking and generally, except for the tow zone activity, little can be done with them in respect to street parking. However, it is feasible to establish contact and to inform them of off-street program developments. One of the methods devised was the institution of planned opening ceremonies and procedures whenever a new major public facility was created. All forms of media were utilized to inform the public of a new facility and the entire public was invited to use the facility free for some limited time period after opening. In addition, specific maps showing approach routes to the facility were distributed to all users, and going further, in publicly owned facilities which became crowded, leaflets were distributed directing those who were turned away to the best routes to reach other facilities. By these means the public came to understand the parking layout and to appreciate the efforts being made to cover their parking needs.

NEIGHBORHOOD GROUPS

Whenever specific actions which will affect a defined neighborhood are to be undertaken, it is possible to establish direct contact. One example involved a short street, one block in length, which was customarily used by through traffic to switch from one artery to another because it enabled drivers to avoid a signalized intersection. There was no traffic capacity or movement hindrance at the signalized intersection that required this movement. It was nothing more than a hazard and a nuisance to the residents of the street. Studies demonstrated that installation of one-way movement on the residential street opposing the flow of the short-cut traffic would solve the problem. It was evident, however, that such one-way operation would provide some inconvenience to the residents of the street. It was quite possible they would fail to understand its purpose and react against it. Accordingly, before installation of the system, notification leaflets were distributed to all residents in the affected area describing the purpose, when it was to go into effect and the alternate routes they could use to and from their places of residence. In addition, an opportunity to express opinion on the plan was given. While all did not agree with the plan, the great majority did, and it was instituted and was successful.

USE OF THE MEDIA

The possibility always exists that news media, especially newspapers, may be antagonistic to any action a particular political administration may take. To preclude this, the stories sent New Haven's local media were well-documented "straight news" announcements. As a result, coverage was achieved that was without bias or prejudice.

In addition, from time to time, the television stations furnished public service time in which major programs were conducted. One such contribution was an attempt to conduct an inexpensive origin-destination survey by television appearance. In this attempt, questionnaire postcards are mailed to all dwelling units in the metropolitan area with a request that they tune in to a particular television program which would describe the purpose of the survey, the use of the forms and how to fill them out. The television program itself came off well and it was evidently successful. Unfortunately, poor timing in the distribution of the postcards resulted in some persons receiving them too long prior to the TV appearance and some did not receive them until after the TV appearance. This fact largely negated the basic purpose.

GENERAL PUBLIC

All traffic improvements, after all, in the long run affect the traveling public as a general group. There is no opportunity to achieve reciprocal contact as such. It did seem to be an obligation, however, to provide the public with the most information possible. Accordingly, all major traffic changes which affected the flow on the street were accompanied immediately prior to and during the change with major distribution of leaflets describing the change and the new pattern. These were distributed to drivers traversing the streets to be affected. Depending on the size of change, the quantity of leaflets varied from 5000 to 50,000. On occasion, as a further effort, necessary major changes in patterns were accompanied by placing oversize temporary signs to supplement standard signing and signaling. These signs gave instructions indicating the direction of new one-way streets, best routes to well-known destinations and otherwise were used as an assist in becoming acquainted with the system during the initial period after installation. Generally, all of the above might be summarized in the slogan which was adopted and appeared on all printed information used in this regard "HELP US

HELP YOU"; a little corny perhaps but it describes the spirit and seemed to be accepted in the spirit it was offered.

CONCLUSIONS

It might be said that obtaining community support for traffic engineering lies in multitude of endeavors all intended to humanize the effort and bring it into proper focus for the affected groups and persons. Too often decisions which come out of local government appear arbitrary and bureaucratic to one that has not studied the problems and devised solutions that sometimes appear to make no sense at all. Lack of information is perhaps the greatest generator of opposition to many public actions.

Addendum
EXAMPLE OF PUBLIC TRAFFIC NOTICE TO RESIDENTS

CITY AND COUNTY OF DENVER

DEPARTMENT OF PUBLIC WORKS
July 10, 1964

TRAFFIC ENGINEERING
CITY AND COUNTY
BUILDING
DENVER 2, COLORADO

Dear Broadway Residents and Businessmen:

Traffic volumes on Broadway between Mississippi Avenue and Bayaud Avenue have continued to increase, and are now well over 20,000 vehicles per day. Among these 20,000 vehicles are many which will be making left turn maneuvers. Under the present traffic design on Broadway in this area, these left turn maneuvers are either prohibited at signalized intersections or must be made from through traffic lanes. The congestion and accident hazard involved in maneuvers of this type are such that we must seek a remedy.

It is therefore planned to prohibit parking on the west side of Broadway between Cedar Avenue and Virginia Avenue. This will provide the necessary space to install left turn lanes on Broadway at all of the intersections between Byers Place and Virginia.

Also included in this project is a re-design of the channelization as it now exists between Virginia Avenue and Mississippi Avenue. Some additional "no parking" regulations may be required, but this will not be extensive.

We believe you will find that this makes Broadway a safer and easier street on which to drive as it provides both a refuge for left turning vehicles and for pedestrians who might find themselves caught between platoons of traffic in the middle of the street.

The sketch below shows a typical block of Broadway as it will look under the new design. If you have any questions concerning this project, please contact me or Assistant Traffic Engineer Dick Thomas at 297-2763.

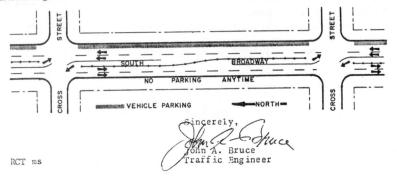

Sincerely,

John A. Bruce
Traffic Engineer

RCT ms

The Traffic Engineer's Relationships
With Local Officials, Boards and Commissions
(Cities Less Than 100,000)

DELBERT F. KARMEIER
Traffic Commissioner
St. Louis County, Mo.

The many subjects covered in the Street Utilization Conference constitute a comprehensive listing of engineering techniques available to the traffic engineer. There is ample evidence to show conclusively that street capacity, efficiency and safety can be achieved by implementation of these procedures. Frequently, however, the major obstacle to translating studies and plans into completed projects is obtaining necessary approval from public officials who are charged with the final decision-making responsibility. A traffic engineer cannot simply determine the action necessary to achieve a desirable result. He must also devote time and energy to the process of obtaining funds and approval from councils, mayors, or board and commission members.

It must be recognized that the traffic engineer who works with and through officials in smaller cities is not necessarily a full-time municipal employee. In fact, because of the shortage of trained traffic engineering personnel, few cities with a population of less than 50,000 are able to employ a professional traffic engineer on a full-time basis. Therefore, the subject of traffic engineering relations must be approached from two viewpoints: (a) a traffic engineer who is a full-time employee of the local government; and (b) a traffic engineer who serves as a consultant to the city, or who is affiliated with a regional governmental agency.

St. Louis County, Mo., has 95 incorporated cities, towns and villages ranging in population from 50 to 51,000. It provides an excellent challenge for the traffic engineer to establish working relationships with officials, boards and commissions. Almost every conceivable form of municipal government is represented. The following listing based on 1960 Census figures summarizes the number of cities in the county according to population:

Population Range	Number of Cities
Below 1,000	31
1,000 to 5,000	32
5,000 to 10,000	15
10,000 to 25,000	13
25,000 to 50,000	3
Over 50,000	1
Total	95

Regardless of the size of the community, the traffic engineer must work in cooperation with all three branches of government: legislative, administrative and judicial. Frequently, much can also be accomplished through the efforts of boards and committees whose functions may be limited to advisory services and the development of general policy. Table 1 contains a typical listing of the officials and agencies with whom the traffic engineer must cooperate.

In order to implement plans and programs for traffic engineering improvements, official and public support for the proposals must be obtained. A prerequisite to gaining this support is the development of effective communications with those officials,

TABLE 1

OFFICIALS, BOARDS, COMMISSIONS AND ORGANIZATIONS

Legislative

City Council, Village Board
County Board or Council
State Legislature
Regional or District Council

Administrative

Mayor, City Manager
City Department Heads
    Director of Planning
    Superintendent of Police
    Director of Public Works
    Fire Chief
    Director of Budget
    Director of Personnel
State Highway Department
State Highway Patrol
County Manager or Supervisor
County Highway Division
County Police Dept. or Sheriff's Office
County Planning Department
Regional Planning Agency

Judicial

Municipal and Magistrate Judges
Clerks of the Court
City Attorney, County Attorney

Advisory

Traffic Commission (City or County)
Planning and Zoning Commission (City or County)
State Highway Commission
Regional Planning Commission
State Legislative Committees
City Council Streets and Traffic Committee

commissions or boards who may be instrumental in approving or disapproving the project. The methods which can be utilized in establishing the lines of communications include:

1. Formation of a Traffic Commission which may number among its membership officials such as the Chief of Police, the Director of Planning, and a member of the City Council. Such a commission should also have citizen participation in order to provide necessary public support.

2. Regular attendance and appropriate participation in official meetings of the legislative body and the administrative staff.

3. Frequent conferences and meetings with specific officials to discuss matters of mutual concern.

4. Membership and participation in area-wide coordinating agencies, such as the Municipal League and the Regional Planning Commission.

5. Formation of an organization which will bring together traffic engineers, enforcement officials, representatives of private industry, citizen groups, etc., who share a common interest; e.g., Traffic Engineering Association of Metropolitan St. Louis.

ASSISTANCE OF TRAFFIC COMMISSION

A traffic commission or committee can be especially helpful in the early stages of the development of a traffic engineering program. In this regard, an important project is the preparation and adoption of the Model Traffic Ordinance which establishes the authority and duties of the traffic engineer. The role of the St. Louis County Traffic Commission in revising its Traffic Code will be cited as an example.

The St. Louis County Traffic Commission is composed of nine citizen members, the Director of Planning, the Superintendent of Police and the Traffic Commissioner. In 1960, the Commission Chairman appointed a subcommittee to review the existing county traffic ordinances and prepare amendments necessary to bring the Traffic Code into conformance with the Model Traffic Ordinance. This subcommittee was assisted by a representative of the Department of Law and the Division of Traffic staff. After numerous meetings over a space of several months, an entirely new Traffic Code was submitted to the Commission.

After study by the entire Commission, the proposed Traffic Code was formally submitted to the County Council with the recommendation that it be enacted. After several months of study by the Council, the code was enacted into law. Adoption of this Model Traffic Legislation permitted the Division of Traffic to establish a master traffic control plan for all county-maintained streets and roads.

The Traffic Commission's role included assisting in drafting the ordinance, generating public support for its enactment, and informing individual council members of the importance of early enactment. Since 1962, several St. Louis County municipalities have reviewed their traffic laws and taken steps to bring them into conformance with the Model Traffic Ordinance.

A major step forward toward uniformity in traffic regulations in Missouri was made by the General Assembly in 1965. At that time the state legislature enacted the "Model Traffic Ordinance for Missouri Municipalities" which can be adopted by reference. The Traffic Commission wholeheartedly supported this legislation and has urged all St. Louis County municipalities to enact it at the earliest possible date.

PARTICIPATION IN OFFICIAL MEETINGS

When a traffic engineer is an employee of a municipal government, he must be an active participant in the regular meetings of the administrative staff and should regularly attend all meetings of the City Council. The staff meetings, in particular, will help to maintain the lines of communications with other departments of the city government. Examples of routine procedures which can be established are as follows:

1. All street improvement plans prepared by the Public Works Department are forwarded to the traffic engineering office for review and approval.

2. The traffic bureau of the Department of Police provides the traffic engineering office with a monthly summary of accident reports as tabulated by data processing equipment.

3. At regular intervals, the traffic engineering agency forwards results of its vehicular volume surveys, travel time, etc., to the Department of Planning and the street design division of the Department of Public Works.

4. When new traffic regulations are established, appropriate information is provided to the City Clerk for the reference of the Department of Law and the municipal court.

Every traffic engineer can cite numerous examples of instances where cooperation between departments of a city or county government has resulted in a substantial improvement in terms of increased capacity or safety. In 1964, the St. Louis County Division of Highways forwarded to the Division of Traffic plans for resurfacing an existing two-lane roadway to provide a 20-ft pavement and 8-ft shoulders. Traffic count information indicated that this street already carried 10,000 veh/day and that annual increases of 5 to 10 percent could be anticipated. Therefore, the Traffic Commissioner recommended that every possible effort be made to revise the roadway cross section to provide four lanes for moving traffic.

Following a field inspection with the highway engineer, the plans were revised to provide four lanes within the limits of the existing 60-ft right-of-way. Volume studies conducted in 1967 indicated that this street now carries in excess of 15,000 veh/day. Although it would be desirable to secure additional right-of-way and increase the lane width to a higher standard, the cooperation between the Division of Highways and the Division of Traffic in 1964 has resulted in the construction of a facility with greater traffic capacity than would otherwise have been possible.

REGULAR CONTACTS WITH MUNICIPAL OFFICIALS

In those instances where the traffic engineer is not a full-time employee of a single municipality, it is necessary that he arrange informal meetings with key municipal officials at appropriate intervals. In St. Louis County, the Traffic Commissioner engages in several phone conversations daily with traffic commission chairmen, city engineers, police traffic officials, councilmen, etc. Many times, it is convenient to meet with part-time officials at lunch in order to discuss current or future projects. Informal contacts of this nature can be used to lay the groundwork for improvements ranging from the simple act of establishing a parking regulation to a major road improvement.

The initiating, planning, design and construction of an intersection "spot improvement" in St. Louis County provide a case history of the value of informal contacts. The Chairman of the Citizens Traffic Commission of the City of Ladue frequently calls upon the County Division of Traffic for day-to-day advice on such matters as traffic signing and marking. During one such phone conversation, he indicated that his commission was concerned about traffic congestion at an intersection of two major arterial streets at the edge of the community. The centerline of one street forms the dividing line between Ladue and the adjacent city, Richmond Heights. Although Ladue was interested in proceeding with the improvement, the commission was uncertain if Richmond Heights had any interest in the project.

Through a similar conversation with a Richmond Heights official, it was learned that the City Council also recognized the need for improvement and would seriously entertain entering into a joint project. The Division of Traffic then offered its services in preparing a preliminary geometric plan of improvements needed to achieve necessary capacity.

After study and review of the preliminary plans, a consulting engineering firm was engaged to prepare detailed construction plans. At this stage, the county government initiated a new "Urban Road Program" whereby county road funds were made available for projects in municipalities on a cost-sharing basis. The two cities immediately requested the County to participate in the intersection "spot improvement."

The actual construction of the project was initiated and completed in the summer of 1966. The improvement included the following features:

1. Widening the four-lane, east-west arterial street to provide a separate left-turn storage lane on both approaches.

2. The addition of a "Right Turn Only" lane and channelizing island on the south approach to the intersection.

3. The construction of an additional lane for through and right-turning traffic on the north approach.

4. Revision of signal phasing from a three-phase operation to a basic two-phase system with a left-turn minor phase.

A before-and-after capacity analysis indicates that the intersection improvement has produced the following results:

Approach	Capacity Increase (%)
East	61
West	150
North	73
South	196

Implementation of this project required action by two city councils and the legislative body of St. Louis County. Obviously, when three agencies attempt to work together, there will be many opportunities for the entire proposal to become stalled and possibly canceled because of procedural problems. The continuing contacts by the Division of Traffic and local officials was apprently an important factor in the successful completion of this improvement.

USE OF COORDINATING AGENCIES

In a metropolitan area composed of many small cities, such traffic engineering objectives as uniformity in control devices and regulations can only be achieved through joint action by many officials and governments. By working through the St. Louis County Municipal League, a notable improvement in the uniformity of speed limits on residential streets has been achieved in the St. Louis Metropolitan area. As recently as 1961, residential speed limits in the 95 incorporated cities could be 15, 20, 25 or 30 mph. Of greater importance, there was no single value which was in effect in a majority of the area.

Following a series of speed surveys conducted according to proper traffic engineering procedures, University City amended its Traffic Code to provide for a basic 25-mph speed limit on all streets except those which were designated as "through streets." Speed regulations on through streets were determined on the basis of engineering and traffic surveys and established at 30 mph, 35 mph, or higher where conditions permitted.

Shortly thereafter, the City of St. Louis, which adjoins St. Louis County, adopted a basic 25-mph residential speed limit. The revised St. Louis County Traffic Code, which was enacted in July 1962, also provided for a 25-mph residential speed limit in the entire unincorporated area of St. Louis County. The Traffic Engineering Association of Metropolitan St. Louis (TEAM) endorsed the standard speed limit concept and the Division of Traffic with the cooperation of the Municipal League began efforts to extend this program to all 95 communities in St. Louis County.

The engineering staff of the Division of Traffic is always represented at the monthly meeting of the Municipal League. These gatherings provide an excellent opportunity to become acquainted with mayors, aldermen, city managers and other officials. For several years, the Traffic Commissioner served on the Municipal League Highway and Traffic Committee. On three occasions during the past five years, the Division of Traffic presented a special program which related to uniformity in traffic regulations and devices.

The methods used in advancing the concept of a uniform basic speed limit may be illustrated by review of the "conversion" of one small village. A newly elected Trustee of this village happened to read an article on proper methods of establishing speed limits which had been prepared by the Division of Traffic for the Missouri Municipal League Magazine. He contacted the Division office asking for help in revising his village's traffic laws, and received an offer to collect necessary data, analyze it and prepare a report with appropriate recommendations.

The Trustee then secured formal approval for the study from the Village Board and the speed limit survey was initiated. After data had been collected, tabulated and analyzed, and preliminary conclusions drawn, a meeting was held with two members of the Board of Trustees to outline the proposals.

Since this was a small village, the meeting was concluded with a field trip to each of the sites where speed studies were made. During the course of the field trip, it was noted that the group was traveling at a speed of 30 mph on a street which had an unrealistically low 20-mph speed limit. This incident helped convince the two Trustees that the recommendations were not only based on scientific procedures but were also reasonable and proper.

Subsequently, the written report was formally submitted to the Village Board of Trustees. Within a short time, the Village Traffic Code was amended to provide for the basic residential speed limit of 25 mph. In addition, 30-mph and 35-mph speed regulations were established on arterial streets within the village.

As a result of this continuing program, over 75 percent of the 1,600,000 persons living in St. Louis and St. Louis County now live in areas which have enacted the standard speed limit program endorsed by the St. Louis County Municipal League and TEAM. Furthermore, over 90 percent of the land area of St. Louis and St. Louis County lies within the boundaries of these jurisdictions. The gains which have been made toward complete uniformity in speed regulations have reduced driver confusion and obtained much greater voluntary compliance with speed regulations. Table 2 gives the results of before and after speed studies on several streets in St. Louis County.

FORMATION OF A TRAFFIC IMPROVEMENT ORGANIZATION

This method of dealing with officials and official groups can be applied most successfully in metropolitan areas. In the case of the single, isolated city, the traffic commission and administrative staff should be the vehicles for bringing together the traffic engineer and key officials. In a metropolitan area, an organization encompassing traffic officials from all governmental jurisdictions is necessary to achieve coordination.

In St. Louis, a group originally known as Metropolitan St. Louis Traffic Engineers began holding regular meetings in 1959. Subsequently, the membership of the organization was expanded to include city engineers, police traffic officers, representatives of industry and citizen groups with an interest in the furtherance of traffic engineering. A new name, the Traffic Engineering Association of Metropolitan St. Louis, and a most appropriate insignia "TEAM" was adopted.

The TEAM organization holds monthly luncheon meetings to hear guest speakers on pertinent traffic topics. These gatherings also provide an occasion for area traffic

TABLE 2

EFFECT OF INCREASED SPEED LIMITS IN ST. LOUIS COUNTY

Street or Road	Posted Speed Limit (mph)		50th Percentile Speed (mph)			85th Percentile Speed (mph)			Percent Above Speed Limit	
	Before	After	Before	After	Change	Before	After	Change	Before	After
Big Bend Road	30	35	32	34	+2	36	38	+2	69	31
Craig Road	30	35	34	33	-1	43	38	-5	64	35
Larimore Road	30	35	30	30	0	35	36	+1	48	20
Lucas-Hunt Road	30	35	32	32	0	35	35	0	70	15
Redman Avenue	30	35	35	34	-1	41	39	-2	76	35
Rock Hill Road	30	35	32	34	+2	37	39	+2	67	22
Schuetz Road	30	35	33	33	0	38	38	0	61	28

Note: The 50th Percentile and 85th Percentile values are the speeds at or below which 50 percent and 85 percent of all vehicles observed were traveling.

officials to become acquainted and initiate joint action on mutual problems. In 1961, TEAM sponsored the first workshop on the newly published Manual on Uniform Traffic Control Devices. This has become an annual event featuring prominent national speakers and attracting an average attendance of 100 persons.

TEAM also establishes technical committees to recommend programs and standards for uniformity in traffic control devices and regulations. The first important project backed by this organization was the Uniform Street Name Sign Program. TEAM endorsed the concept that all street name signs should be fully reflectorized with a white legend on a green background. The organization prepared standard specifications for the design and installation of street name signs and distributed copies of the booklet to several hundred municipal officials.

Today, the City of St. Louis, St. Louis County, East St. Louis and more than 40 of the largest municipalities have installed the standard green and white reflectorized street name signs. In fact, a recent tabulation indicates that more than 90 percent of the land area of St. Louis and St. Louis County is now included within the Uniform Street Name Sign Program. Other individuals and organizations such as the St. Louis County Municipal League contributed greatly to the success of this program. The original concept was initiated, however, among the members of TEAM.

In 1966, a TEAM technical committee produced a Uniform Design Standard booklet for residential subdivision entrances. Several municipalities and the county government have already adopted the requirements of this standard in their regulations which govern the construction of subdivision entrances. Another semiannual TEAM activity is the preparation of a state traffic safety legislative program.

CONCLUSIONS

In reviewing the accomplishments of this traffic engineering organization, its principal objective can be summarized as enabling engineers, officials and citizens who are devoted to the furtherance of traffic engineering to become better acquainted. In this way, a basis for a coordinated attack on traffic safety and congestion problems is established.

Effective communication with officials, commissions or boards is an essential ingredient in the establishment of a successful traffic engineering improvement program. The traffic engineer should cooperate with and utilize the services of traffic commissions, fellow governmental officials, and coordinating organizations and agencies in achieving the desired goal of safe, efficient and economical traffic movement.

REFERENCES

1. Traffic Engineering Handbook, 3rd Edition. (John E. Baerwald, Ed.) Institute of Traffic Engineers, pp. 724-766, 1965.
2. Matson, Theodore M., Smith, Wilbur S., and Hurd, Frederick W. Traffic Engineering. McGraw-Hill Book Company, pp. 559-587, 1955.
3. Setting Up Traffic Engineering in Your City. Public Safety Memo No. 101, National Safety Council, 1952.
4. Hanson, D. J. Urban Development in the County. Northwest Roads and Street Conference, Corvallis, Oregon, 1964.

Traffic Engineer—Official Contact
(Cities of Over 100,000)

PAUL W. RICE
City Manager
Bethany, Okla.

This paper deals with the actual experiences of a traffic engineer employed in three different cities of over 100,000 population. In two of the cities, the traffic engineer was the first city traffic engineer. In the third city, he was the second traffic engineer employed. Furthermore each of the three cities had a different type of government.

The first city was Tulsa, Okla., a city of over 200,000 population. The employment was the result of the recommendation of a consultant engineer who had been called in to help determine the city's traffic needs. The new traffic engineer, a new graduate of the Yale Bureau of Highway Traffic, was employed by the Commissioner of Fire and Police, and assigned to the Police Department under the Captain of Traffic.

Tulsa had a mayor-commissioner form of government, all being elected to office. Many positions were filled by political patronage, hence, the new traffic engineer had to fit into the organization in an unassuming position and attempt to prove himself in the midst of politicians and veteran police officers. After 18 months in this position as traffic engineer under the Captain of Traffic, the Chief of Police and the Fire and Police Commissioner, the traffic engineer succeeded in being reassigned to the Commissioner of Streets and placed under the Director of Public Affairs (Director of Public Works). It was in this new assignment that the traffic engineer began to function as he should and find a place in the city organization.

The official organizations with which the traffic engineer had to deal were the City Commission, the commissioners individually, the Director of Public Affairs, City Departments, the Planning Commission and individual politicians.

The second city was Evansville, Ind., a city of approximately 130,000 population located in southern Indiana. The Mayor and City Council were elected with the Mayor serving full time as the Chief Executive. The Mayor did not officiate at the weekly council meetings, but rather a President of the Council was elected by the other councilmen for this purpose. All matters of business were submitted through Boards or Department Heads to the Mayor for his presentation to the City Council. This did not usually occur in a public meeting, but rather in a work session prior to the regular council meeting.

Evansville had a Board of Public Safety, a three man citizen board which supervised the activity of the Fire, Police and Traffic Engineering Departments. While their authority was limited, their recommendations were usually followed by the Mayor and the City Council.

In addition to the official Board of Public Safety, there was an official group known as the Mayor's Traffic Safety Commission. While this organization may appear cumbersome, in actual practice many fine accomplishments were made in a relatively short time, with the support of these two official bodies.

The third city served was Corpus Christi, Texas, a rapid growing city of approximately 160,000 population located on the Gulf Coast. Corpus Christi was growing and developing in shipping, industry, ranching, farming and oil production.

The city had evolved a strong Council-Manager form of government with a capable City Manager and qualified Department Heads. The traffic engineer was employed as a department director with equal department status and given all the traffic engineering functions.

This city government functioned about as ideally as could be desired. The elected Mayor and City Council confined their activity to policy and approvals. The City Manager ran the city through his department heads.

CASE HISTORY NO. 1
(Size of City—200,000)

The Problem

This rapid growing city was being choked with traffic congestion in the CBD area. The merchants were complaining, the public was demanding relief, and the Police Department and City Officials were at a loss as to just what to do.

The streets were congested to the point that traffic could hardly move, especially during peak hours. Customers were refusing to come into the area, and workers were finding it hard to get into the central core area to work. Relief was a necessity. People were getting desperate, the time was right for a progressive program, but what would it consist of? Who would initiate it? Who would pay the bill? These and many other questions were being asked. Where were the answers?

In an aroused situation, at least two basic premises must prevail: (a) the analysis of the situation should be correct, and (b) the program should bring effective relief.

Proposal

Two programs were proposed at the same time as the result of aroused citizens serving officially as a Citizens Traffic Improvement Committee.

1. One-way business streets, and
2. All rolling traffic 7:00 to 9:00 a. m. and 4:00 to 6:00 p. m. (a peak-hour parking restriction).

The attitude of the city government had been somewhat passive. They had no traffic engineer, nor were they trying to employ one. The official city did recognize a need but lacked leadership in identifying the problem, let alone solving it.

The official committee was appointed to study and identify the problem, and to make recommendations for a solution. Fortunately the "right" people were selected for the committee and things began to happen:

1. A traffic engineering consultant was engaged to analyze the problems;
2. The committee recommended the employment of a full-time professional traffic engineer;
3. The committee initiated a program for traffic relief in the CBD;
4. The committee initiated a program of citizen support and information; and
5. The committee supported the relief program through official channels, the City Commission and with the general public.

The consultant made a brief, but impressive analysis of the needs and suggested definite action for needed traffic relief. The committee took the recommendations and saw to it that they were adopted and carried out. They overcame opposition by convincing both official and non-official groups that one-way streets increase capacities, increase safety, and improve operations.

The new traffic engineer entered into this project by aiding in the details of furnishing factual data, engineering the project, and by aiding in the general selling of the proposed traffic relief measures to merchants, city officials, and citizens in general.

The desire for relief from congestion in the CBD far outweighed the opposition. The Citizens Traffic Improvement Committee acted as a buffer between the merchants and the city officials, and were also effective between the traffic engineer and the public on the one hand, and the City Commission on the other.

Politicians in office are often unacquainted with methods used to solve technical problems. Often they must be educated along with the general public in methods and techniques necessary to solve major problems. In this particular case, the traffic engineer had to work through a maze of officials and committees to get to the point of action. A traffic engineer working under police supervisors to accomplish a sweeping change of travel and parking habits for thousands of citizens, found it hard at times to carry through to the ultimate pre-calculated results.

The recommendations included four one-way pairs of streets on each side of the CBD with "all rolling traffic" on all CBD streets during peak hours. This was quite a project to install at one time. It had to be effective and produce results for the new traffic engineer who had been left with the installation and final selling to the people. The signs had to be fabricated and installed. Street markings had to be installed and traffic signals modified.

There was outstanding cooperation. Interest was high for the proposal. The skeptical were a bit apprehensive, but agreed to go along and see if the proposal would work. Many were on hand the first morning the one-way streets were opened to traffic. They were a success from the very start and the citizens committee, the city officials and the new traffic engineer had succeeded in successfully promoting the project.

In review, the key to the project was that the official Traffic Improvement Committee was willing to accept responsibility for the project. Second, the city government was willing to accept the recommendations and give official approval with necessary ordinances and funds. The traffic engineer by this time, had developed the confidence and support of his program and had educated those involved to its benefits. The project succeeded because of cooperation and mutual confidence among all concerned. After one successful project, the succeeding ones became easier to initiate and install.

CASE HISTORY NO. 2
(Size of City—200,000)

The Problem

Property along an arterial street had been zoned for business and offices, generally one lot deep. If the lots faced a side street, only the 50-ft lot was thus zoned. The case at hand was a doctor's office located on a 50-ft wide lot lying parallel to the arterial street. Parking was at a premium, and off-street parking was badly needed. The doctor purchased the residential zoned lot next to his lot and the second lot from the arterial street. He applied for re-zoning so the lot could be used for parking for his office. The request was denied by the Planning Commission.

Proposal

The traffic engineer who was trying to clear the arterial streets of parking congestion supported the doctor in his appeal and decided to appeal the decision and permit use of the lot for parking. He felt so strongly that parking would have to be extended into the residential area near such arterial street development, that he supported the doctor before the City Board of Zoning Appeals, and later in District Court. The court decided in favor of the doctor and overruled the Planning Commission.

The net result was that the city zoning ordinances were amended to allow parking for businesses adjacent to residential zoned areas, provided proper screening, lighting control and policing were incorporated.

The traffic engineer had taken issue with the Planning and Zoning Commission, the Board of Zoning Appeals and appeared as a witness in District Court to help provide adequate off-street parking for patients, thus, cleaning the arterial street for better traffic movement.

CASE HISTORY NO. 3
(Size of City—130,000)

The Problem

The existing signal system was an outdated simple double-alternate system with absolutely no flexibility. All traffic moved at the same pace, peak and off-peak, night and day. Pedestrians had to guess when to walk, and the narrow streets were clogged at all hours of the day. The merchants were desperate because of the deplorable traffic situation. Many traffic improvements were needed. Very little had been done before the signal system was modernized, and many other improvements would obviously have to follow.

Although the general public realized there was a need for improvements, they were somewhat complacent and had accepted the bad situation.

Proposal

It was the Mayor's Traffic Safety Commission which had been organized as an official organization, who not only had to identify the problem, but also to convince those in authority that adequate relief measures should and could be taken.

The traffic engineer, working with the commission, was able to propose a program for traffic relief: a new signal system for the CBD. While he served under a Board of Public Safety, his real program support came from the Mayor's Traffic Safety Commission.

The recommendation was made and the decision was reached to modernize the signal system. The interested people and organizations had to be convinced that the project, along with the cost, was justified. The Board of Public Safety was ready to support the proposal. The Mayor was not opposed to improvement, for his platform at the time of election, included traffic relief. The real selling came with the City Council when they were presented with a proposal for 56 completely new radio-controlled traffic signalized intersections with pedestrian indications. The cost was about $300,000, and the radio coordination was a completely new concept in traffic signals.

The first success came when the funds were provided for the project. Achieving this goal was difficult and time consuming, and required private and public contacts, day and night, in public meetings and private sessions. It was difficult to convince some that the benefits to the community would equal the cost. To these and to a few of the councilmen who were hard to convince, there had to be a thorough job of selling three basic things: (a) that the need was equal to the cost, (b) that confidence in the traffic engineer's proposal was warranted, and (c) that the proposal would bring the desired relief. These three points were used to convince the majority, and they produced an affirmative vote on the request for funds.

After the approval of the funds came an early approval of the new type of equipment. Although the radio coordination of traffic signals was being tried in isolated cases, this was the first complete CBD system so equipped. There were 56 totally new installations all equipped with double signal indications, radio receivers and pedestrian signals.

The actual installation of the signal equipment at the intersections was enough to gain public support. The public was so pleased with what they saw that they were sold on the project long before the system was ever actually coordinated and programmed to really aid traffic flow. Suffice to say, the program and project were well accepted. Apparently, the public and the press alike were proud to be a part of a new and different traffic control system, coordinated with FM radio tones and programmed from a master controller located in City Hall near the office of the traffic engineer.

All had been accomplished because a commission, a board, a mayor, a council and individual politicians had been convinced that a program of relief was needed, the proposed signal system would do the job, and the general public was willing to pay for the improvements.

CASE HISTORY NO. 4
(Size of City—130,000)

The Problem

The Fire Department Headquarters and No. 1 Fire Station were located on a one-way street, down stream from its intersection with another one-way street. The only possible exit for the fire equipment was to move one-way, and that one-way street led directly into the CBD. The Chief of the Fire Department insisted that he be allowed to move either direction on the one-way street. To move on the one-way street only, he would have to travel three blocks through heavy business traffic to get to an opposite flow one-way street.

Proposal

It was proposed that special signal controls be installed. A simple relay and flashing unit was installed in the traffic signal controller with controls located in the Fire Department. The firemen actuated a time delay switch which turned all the signals at the intersection to red. By the time the equipment was able to enter the street, the intersection was clear and the firemen could move with traffic on the cross one-way street to the companion one-way street one block away. Traffic moved safely and normally on the one-way streets.

CASE HISTORY NO. 5
(Size of City—160,000)

The Problem

This city had grown up around a fishing village which had developed into a seaport of no small proportion. World War II had made it a major training area for Navy pilots. It was a city of contrasts, having both old and new areas, both the progressive and conservative; those who wanted to grow and expand, and those who were satisfied with things as they were.

If the city was to progress as a center for shipping, farming, ranching, oil and industry, there had to be an effort to keep pace with transportation planning for the area. An expanded population in an expanding area requires traffic modernization. Some changes require large sums of money, while other changes are relatively inexpensive.

Proposal

A proposal was made for a high-level bridge because of the following conditions.

With the coming of shipping to this city, came an inland waterway, ship channel, and turning basin. This inland waterway caused a conflict with surface transportation, both the automobile and the railroad. The first relief measure had been the construction of a bascule bridge at surface level. Invariably the bridge was raised for the movement of water transportation at the peak hour of surface traffic.

A technical committee was appointed by the various governmental agencies to attempt to work out the details for relief measures which would allow free flow of water, rail and highway traffic without delay of any. At first, the task seemed insurmountable, but as official bodies worked together, the objective was accomplished. The technical committee represented the City, the navigation district, the county, the railroads, the state highway department and the Corps of Engineers. The details of relocating a railroad, the cost of the removal of the old bascule bridge, the cost for land for interchanges at each end of the high bridge, proposal for two railroads to enter the city over the same line, a new lift span to replace the old bascule bridge far inland were some of the complicated problems with which the committee dealt. The objective, however, was clear and the officials of the official organizations had pledged themselves to complete the job.

This project, when completed, represented an expenditure of over 24 million dollars, and involved every level of government from the Congress, down. All shared in the expense, all had to be willing to compromise at many points. Bond issues were passed by both the City and the County. The navigation district sold revenue bonds, the State and Federal governments both appropriated money. The three railroads were the problem—they were the least interested in the change. Their costs were small compared with others. Their main part in the total project was to be willing to relocate and submit to a program of cooperation. In time, they did cooperate very well with the total plan. This was an outstanding example of cooperation by many agencies to accomplish a common objective. Within a period of less than four years, a six-lane, high-level bridge (150-ft clearance above mean high tide) and a widened dredged ship channel (600 ft wide and dredged to 35 ft, mean low tide) had been constructued. The railroad crossing had been moved about two miles inland. Many concessions had to be made, local business was affected, but the total overall economy of the community surged ahead as never before. They had proved to themselves that they could accomplish much by united effort, a willingness to carry a fair share of the costs, and to give and take as problems would arise.

The traffic engineer was a part of this total project in cooperation with many others, and was able to see much accomplished to aid in his desire to move traffic and reduce delays in a growing city.

Proposal

As the city grew and began to expand, it developed along arterial streets. While many of the arterial streets had been allowed to develop as business streets, the main north-south waterfront street had been maintained as a scenic, residential thoroughfare. As congestion and delays began to be experienced on the other arterial streets more and more traffic found its way to the free-flowing waterfront street. Naturally, the street soon became overloaded and congested. To get traffic onto the street simple, two-phase fixed time traffic signals had been installed. This added to the problem and traffic backed up; something had to be done.

The traffic engineer proposed to the Traffic Safety Advisory Board that a through lane be provided along the opposite curb to the side streets and allow the traffic on the water side of the street to move continuously with a narrow (1 ft) raised island for protection from the side-street traffic. Traffic was allowed to move into the traffic stream on an actuated green light, while one lane of the two inbound waterfront street lanes was stopped as the side-street traffic entered. The curb lane moved continually and was never required to stop.

This was a simple application of channelization with paint and raised islands and with the use of traffic-actuated signals. The result was phenomenal. The public acceptance was gratifying, and from this simple inexpensive application, the engineer was able to move on to bigger and more effective traffic engineering projects.

This project was proposed to the City Council as a recommendation of the Traffic Safety Advisory Board, and while some thought it would never work, others thought differently, and the project was installed.

Proposal

School speed in some 25 public and private school zones was 15 mph from 8:00 a. m. to 4:00 p. m. As is so often the case, most of the schools were located on arterial streets, hence, the flow of traffic was impeded 8 hours each day. There was a conflict of traffic and students for no more than 1 hour each day. The restriction was covered by ordinance. A school official argued, "It has been this way for years, we have a safe record, there is no need of changing."

The first approach was to attempt to use speed control signs with limited hours for reduced speed, such as, 15 mph, 8 a. m. to 9 a. m., 3 p. m. to 4 p. m. and where necessary 12 noon to 1 p. m. This was met with stiff opposition from those who felt no change was necessary on the basis of the safety record. Realizing that traffic would never be able to move well on arterial streets until the number of hours school zone speeds were in effect were reduced, the traffic engineer proposed traffic signal flashers along with the school zone speed signs, on each side of the school and covering the entire zone. This was immediately accepted by the school official as being more and better traffic control. After an entire school year had passed, the "good" safety record had not changed. The flasher system has continued to work and it is still in effect, thus aiding traffic flow on the major arterial streets.

CONCLUSIONS

Traffic engineers must be first and foremost a public relation specialist, a salesman of himself and his abilities. He must be able to work together with other officials and official groups in an atmosphere of mutual confidence. He must be able to communicate his capability to those desiring improvements.

Some improvements are more readily accepted than others because the public is prepared to pay for the relief measure. Wrong engineering techniques can be applied at this point. The careful traffic engineer will take time to determine the best possible action for the needed relief, then carefully apply the program, watching, analyzing results, and never being quite satisfied until the action brings the necessary results.

In reviewing the techniques of working with boards, commissions, and elected officials, it can again be said that the traffic engineer must be qualified, able to communicate and have confidence in his ability and himself. He must be able to convey that confidence to others. When the traffic engineer has done this, he is ready to perform, to accept the challenge of his position. Boards and commissions are people. They, like the general public, want results. They can be educated to a program of development that the public will accept and support.

The real work with boards and commissions is not always accomplished in the public or official meeting place. Sometimes the most beneficial contacts come in the casual meeting place, planned or otherwise. Sometimes it develops from "small talk" or a carefully planned conference. This is especially true of boards, commissions, councils or other official groups and individuals, where the principals are active, busy community leaders. The importance of these contacts must never be minimized, for they often lay the foundation on which to build programs for the future. They establish the basis for mutual confidence among all concerned.

THE NATIONAL ACADEMY OF SCIENCES is a private, honorary organization of more than 700 scientists and engineers elected on the basis of outstanding contributions to knowledge. Established by a Congressional Act of Incorporation signed by Abraham Lincoln on March 3, 1863, and supported by private and public funds, the Academy works to further science and its use for the general welfare by bringing together the most qualified individuals to deal with scientific and technological problems of broad significance.

Under the terms of its Congressional charter, the Academy is also called upon to act as an official—yet independent—adviser to the Federal Government in any matter of science and technology. This provision accounts for the close ties that have always existed between the Academy and the Government, although the Academy is not a governmental agency and its activities are not limited to those on behalf of the Government.

The NATIONAL ACADEMY OF ENGINEERING was established on December 5, 1964. On that date the Council of the National Academy of Sciences, under the authority of its Act of Incorporation, adopted Articles of Organization bringing the National Academy of Engineering into being, independent and autonomous in its organization and the election of its members, and closely coordinated with the National Academy of Sciences in its advisory activities. The two Academies join in the furtherance of science and engineering and share the responsibility of advising the Federal Government, upon request, on any subject of science or technology.

The NATIONAL RESEARCH COUNCIL was organized as an agency of the National Academy of Sciences in 1916, at the request of President Wilson, to enable the broad community of U.S. scientists and engineers to associate their efforts with the limited membership of the Academy in service to science and the nation. Its members, who receive their appointments from the President of the National Academy of Sciences, are drawn from academic, industrial and government organizations throughout the country. The National Research Council serves both Academies in the discharge of their responsibilities.

Supported by private and public contributions, grants, and contracts, and voluntary contributions of time and effort by several thousand of the nation's leading scientists and engineers, the Academies and their Research Council thus work to serve the national interest, to foster the sound development of science and engineering, and to promote their effective application for the benefit of society.

The DIVISION OF ENGINEERING is one of the eight major Divisions into which the National Research Council is organized for the conduct of its work. Its membership includes representatives of the nation's leading technical societies as well as a number of members-at-large. Its Chairman is appointed by the Council of the Academy of Sciences upon nomination by the Council of the Academy of Engineering.

The HIGHWAY RESEARCH BOARD, an agency of the Division of Engineering, was established November 11, 1920, as a cooperative organization of the highway technologists of America operating under the auspices of the National Research Council and with the support of the several highway departments, the Bureau of Public Roads, and many other organizations interested in the development of highway transportation. The purposes of the Board are to encourage research and to provide a national clearinghouse and correlation service for research activities and information on highway administration and technology.